MODULAR SCIENCE

for AQA

Heinemann

MODULAR SCIENCE

for AQA

Keith Hirst
Mike Hiscock
David Sang
Martin Stirrup

Heinemann Educational Publishers
Halley Court, Jordan Hill, Oxford OX2 8EJ
Part of Harcourt Education

Heinemann is the registered trademark of Harcourt Education Limited

© Keith Hirst, Mike Hiscock, David Sang and Martin Stirrup, 2002

First published 2002

ISBN 0 435 57195 8

05 04 03
10 9 8 7 6 5 4 3

Edited by Teresa Brady, Gina Walker and Tim Jackson

Index compiled by Paul Nash

Designed and typeset by Hardlines, Charlbury

Illustrated by Hardlines, Charlbury

Printed and bound in Spain by Edelvives

Acknowledgements
The authors and publishers would like to thank the following for permission
to use photographs:

Cover photos: Osprey catching fish courtesy of Oxford Scientific Films/Tom
Ulrich; Diamond courtesy of Science Photo Library/Alfred Pasieka; Biker
courtesy of Image Bank.

T = top *B* = bottom *R* = right *L* = left *M* = middle

1 *TL* Corbis/Richard Hamilton Smith, *B* Science Photo Library/Richard T
Nowitz/, *TR* BBC Natural History Unit/Karl Amman; 2 Image Bank/Vikki
Hart; 3 EMPICS/Tony Marshall; 4 Science Photo Library/John Greim; 5
Science Photo Library/Claude Nuridsany & Marie Perennou; 6 *T* Science
Photo Library/Petit Format/Nestle, *B* Science Photo Library J C Revy; 9 *L*
Bruce Colman, *R* CEC/Malcolm Boulton; 10 Holt Studios/Nigel Cattlin; 12
Science Photo Library/John Giannicchi; 13 *T* Science Photo Library/Saturn
Stills, *M* Corbis/Patrick Bennett; 14 Mary Evans Picture Library; 16 *B* Science
Photo Library/Hattie Young; 20 *T* FoodPix/Burke/Triolo Productions, *ML*
Holt Studios/Bob Gibbons, *MR* Holt Studios/Nigel Cattlin; 21 *TL* Bruce
Coleman/Jane Burton, *TR* Holt Studios, *M* Corbis/Yann Arthus-Bertrand, *B*
Woodfall Wild Images/David Woodfall; 22 Corbis/Jonathan Blair; 24
Empics/Neal Simpson; 27 Mary Evans Picture Library; 28 *M* Science Photo
Library/Sinclair Stammers, *B* Science Photo Library/J Koivula; 30 *T* Oxford
Scientific Films/Tony Tilford, *M* Science Photo Library/Philippe Plailly; 32 *T*
Science Photo Library/David M Schleser/Nature's Images, *M* Bruce
Coleman/Sarah Cook, *B* Oxford Scientific Films/Robin Bush; 33 Science
Photo Library/Claude Nuridsany & MariePerennou; 34 Corbis; 35 Oxford
Scientific Films/Robin Bush; 37 Science Photo Library/David Campione; 40
Mary Evans Picture Library; 43 Science Photo Library; 45 Peter Gould; 47
Peter Gould; 54 Martin Stirrup; 55 Mary Evans Picture Library; 59
Corbis/Bettmann; 60 Peter Gould; 62 *T* Peter Gould, *M* Trevor Clifford; 63
(all) Peter Gould; 65 *T* MWMPC, *M* Peter Gould; 69 Ed.Pecheur
d'images/Guillaume Plisson; 70 Ed.Pecheur d'images/Philip Plisson; 73 Getty
Images/Peter Sterling/FPG International; 74 Bruce Coleman; 76 *L* David Sang,
T Aerofilms, *R* Trevor Clifford; 78 *T* CEC/Mark Bolton, *M* Science Photo
Library/David Parker; 80 Science Photo Library; 81 *TL* Science Photo
Library/Martin Bond, *TR* Science Photo Library/David Ducros, *B* CEC/Mark
Bolton; 82 *T* Panos Pictures/Caroline Penn, *M* Science Photo Library/Pascal
Goetgheluck, *B* Science Photo Library/Dave Roberts; 83 Mediscan.co.uk; 84
Science Photo Library/Deep light productions; 85 Science Photo Library;
86 John Birdsall Photography; 87 Science Photo Library; 88 Trevor Clifford; 92
Trevor Clifford; 94 *T* Science Photo Library/Maximilian Stock Ltd, *M* Science
Photo Library/Martyn F Chillmaid, *BR* Science Photo Library, *BL* Beaumont
Veterinary Practice/Ginny Stroud-Lewis; 100 *T* Corbis/James L Amos, *B*
Science Photo Library/Peter Menzel; 101 *T* Mary Evans Picture Library, *M*
Camera Press, *B* Hutchison Library/Andrew Sole; 102 Bruce Coleman/Kim
Taylor; 103 *T* Science Photo Library/Jesse, *M* Science Photo Library/Rosenfeld
Images Ltd; 104 *M* Rex Features/Shigeo Kogure/Time, *BL* Science Photo
Library/Carlos Munoz-Yague/Eurelios, *BR* Corbis/Vince Streano; 115 *TL*
Photodisc, *TM* Photodisc, *TR* Photodisc, *MR* Photodisc, *B* Photodisc; 116 *T*
Corbis/Bettmann, *M* Oxford Scientific Films/Doug Allan, *B* Oxford Scientific
Films/Doug Allan; 117 *T* BBC Wild/Niall Benvie, *TM* Oxford Scientific
Films/Doug Allan, *TB* Oxford Scientific Films/Owen Newman, *BR* Science
Photo Library/ER Degginger, *B* Science Photo Library/Stephen J Krasemann;
118 *T* BBC Wild/Mark Payne-Gill, *TML* Oxford Scientific Films/Kathie
Atkinson, *MR* BBC Wild/Graham Hatherley/, *B* Bruce Coleman/Natural
Selection, *BML* Oxford Scientific Films/William Gray; *BMR* Science Photo
Library/Tom McHugh, 119 *T* Oxford Scientific Films/Tim Jackson, *M* BBC
Wild/Mary Ann McDonald; *MR* BBC Wild/Gertrud & Helmut Denzau, 120 *T*
Bruce Coleman/John Cancalosi, *M* Corbis/Ecoscene; 121 Oxford Scientific
Films/Kjell Sandved; 122 *TL* Hutchison Library/Lesley McIntyre, *TR* Science
Photo Library/Phillip Wallick/Agstock; 124 Corbis/Papilo; 125 Oxford
Scientific Films/Mark Hamblin; 126 *T* Oxford Scientific Films/Jeff
Foott/OKAPIA/, *BL* Bruce Coleman/Kim Taylor, *BR* Andy Purcell; 127 *T*
Bruce Coleman/Robert Maier, *B* Science Photo Library; 128 *T* CEC/Mark
Boulton, *M* Bruce Coleman; 129 Science Photo Library/Roger Wilmshurst; 130
T Hutchison Library/NickHaslam, *M* Bruce Coleman/Hans Reinhard, *BM*
Bruce Coleman/Robert Maier, *B* Bruce Coleman/Hans Reinhard; 132 *TL*
Science Photo Library/Jim Gipe/Agstock, *TR* Still Pictures/Joerg Boethling,
M Science Photo Library/Tony Craddock, *B* CORBIS/Natalie Fobes; 134 *T*
Corbis/Jonathan Blair, *M* Science Photo Library/Rosenfeld Images Ltd, *B*
Science Photo Library/Martin Bond; 135 Holt Studios/Nigel Cattlin; 136
Bruce Coleman/Luiz Claudio Marigo; 137 BBC Wild/Mary McDonald; 138
EMPICS/Neal Simpson; 140 *T* Woodfall Wild Images/David Woodfall, *M*
Science Photo Library/Martin Bond, *BM* Still PicturesJim Wark, *B* Science
Photo Library/David Nunuk; 142 *T* Getty Images/Stone, *B* Science Photo
Library/Simon Fraser; 144 *M* Woodfall Wild Images/John Macpherson, *B* Still
Pictures/Mark Edwards; 145 Corbis/Keren Su; 146 *T* Panos Pictures/Jeremy
Hartley, *M* Science Photo Library/Peter Menzel, *B* Still Pictures/Mark
Edwards; 147 Still Pictures/Mark Edwards; 148 *T* Science Photo
Library/Doug Allan, *B* BBC Wild/Ron O'Connor; 151 Gareth Boden; 154 Peter
Gould; 156 *M* Peter Gould, 160 *T* Corbis/Adam Woolfitt, *B* Hutchison
Library/Tony Souter; 161 *T* Peter Gould, *M* CEC/Mark Boulton; 162 *T*
CEC/Mark Boulton, *M* CEC/Mark Boulton, *B* Science Photo Library/Nigel
Cattlin/Holt Studios; 163 CEC/Mark Boulton; 166 *T* Science Photo
Library/Martin Land, *M* Andrew Lambert, *B* Science Photo Library/Martin
Land; 167 *T* Andrew Lambert, *B* Corbis; 168 *(all)* Peter Gould; 169 Milepost 92
1/2; 170 *(all)* Peter Gould; 172 *T* Trevor Clifford, *B* Corbis/Galen Rowell; 173
Trevor Clifford; 174 *T* Science Photo Library/Oscar Burriel, *M* Peter Gould, *B*
Peter Gould; 176 Science Photo Library; 179 *T* Andrew Lambert, *M* Science
Photo Library/David Campione; 183 Science Photo Library/European
Southern Observatory; 187 *T* Alvey & Towers, *M* Alvey & Towers; 188 *T*
Trevor Clifford, *B* Getty Images/FPG International; 190 *T* Alton Towers, *BL*
Trevor Clifford, *BR* Trevor Clifford; 191 Science Photo Library/Erich
Schrempp; 193 Alvey & Towers; 194 *T* Frank Spooner Pictures/John Paul, *B*
Rex Features; 196 *(all)* Rex Features; 197 Science Photo Library/Jim Varney;
198 Genesis Space Photo Library; 200 *T* Alvey & Towers, *B* Corbis/George
Hall; 201 EMPICS; 204 Science Photo Library/David Nunuk; 205 Science
Photo Library/Jerry Schad; 206 Science Photo Library/M-SAT Ltd; 207 Rex
Features/Lucy Kelaart; 208 *T* Science Photo Library/Frank Zullo, *B* Science
Photo Library/James King-Holmes; 209 Science Photo Library; 210 Science
Photo Library/NASA; 212 *T* Science Photo Library, *ML* Science Photo
Library/NASA, *MR* Science Photo Library/NASA, *B* Genesis Space Photo
Library; 213 Science Photo Library/John Mead.

Picture research by Liz Savery.

About this book

This is the second book in the AQA Modular Science series and is designed to guide you through the second year of GCSE study. It has been written to help you find everything you need to prepare for your exams.

For ease-of-use the book has been separated into sections by exam. Modules from Year 10 that are in the exams have recap material to aid revision.

The introductory page to each module will help you get a feel of the module. It explains the topics covered and gets you thinking about the science that you already know.

To help you study we have included some useful features in the book. Here are a few:

Double-page spreads
Everything you need to know for each module is covered in double-page spreads. These pages will cover all the topics you need to understand for your exams. To help you find all of the important points we have included questions to test yourself as you learn.

End of module questions
At the end of each module you will find some test questions. Answering lots of questions will help you check what you have learnt and prepare for exams.

Digging Deeper
These boxes contain extra information about the topic that you are studying. The information in these boxes will not be tested in module tests or exams.

Summary
The information in these boxes summarises the most important points on the page. In your exams you will be tested on your knowledge of the points in the summary boxes. These boxes will also help you make notes and answer questions.

Glossary pages
When a new scientific word appears for the first time in the text, it will appear in **bold** type. All words in bold are listed with their meanings in the glossary at the back of the book. Look there to remind you what they mean.

Data sheet pages
When you sit your exams you will be given data sheets. At the back of the book you will find the information that will be on these data sheets.

Contents

Module 4 – Inheritance and selection

Why do you have some of your father's features and some of your mother's features? Some of your characteristics are due to information in your body's cells, which you **inherited** from your parents. Other characteristics are affected by the environment in which you live and grow.

Breeding from animals and plants with desired characteristics has produced many types of pet and farm animals, as well as garden and crop plants. New breeds have been developed with useful characteristics by **selecting** which animals and plants will reproduce.

Scientists think that life on Earth began about 400 million years ago. Since then more species of animals and plants have developed – and are still developing. This is the process of **evolution**.

This module will help you to understand how information can be passed from parents to their offspring. You will study how useful breeds of animals and plants have been developed and how scientists can even control the characteristics of an organism by changing the material of inheritance found inside cells. You will also learn how species of organisms have evolved and why some species no longer exist.

Before you start, try these questions to check what you know about inheritance and selection.

These children are very different from the orang-utan they are looking at, and different from each other. There are differences between species and between individuals of the same species.

These kittens have many attractive characteristics, which are the result of many generations of breeding.

Fossils are formed from animals and plants that lived many years ago. By studying fossils we can find out how organisms have changed over a long period of time.

1 Where in a cell is inherited information stored?

2 What cells pass information from parents to offspring?

3 Give one example of a characteristic that is inherited, and one that is affected by the environment in which people live and grow.

4 Some animals and plants that lived in the past do not exist today. Suggest reasons why some species no longer exist on the Earth.

4:1 There is no-one like you!

You are unique

There are many different kinds of animals and plants. We call these **species**. You look very similar to other people around you because you belong to the same species.

Even though you look similar you can still be recognised as different from other people around you. This is because of your **characteristics**, or features, such as your hair colour, eye colour and height. These are just a few of the many characteristics that distinguish you from everyone else. There are millions of people in the world, yet no two people are exactly the same. You are unique!

a What important characteristic do the police use to identify criminals even if they have left the scene of a crime?

Spot the difference

Young animals and plants often look like their parents.

b Give two examples of characteristics the puppy in the photograph has in common with:

   i all other dogs

   ii the parent dog.

Young animals and plants look like their parents because some characteristics are **inherited** – they are passed from parents to their offspring.

The puppy in the photograph has many similar characteristics to its parents.

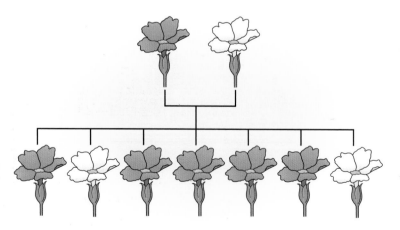

Flower colour is an inherited characteristic.
Some inherited characteristics are more common than others.

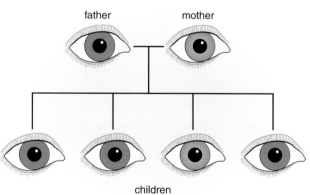

Eye colour is a characteristic that is inherited.

Talent or training?

Not all characteristics are passed on from parents. You cannot just be born with all that it takes to become a world class musician, for example – it depends on years of practice as well as having natural talent. This is because some characteristics are affected by the environment in which you live and grow.

The characteristics of individuals may be due to:

◆ inherited causes

◆ environmental causes

◆ a mixture of both.

It takes more than natural talent to become a world class gymnast.

It runs in the family

It is possible to find out if a characteristic is inherited by tracing it in a family tree.

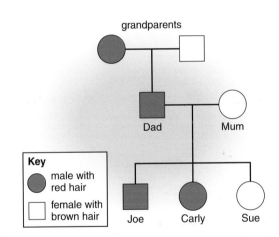

grandparents

Dad   Mum

Key
- male with red hair
- female with brown hair

Joe   Carly   Sue

This family tree shows hair colour in members of a family. Do you think hair colour is an inherited characteristic?

Questions

1 Copy and then complete the table below using words from the list. One example has been filled in for you.

scars	freckles	fingerprints
eye colour	height	body mass
running ability	number of tooth fillings	

Inherited causes	Environmental causes	Mixture of both inherited and environmental causes
		height

2 Look at the family tree diagram.

a Which of the children's parents had red hair?

b Which of the children had brown hair?

c Describe the evidence suggesting that red hair is inherited.

Summary

- Young plants and animals have similar characteristics to their parents.

- Characteristics may be inherited, caused by the environment or caused by both environmental and inherited factors.

4:2 Passing on information

Inheriting features

'Doesn't she have her mother's eyes?' 'Isn't she like her father?' These are typical comments that people make when they first see a baby. Children have similar characteristics to their parents because of the **genes** they inherit. Different genes control the development of different characteristics. For example, the baby in the photograph may have inherited genes that will produce curly hair or freckles.

Children inherit characteristics from their parents.

Genes and chromosomes

The genes that control characteristics are carried on the **chromosomes** contained in the nucleus of a cell. Each chromosome carries a large number of genes.

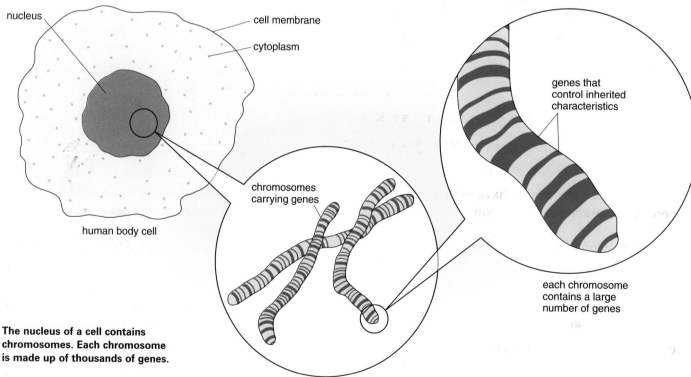

nucleus

cell membrane

cytoplasm

human body cell

chromosomes carrying genes

genes that control inherited characteristics

each chromosome contains a large number of genes

The nucleus of a cell contains chromosomes. Each chromosome is made up of thousands of genes.

Passing on genes

Young animals and plants have similar characteristics to their parents because of the genes that are passed on to them.

Genes are passed from parents to their children in sex cells called **gametes**. In male animals, the sex cells are called **sperm** cells. Sperm cells are made in sex organs called **testes**. In female animals, the sex cells are called **egg** cells. Egg cells are made in sex organs called **ovaries**.

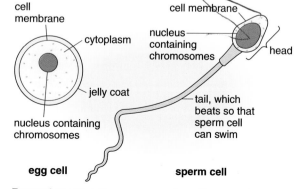

cell membrane

cytoplasm

jelly coat

nucleus containing chromosomes

egg cell

cell membrane

nucleus containing chromosomes

head

tail, which beats so that sperm cell can swim

sperm cell

Egg and sperm cells carry genes from the parents.

a Where are the genes in a sperm cell?

b Why do sperm cells have tails?

Eggs and pollen

Plants also produce sex cells to pass on genes to young plants. Male sex cells are made inside **pollen grains**. Female sex cells are made inside **ovaries**.

Flowers are a plant's reproductive system.

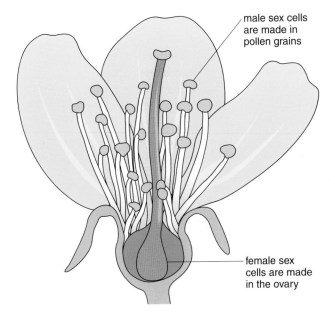

male sex cells are made in pollen grains

female sex cells are made in the ovary

Questions

1 Use words from the list to complete the sentences.

gametes   inherited   chromosomes

genes   characteristics

Young animals and plants have similar _____ to their parents. Characteristics are controlled by _____, which are carried on _____. Inherited information is passed on from parents in special cells called _____.

2 Where are the following cells made?

a sperm cells in an animal

b egg cells in an animal

c female gametes in a plant

d male gametes in a plant

Summary

- The nucleus of a cell contains chromosomes.
- Chromosomes carry a large number of genes.
- Genes control inherited characteristics.
- Genes are passed on from parents to their young in sex cells called gametes.
- In animals, the sex cells are egg cells and sperm cells. In plants, the sex cells are found in the ovaries and pollen grains of flowers.

4:3 Making new cells

The start of life

Your life started from a single cell. The thousands of cells that make up your body developed from this single cell by **cell division**.

Dividing cells

When a cell divides new cells are made.

New cells are needed as organisms grow. Many new cells were made in your body as you developed from a fertilised egg into a baby and then from a baby into a young adult.

New cells are also made as body cells become damaged and need to be replaced. For example, new cells are needed to heal a cut in your skin.

Chromosomes are usually found in pairs in body cells. For example, human body cells contain 23 pairs of chromosomes. When body cells divide new cells are made that are exact copies of the original cell. This means that all your body cells contain the same chromosomes and genes.

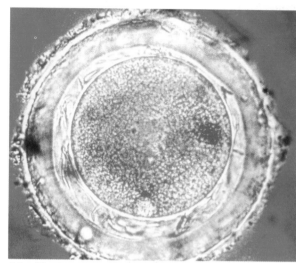

A fertilised egg is the start of a whole new organism.

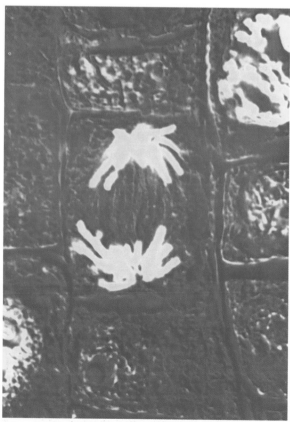

When a cell divides, each chromosome is copied. One copy goes to each new cell, so they both get the same number of chromosomes as the original cell.

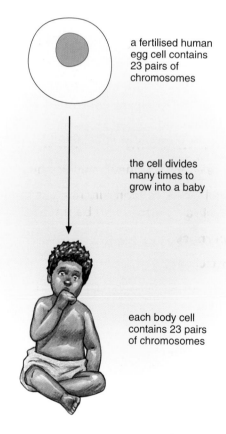

a fertilised human egg cell contains 23 pairs of chromosomes

the cell divides many times to grow into a baby

each body cell contains 23 pairs of chromosomes

All the cells in an organism's body contain exactly the same chromosomes.

Forming gametes

A new life starts from special sex cells called **gametes**, made in the reproductive organs. Cells in the testes form **sperm** cells. Cells in the ovaries form **egg** cells.

Gametes contain only one chromosome from each pair of chromosomes in a normal body cell. Human sperm and egg cells contain 23 *single* chromosomes.

Fusing gametes

The first cell of a new individual is formed when male and female gametes fuse (join together) at **fertilisation**.

Gametes contain *single* chromosomes. When gametes fuse, a cell is formed containing *pairs* of chromosomes.

For example, in humans at fertilisation a sperm cell containing 23 chromosomes fuses with an egg containing 23 chromosomes. The fertilised egg contains 23 *pairs* of chromosomes.

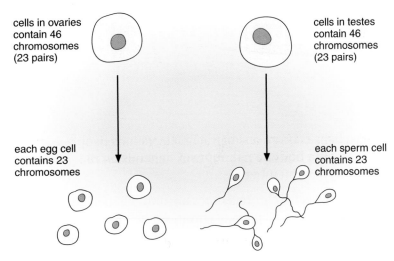

cells in ovaries contain 46 chromosomes (23 pairs)

cells in testes contain 46 chromosomes (23 pairs)

each egg cell contains 23 chromosomes

each sperm cell contains 23 chromosomes

Gametes are formed in reproductive organs.

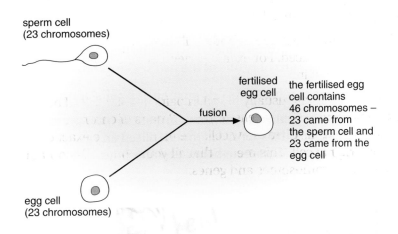

sperm cell (23 chromosomes)

fusion

fertilised egg cell

the fertilised egg cell contains 46 chromosomes – 23 came from the sperm cell and 23 came from the egg cell

egg cell (23 chromosomes)

When gametes fuse, the fertilised cell has the right number of chromosomes for a normal body cell.

Questions

1 State two reasons why new cells are needed.

2 The body cells of a cat contain **19 pairs** of chromosomes. How many chromosomes will be found in:

   a a cat sperm cell

   b a cat muscle cell

   c a cat egg cell that has been fertilised.

3 Use words from the list to complete the sentences.

> fertilised   fuse   chromosomes   divides
>
> genes   gametes   parents

Human egg and sperm cells are called _____. They contain 23 _____. When sperm and egg cells _____, a _____ egg cell is made. This cell then _____ many times to make body cells. Each body cell contains chromosomes from both _____.

Summary

- Body cells divide to produce additional cells during growth or to produce replacement cells.

- In body cells chromosomes are usually in pairs.

- Sex cells contain a single set of chromosomes.

- Sex cells fuse during reproduction.

- Fusion of sex cells forms new cells containing chromosomes from both parents.

4:4 Chromosomes and genes

Boy or girl?

When a baby is born, one of the first questions people ask is whether it is a boy or a girl. Your sex depends on the chromosomes you inherit.

In your body cells, chromosomes are found in pairs. Human body cells contain 23 pairs of chromosomes. One of these pairs is the **sex chromosomes**. In females, the two sex chromosomes are the same (XX). In males, they are different (XY).

Chromosomes in sex cells

Sex cells (sperm and egg cells) contain only one chromosome from each pair of chromosomes. This means that each sperm and egg cell contains only one of the two sex chromosomes.

a How many chromosomes do human sex cells contain?

Your sex was set by the chromosome present in one sperm cell from your father – the sperm cell that fertilised an egg and started your life. The diagram below explains how.

b Why is there a 50% chance of a baby being a girl?

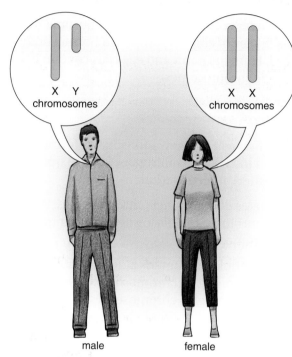

Male humans have XY sex chromosomes. Female humans have XX.

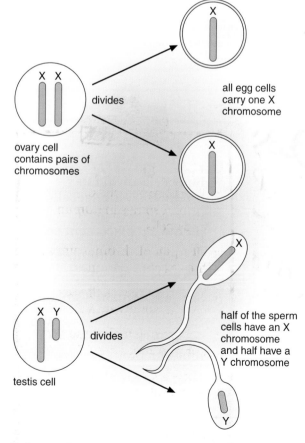

Each sex cell contains only one sex chromosome – an X or a Y.

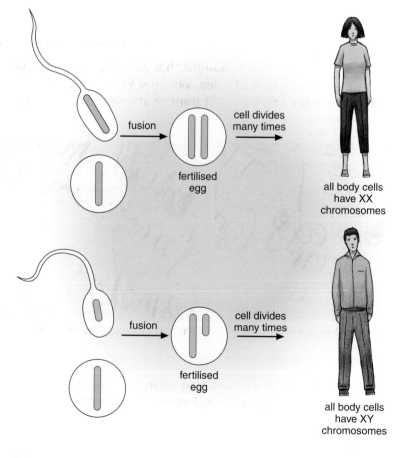

If the sperm cell contains an X, the fertilised egg becomes a female. If it contains a Y, the fertilised egg becomes a male.

Pairs of genes

The diagram shows a pair of chromosomes. Because paired chromosomes are identical, the same genes are carried along the length of each one. This means that genes, like chromosomes, are found in pairs.

Different forms of genes

Many genes have different forms called **alleles**. For example, the gene that controls the colour of a rabbit's fur has two alleles. The diagram shows the alleles that may be present and the colour of the rabbit's fur.

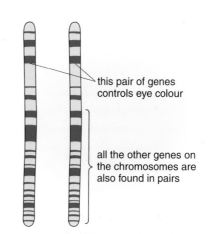

this pair of genes controls eye colour

all the other genes on the chromosomes are also found in pairs

Body cells contain pairs of chromosomes. The genes carried on the chromosomes also come in pairs.

c i Which alleles are present in rabbits with white fur?

ii Which alleles are present in rabbits with black fur?

Dominant and recessive

Rabbits will always have black fur if the B allele is present. This is an example of a **dominant** allele.

A rabbit will have white fur only when there is no dominant B allele, and both alleles are b. Allele b is an example of a **recessive** allele.

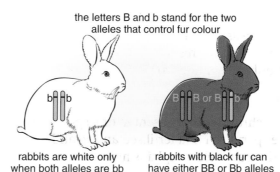

the letters B and b stand for the two alleles that control fur colour

rabbits are white only when both alleles are bb

rabbits with black fur can have either BB or Bb alleles

The different colours of rabbits are caused by different alleles.

Questions

For a long time scientists thought that panthers and spotted leopards were different species. We now know that they are the same species and their different coat colours are due to different alleles.

The panther has alleles ss.

The leopard has alleles SS or Ss.

1 Which allele is recessive?

2 If two panthers mated and had young, predict what the cubs' coat colour would be. Explain your answer.

Summary

- There are 23 pairs of chromosomes in human body cells.

- One pair of chromosomes is the sex chromosomes.

- In human males, the sex chromosomes are XY.

- In human females, the sex chromosomes are XX.

- Some genes have different forms called alleles.

- Alleles may be dominant or recessive.

Joining sex cells

To produce a young animal or plant, a male sex cell **fuses** with a female sex cell.

Your life began when a sperm cell from your father fused with an egg cell from your mother.

Producing young animals or plants by the fusion of male and female gametes is called **sexual reproduction**. This type of reproduction produces individuals who have a mixture of genes from two parents. This is why you look like your father in some ways and your mother in other ways.

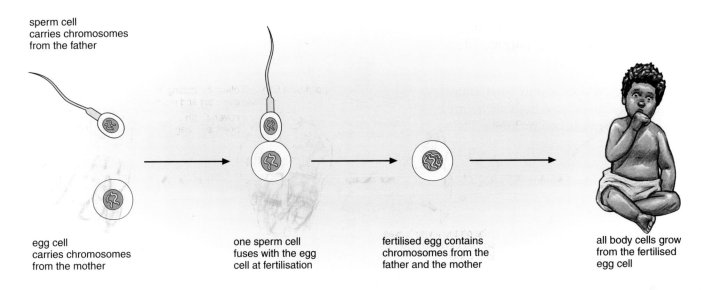

sperm cell
carries chromosomes
from the father

egg cell
carries chromosomes
from the mother

one sperm cell
fuses with the egg
cell at fertilisation

fertilised egg contains
chromosomes from the
father and the mother

all body cells grow
from the fertilised
egg cell

Sexual reproduction means you are similar to both your parents, but not identical to them.

a Why does a child show characteristics from both parents?

Young plants from seeds

Young plants can also be formed from sexual reproduction. Plants produce gametes in their flowers. After the gametes have fused, an embryo plant develops inside a seed.

Pips contain seeds. Seeds contain chromosomes from the parents.

The strawberry plant, like many others, can make new plants by sexual reproduction.

Young plants without seeds

Young plants do not always grow from seeds. They sometimes grow from the ordinary body cells of plants. The diagram shows young strawberry plants being made from one parent plant. The parent plant does not use gametes to reproduce in this way. This type of reproduction is called **asexual reproduction**.

Asexual reproduction produces individuals with identical genes to the parent. These identical individuals form a **clone**.

Young plants from cuttings

Young plants can be grown from older plants by taking **cuttings**. Plants grown from cuttings from the same parent plant will have identical genes. Cuttings can be taken from the stems, leaves or roots of plants.

By taking cuttings, gardeners can produce many young plants with the same characteristics quickly and cheaply.

parent plant

new plant formed by asexual reproduction

The strawberry plant can also make identical new plants by asexual reproduction.

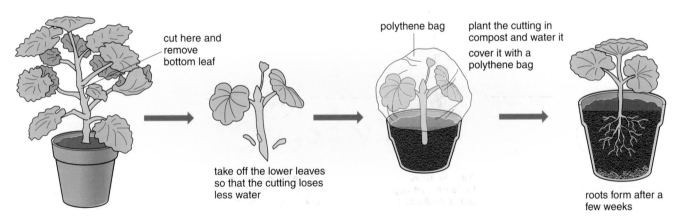

cut here and remove bottom leaf

take off the lower leaves so that the cutting loses less water

polythene bag

plant the cutting in compost and water it

cover it with a polythene bag

roots form after a few weeks

Taking cuttings from a plant.

Questions

1 a Why do gardeners place a polythene bag over cuttings?

 b Explain why cuttings grown from the same plant are identical.

 c Give two advantages of growing plants from cuttings.

2 a Explain why strawberry plants grown from runners are identical.

 b Explain why strawberry plants grown from seeds have different characteristics.

3 Sometimes a fertilised egg splits into two and grows to make identical twins. Suggest why identical twins have the same genes as each other.

Summary
- Sexual reproduction involves the fusion of gametes.
- The young produced by sexual reproduction have a mixture of genes from both parents.
- In asexual reproduction there is no fusion of gametes.
- The young produced by asexual reproduction have identical genes to the parent.

The start of your life

An egg is released from one of a woman's ovaries about every 28 days. The egg passes out of the ovary into an oviduct (egg duct). The egg moves along the oviduct towards the **womb**.

If sperm cells are present in the oviduct, one of the sperm cells may fuse with the egg cell. This is called **fertilisation**. If an egg is not fertilised it soon dies.

The fertilised egg cell grows to form an embryo, which attaches to the lining of the womb.

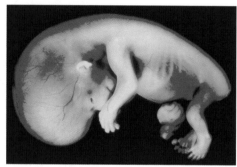

An eight week old embryo attached to the womb of the mother.

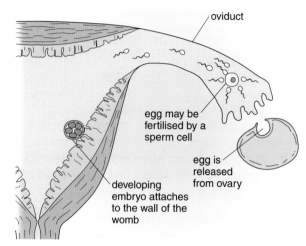

oviduct

egg may be fertilised by a sperm cell

egg is released from ovary

developing embryo attaches to the wall of the womb

A woman has two ovaries (only one is shown here). Each month, one of the ovaries releases an egg.

Getting the timing right

The lining of the womb needs to be ready to receive a growing embryo. At the same time that an egg is developing inside an ovary, the lining of the womb becomes thicker. The thick lining contains many blood vessels to supply the developing embryo with food and oxygen.

If the egg is not fertilised, the lining of the womb breaks down causing bleeding. This is the woman's monthly period.

The release of an egg and the growth of the womb lining are both controlled by chemicals called **hormones**. These hormones are released from the **pituitary gland** and from the **ovary glands**.

Controlling fertility

The hormones that control the release of eggs and the growth of the womb lining can be used to control **fertility**.

Hormones can be used to:

 ◆ stop a woman becoming pregnant

 ◆ help a woman to become pregnant.

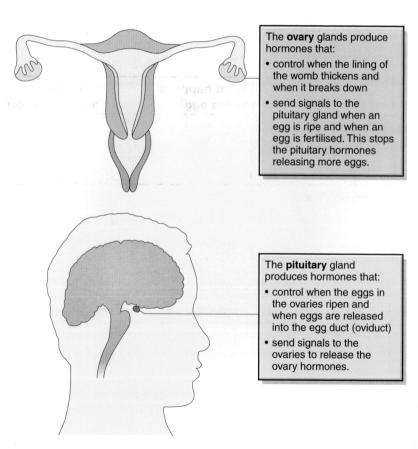

The **ovary** glands produce hormones that:
• control when the lining of the womb thickens and when it breaks down
• send signals to the pituitary gland when an egg is ripe and when an egg is fertilised. This stops the pituitary hormones releasing more eggs.

The **pituitary** gland produces hormones that:
• control when the eggs in the ovaries ripen and when eggs are released into the egg duct (oviduct)
• send signals to the ovaries to release the ovary hormones.

Glands make and release chemical messengers called hormones.

Stopping egg release

Some couples want to have sexual intercourse but do not want the woman to become pregnant. The woman can take the **contraceptive pill**. The pill contains hormones that stop eggs being released from the ovaries.

The pill has to be taken every day. It is a very reliable method of stopping pregnancy but it can produce side effects. Some women get headaches or feel sick. In a very small number of women, the contraceptive pill can cause heart problems.

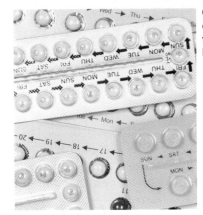

Contraceptive pills contain hormones that stop eggs being released.

Stimulating egg release

Some couples want to have children but the woman cannot become pregnant because her ovaries do not release eggs. She is infertile.

The woman can be treated by having a hormone injected regularly into her blood. The hormone acts as a **fertility drug** by stimulating the release of eggs from the ovaries.

Fertility treatment does not always work. Or, sometimes, it may cause more than one egg to be released. This can result in twins, triplets, quadruplets or even more!

Sometimes fertility drugs do not work – sometimes they work too well!

Questions

1 Copy and complete the table.

	What happens to the egg?	What happens to the lining of the womb?
Egg is not fertilised		
Egg is fertilised		

2 Copy and complete the table.

	Benefits	Problems
Using hormones as a contraceptive pill		
Using hormones as fertility drugs		

Summary

- Hormones control the release of eggs from the ovaries.

- Hormones also control changes in thickness in the lining of the womb.

- These hormones are produced by the pituitary gland and by the ovaries.

- Hormones that stimulate the release of eggs can be used as fertility drugs.

- Hormones that prevent the release of eggs are used in the contraceptive pill.

- Using hormones as contraceptives or as fertility drugs can have both benefits and problems.

4:7 Investigating inheritance

Early genetics

In the 1860s, Gregor Mendel carried out some very important investigations to find out how characteristics are inherited. At this time, no-one knew about chromosomes or genes because they were not yet discovered.

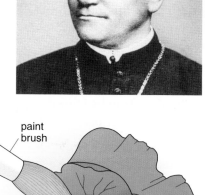

Gregor Mendel (1822–84) carried out investigations to find out how characteristics are inherited.

Controlling breeding

In his investigations, Mendel used pea plants with distinctive characteristics such as flower colour and height. He also controlled which parent plants produced young plants by transferring pollen from one plant to another. He used hundreds of plants in his experiments.

From his results, he made predictions about the way characteristics are passed from one generation to the next.

a Why did Mendel use very large numbers of plants in his investigations?

b What is transferred when pollen is taken from one plant and put onto the flower of another plant?

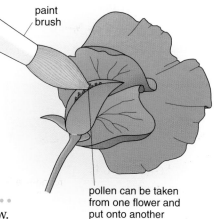

paint brush

Pollen from a chosen plant can be transferred to another chosen plant to find out which characteristics are inherited.

pollen can be taken from one flower and put onto another

Finding a pattern

One of the investigations carried out by Mendel is shown below.

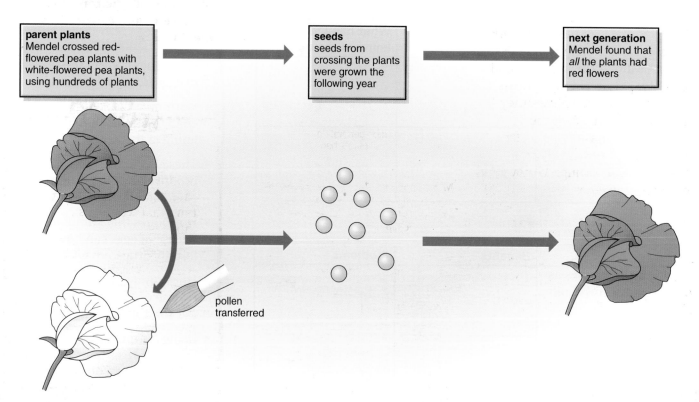

parent plants	seeds	next generation
Mendel crossed red-flowered pea plants with white-flowered pea plants, using hundreds of plants	seeds from crossing the plants were grown the following year	Mendel found that *all* the plants had red flowers

pollen transferred

This investigation looked at how flower colour is inherited in pea plants.

Making conclusions

From the results of this investigation, and many others, Mendel concluded that:

- some characteristics, such as flower colour, are controlled by a pair of 'inherited factors'
- only one of these factors is present in a gamete
- 'inherited factors' can be dominant or recessive.

The diagram shows how Mendel explained the results of his investigation with red and white flowered pea plants.

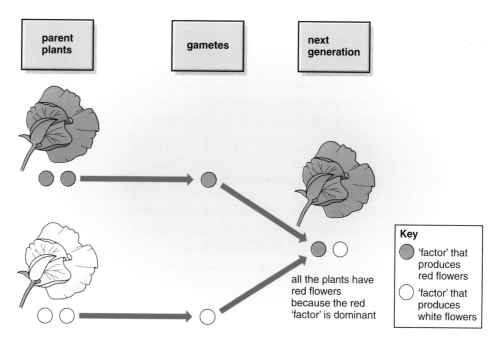

all the plants have red flowers because the red 'factor' is dominant

Key
- 'factor' that produces red flowers
- 'factor' that produces white flowers

What Mendel called 'factors' we call 'genes' or 'alleles' today.

Testing his ideas

Once Mendel had made his conclusions, he carried out more investigations to make sure his findings were accurate. The diagram shows an investigation carried out with pea plants that had round seeds and plants with wrinkled seeds.

Important findings

The importance of Mendel's work was not recognised until after his death. By then chromosomes had been discovered. Once scientists knew about chromosomes, they could then explain how the 'inherited factors' suggested by Mendel could be passed from parents to their young. We now call these 'factors' genes.

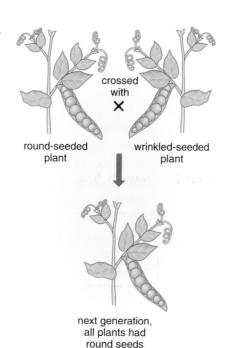

round-seeded plant crossed with ✕ wrinkled-seeded plant

next generation, all plants had round seeds

Mendel found when he crossed round-seeded and wrinkled-seeded plants, all the seeds produced grew into round-seeded plants.

Question

The diagram explains the results of the investigation using round-seeded and wrinkled-seeded plants.

Copy the diagram. Fill in the boxes using the letters R and r to represent the alleles for round-seeded and wrinkled-seeded plants. One of the boxes has been filled in already.

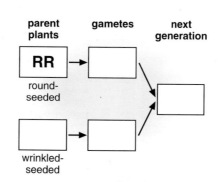

parent plants | gametes | next generation

RR
round-seeded

wrinkled-seeded

DIGGING DEEPER

Tomatoes grown in the UK are usually round. The round shape is due to a single allele. Italian tomatoes found in many cans of tomatoes contain a different allele – they are long rather than round. When plant breeders crossed the two types of tomato, all the tomatoes produced were round. Which is the dominant allele?

Summary

- Mendel carried out investigations to find out how characteristics are inherited.
- He suggested the idea of 'inherited factors', which we now call genes.
- His discoveries were not recognised until after his death.
- By that time other scientists had discovered chromosomes.

4:8 Harmful genes

Inheriting illness

Most illnesses are caused when microbes get into your body. For example, measles and flu are diseases caused by certain viruses that get inside your body and cells.

There are some diseases that are not caused by microbes. Some health problems are caused by the genes passed on to children from their parents. These are called **inherited disorders**.

Cystic fibrosis

One child in every 2000 is affected by an inherited disorder called **cystic fibrosis**. The photograph below shows a girl who suffers from cystic fibrosis. Her body produces a thick, sticky mucus. This blocks the air passages in her lungs. Because of the blockages, the girl will get a lot of chest infections. She will also have difficulty digesting and absorbing food because a lot of mucus is produced by her digestive system.

Regular physiotherapy and strong antibiotics help, but each time the girl gets an infection she becomes more and more ill.

There is no cure for cystic fibrosis yet. Scientists are working on ways to replace the faulty allele.

Inheriting faulty genes

Cystic fibrosis is caused by a faulty *recessive* allele. The faulty alleles must be passed on from both parents. The parents may be **carriers** of the disease without having the disease themselves.

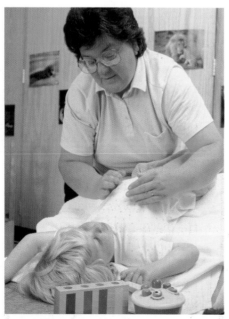

Physiotherapy helps to shift the mucus from the lungs and unblock the air passages.

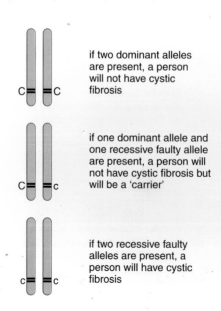

If both parents are carriers, they may produce a child with cystic fibrosis.

if two dominant alleles are present, a person will not have cystic fibrosis

if one dominant allele and one recessive faulty allele are present, a person will not have cystic fibrosis but will be a 'carrier'

if two recessive faulty alleles are present, a person will have cystic fibrosis

Key
C   dominant allele
c   recessive allele

Huntington's disease

Huntington's disease is an inherited disorder that damages the brain and other parts of the nervous system. People with the disease lose control of their movements and cannot remember things.

Sadly, there is no cure. People with Huntington's disease need a lot of care and eventually die from the disease.

Faulty dominant alleles

Huntington's disease is caused by a faulty *dominant* allele, so only one allele needs to be present for the person to have the disease. It is passed on even if only one parent has the disease.

Signs of the disease do not appear until people are 30–50 years old. This means that people may have children before finding out that they have a disease that can be inherited.

even if just one dominant faulty allele is present, a person will have Huntington's disease

a person will not have Huntington's disease if two recessive alleles are present

Key
H dominant allele
h recessive allele

Huntington's disease is caused by a faulty dominant allele.

Questions

1 a Sue has Huntington's disease. Which of her parents also has the disease?

 b What evidence shows that Huntington's disease is inherited?

 c Sammy has cystic fibrosis. Neither of his parents have this disease but are 'carriers'. Explain what this means.

 d Using the letters c and C, say what alleles are present in the body cells of:

   i Sammy

   ii Sammy's father.

2 Use words from this list to complete the sentences.

   contagious   recessive   inherited

   Huntington's   Mendel's

   Some diseases are passed on by genes. These are called _____ diseases. An example is cystic fibrosis, which is caused by a faulty _____ allele. An example of a disease caused by a dominant allele is _____ disease.

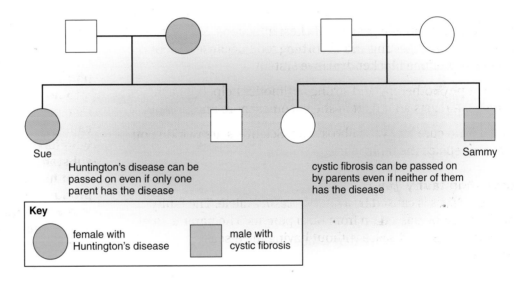

Huntington's disease can be passed on even if only one parent has the disease

cystic fibrosis can be passed on by parents even if neither of them has the disease

Key

female with Huntington's disease

male with cystic fibrosis

Inheritance of Huntington's disease and cystic fibrosis.

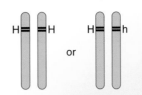

Summary

- Some diseases are caused by faulty alleles.
- These diseases can be inherited.
- Cystic fibrosis is caused by a faulty recessive allele.
- Huntington's disease is caused by a faulty dominant allele.
- Parents may be carriers of an inherited disease.

4:9 Blood disorders

Blocking blood vessels

Sickle cell disease is an inherited disorder.

The disorder affects red blood cells, which carry oxygen from the lungs to all parts of your body. It is also called sickle cell **anaemia** – anaemia occurs when not enough oxygen gets to body organs.

People with sickle cell disease have red blood cells that are rigid and sickle-shaped. Healthy red blood cells can bend easily and have a doughnut shape.

Healthy red blood cells can bend to squeeze through small blood vessels. Rigid sickle red blood cells cannot get through small blood vessels. This causes blood vessels to become blocked and oxygen cannot get to where it is needed. Organs become damaged, causing a lot of pain.

a What is the job of red blood cells?

b What happens when red blood cells become faulty?

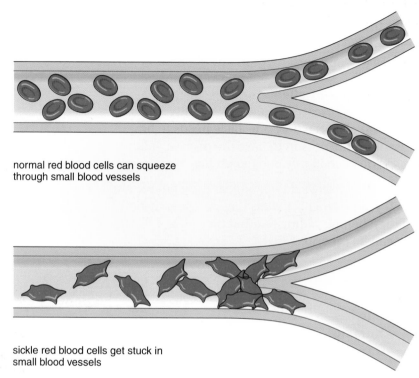

normal red blood cells can squeeze through small blood vessels

sickle red blood cells get stuck in small blood vessels

The shape and stiffness of sickle red blood cells mean they clog up small blood vessels.

Inheriting sickle cell disease

Sickle cell disease is caused by a faulty allele.

People with sickle cell disease have two faulty alleles. This causes their red blood cells to be sickle-shaped.

People can inherit just one faulty allele and one 'normal' allele. They will be **carriers** of the disease. They do not usually have anaemia, but they have to be careful when they are doing an activity where there is less oxygen than usual, such as scuba diving.

c What is a 'carrier' of an inherited disease?

A puzzling pattern

In parts of Africa more babies are born with sickle cell disease than in other parts of the world. Doctors could not explain this for many years.

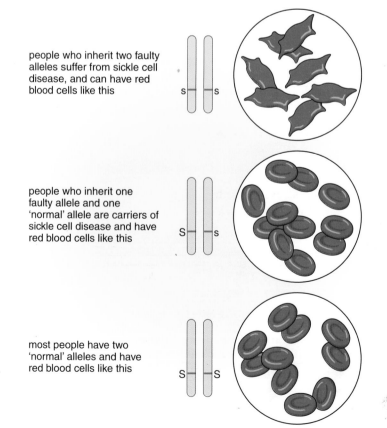

people who inherit two faulty alleles suffer from sickle cell disease, and can have red blood cells like this

people who inherit one faulty allele and one 'normal' allele are carriers of sickle cell disease and have red blood cells like this

most people have two 'normal' alleles and have red blood cells like this

Sickle cell disease is inherited.

These maps give an explanation.

The maps show that areas where sickle cell disease is common match areas where malaria is common. Malaria is a disease that also affects red blood cells. Thousands of babies die from malaria every year.

People who are carriers of sickle cell disease do not have anaemia and they do not get malaria. In parts of the world where malaria is common it is an advantage to have the faulty allele.

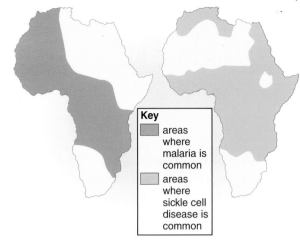

In Africa, sickle cell disease is common where malaria is common.

Key
- areas where malaria is common
- areas where sickle cell disease is common

alleles that may be present	 SS alleles	 Ss alleles	 ss alleles
effects of alleles	normal red blood cells no anaemia no resistance to malaria	normal red blood cells slight risk of anaemia resistance to malaria	sickle-shaped red blood cells sickle cell disease causing anaemia resistance to malaria

In some circumstances, a 'faulty' gene can be helpful.

Questions

1 a Describe evidence that shows there is a link between malaria and sickle cell disease.

   b Explain why it may be beneficial to be a carrier of sickle cell disease in countries in Africa.

2 The diagram shows which members of a family have sickle cell disease.

   a Which member of the family has sickle cell disease?

   b Which alleles for this disease are present in Farah's cells?

   c Even though Farah and Joseph do not have sickle cell disease, could they have children with the disease? Explain your answer.

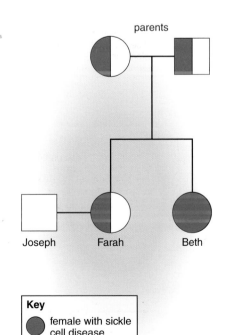

parents

Joseph   Farah   Beth

Key
- female with sickle cell disease
- male carrier

Summary

- Sickle cell disease is an inherited disease that affects red blood cells.

- This disease reduces the ability of red blood cells to carry oxygen to body organs.

- It can be beneficial to be a carrier of this disease in countries where malaria is common.

4:10 Selecting the best

Tasty foods

The shelves of your local supermarket are stacked with a wide choice of good quality foods. This food has been produced from plants and animals bred by farmers.

Farmers choose which plants and animals have useful characteristics and then use them for breeding. This means that these characteristics will be passed on to young plants and animals. Selecting the plants and animals used for breeding is called **artificial selection**.

Breeding better plants

The very first plants used to produce food were wild plants. By choosing which plants were used for breeding, farmers produced new varieties.

Broccoli is a plant grown for food. We use the flower heads as a vegetable. The photograph shows the flower head from the modern variety of broccoli. Wild broccoli contains several much smaller flower heads.

a What characteristic makes the modern variety more useful to farmers than wild broccoli?

Wheat is a very important plant grown by farmers. It is used to make flour to make bread, cakes and other foods. Modern varieties of wheat have characteristics more useful to farmers than older varieties.

b The diagram below shows the modern and old varieties of wheat. What characteristics make the modern variety a better plant?

We need plants and animals with the best characteristics to produce the foods we buy.

Many years of breeding have produced more useful varieties of broccoli.

The ears of wild wheat are small and have few seeds.

This is an ear of modern wheat. It is large and has many seeds. The seeds are used to make flour.

The ears ripen at different times and can be diseased.
The stalks grow to different heights, making it hard to cut the crop.

The ears all ripen at the same time and are resistant to disease.
The stalks grow to the same height, making it easier for farmers to cut the crop.

wild wheat

modern wheat

Advantages of modern varieties of wheat.

Breeding better animals

New breeds of farm animals have been produced by choosing which animals are used for breeding. The new breeds have characteristics that are wanted by farmers.

For example, the hens used by farmers many years ago produced about 20 eggs per year. Modern varieties of hen lay eggs for most of the year and produce about 240 eggs per year.

This is what the first hens were like.

Hens have been bred to increase the number of eggs they lay.

More milk

The black and white cows you often see in fields are a breed called Friesian. This breed is used by farmers to produce milk.

Dairy Shorthorns used to be a more common breed used by farmers for milk.

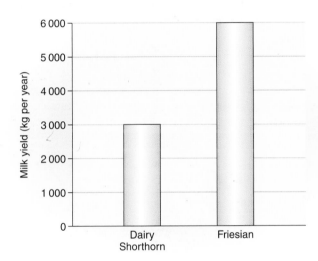

The amounts of milk produced by Dairy Shorthorn and Friesian cows each year.

A Dairy Shorthorn cow.

A Friesian cow.

Questions

1 a How much milk is produced by:

  i Dairy Shorthorns

  ii Friesians?

 b Explain why dairy farmers developed the Friesian breed of cows.

2 Use words from the list to complete the sentences.

   artificial   **breeding**   **characteristics**

   chromosomes   **selecting**

Light Sussex hens are a breed of chicken. This breed was developed by _____ chickens with the most useful _____ and _____ from them. This is an example of _____ selection.

3 a List four characteristics of modern wheat that make this variety more useful than wild wheat.

 b Explain why each characteristic is useful.

Summary
- Selective breeding has produced new varieties of plants and new breeds of animals.
- Using modern varieties of plants and breeds of animals has increased food production.
- Choosing which animals and plants are used for breeding is an example of artificial selection.

4:11 High-tech breeding

Modern technology

Selective breeding has been used for many years to produce new varieties of plants and new breeds of animals.

Modern techniques are now used to make breeding more efficient.

Test tube plants

The photograph shows plants growing on a special jelly. The jelly contains nutrients and hormones to help the plants to grow. Tiny pieces of plant are placed on the jelly. The tiny pieces form roots and shoots and develop into whole plants. This technique is called **tissue culture**.

Using tissue culture, plant breeders can grow large numbers of plants containing the same genes, from just one plant. The new plants form a **clone**.

Tissue culture can be used to produce identical new plants.

a Why are the new plants grown from a single plant called a clone?

Breeding without mating

Farmers can produce calves without a cow and bull even mating.

They do this by collecting sperm cells from a bull with the most useful characteristics. The sperm cells are then injected into a cow's reproductive system.

b Why will the calves produced by injecting sperm cells inherit characteristics from both the bull and the cow?

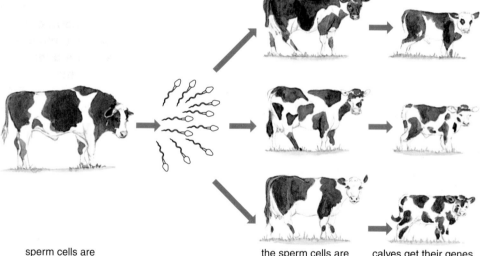

sperm cells are taken from the best bulls

the sperm cells are used to fertilise the best cows

calves get their genes from both the best bull and one of the best cows

Injecting sperm cells to produce the best animals.

Transplanting embryos

Breeders also use embryo transplants to produce young animals with the characteristics they want. The diagram on the next page shows how embryo transplants are carried out.

All the young animals produced from a single fertilised egg will have identical genes – they will be a **clone**. This means that a breeder can produce more young animals with chosen characteristics.

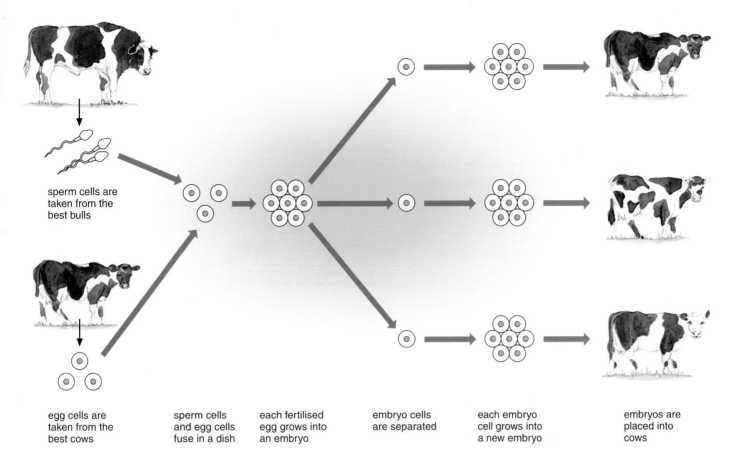

sperm cells are
taken from the
best bulls

egg cells are
taken from the
best cows

sperm cells
and egg cells
fuse in a dish

each fertilised
egg grows into
an embryo

embryo cells
are separated

each embryo
cell grows into
a new embryo

embryos are
placed into
cows

**Embryo transplantation can be used to breed
many animals with chosen characteristics.**

c Explain why the embryos that are transplanted
   contain identical genes.

Cloning – should it be used?

Some people argue that breeding lots of identical
animals using embryo transplants ('cloning') is not
natural. It is as though the scientists are 'playing God'.

Scientists argue that cloning from embryos is a
method of controlling the breeding of animals that
can be used to do good.

Question

The following examples describe cases where cloning *could*
be used. In each case, explain your views on whether
cloning methods *should* be used.

a A dog breeder wants to use cloning methods to increase
   the number of pups to sell.

b Scientists in a developing country in Africa want to use
   cloning to raise healthy cattle.

c Scientists working in a zoo want to use cloning methods
   to breed from an animal of an endangered species that
   may become extinct.

DIGGING DEEPER

The sperm cells collected from a bull can be stored
at low temperatures. This keeps the sperm cells
alive for a long time. By keeping the sperm cells at
low temperatures, farmers can transport them to
farms all over the country and use them to fertilise
cows. This is easier than transporting bulls!

Summary

- Plants and animals can be
  produced using cloning
  techniques.

- Tissue culture is a cloning
  technique used to grow new
  plants from small groups of
  cells from part of a parent
  plant.

- Cells from a developing
  animal embryo can be split
  apart. The identical
  embryos that form are then
  transplanted into host
  mothers.

4:12 Swapping genes

Missing chemicals

Some illnesses are caused when a person cannot make a substance that is needed for their body to work. For example, some people have **diabetes** because their body cannot make a hormone called **insulin**. This hormone is used in your body to control the amount of sugar in your blood.

a What is the sugar in your blood used for?

b Suggest the effect of a low amount of sugar in someone's blood.

Steve Redgrave (second from the right) needs to inject himself with insulin six times a day just to stay alive. But he was determined that his diabetes would not prevent him winning gold at the Sydney Olympic Games.

Treating diabetes

People who have diabetes control the amount of sugar in their blood by injecting themselves with insulin. Regular insulin injections help people who have diabetes to lead a healthy life.

Over a million people in the UK have diabetes, so large amounts of insulin are needed. Insulin can be obtained from cattle and from pigs. Over recent years, scientists have developed methods of producing human insulin from bacteria.

Cutting and sticking genes

You have a gene in your chromosomes that makes insulin. Scientists have been able to cut this gene out of the chromosome that carries it and then stick it into a chromosome of a bacterial cell. This is an example of **genetic engineering**.

DIGGING DEEPER

Before insulin was available, people with diabetes slowly lost more and more weight and eventually died. In 1922, a 14-year-old Canadian boy with diabetes was treated with extract from the pancreas of a dog. After treatment, the teenager was able to eat a normal diet and began to put on weight and lead an active life. Without this treatment he would have died.

Insulin was then extracted from the pancreas of pigs and cattle and made available for the treatment of diabetes. Now human insulin is made by 'genetic engineering' from bacteria.

stage 1

The gene that makes insulin is cut out from the DNA.

gene for
making insulin

human DNA   special enzymes act   ... 'cutting out' gene
                   like molecular sissors...   from rest of DNA

stage 2

The human gene is inserted into bacterial DNA.

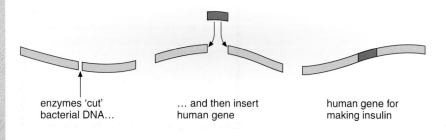

enzymes 'cut'   ... and then insert   human gene for
bacterial DNA...   human gene   making insulin

Cutting and sticking the human gene for insulin into bacterial cells.

Bacterial factories

Bacteria containing the human gene that makes insulin can be grown inside massive storage vessels. The temperature and nutrients inside the vessels are controlled so that the bacteria will grow rapidly.

Rapid growth produces millions of bacterial cells inside the vessels, each cell containing the human gene that makes insulin. This means that large amounts of insulin can be made.

c If a bacterial cell reproduces to form two cells every minute, how many cells will be formed in five minutes?

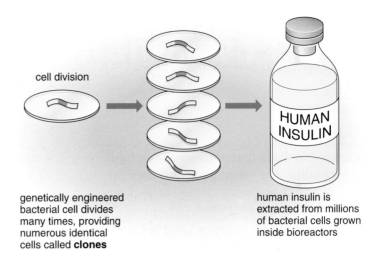

cell division

genetically engineered bacterial cell divides many times, providing numerous identical cells called **clones**

human insulin is extracted from millions of bacterial cells grown inside bioreactors

Human insulin produced by bacteria is now available to people with diabetes.

Adding genes to plants

Recently scientists have found ways of cutting genes from bacteria and sticking them into the crops grown by farmers. For example, some bacteria produce a protein that is poisonous to some insects. The gene that makes the protein can be cut out and added to the genes of a crop plant. Because the crop plant makes the poisonous protein, farmers will need to use smaller amounts of insecticides to kill insects that damage the crop.

Other genes can be changed to make crops resistant to disease or to increase their vitamin content.

The Daily Glob

Activists destroy GM crops

Quest

'Gene crops are food for future', say scientists

NEWSDAY

BAN GENETIC POLLUTION

Crops that have had their genes changed in this way are called genetically modified crops (**GM crops**).

Some people are against the use of GM crops. They say they are unsafe and we do not know the long-term effects of adding and replacing genes.

Questions

1 Use words from the list to complete the sentences.

    gene   chromosome   insulin   bacteria   sugar   protein

Someone with diabetes needs regular injections of a hormone called _____ to control the amount of _____ in their blood. This hormone is made by a _____, which can be cut out and added to _____.

2 GM crops are grown in countries such as the USA. They cannot be grown in the UK except on test sites. Give two reasons:

a in support of growing GM crops

b why GM crops should not be grown.

Summary

- Genes from the chromosomes of humans and other organisms can be cut out using enzymes.

- The genes can then be put into bacterial cells.

- The swapped gene makes the same protein in the bacterial cell.

- Bacteria can be grown on a large scale to manufacture drugs such as human insulin.

- Genes can be transferred to the cells of animals and plants to give them useful characteristics.

4:13 Forming new species

Changing species

People used to think that all living things had always remained the same. They also thought that living things had been created at the same time that the Earth was created.

As scientists learned more and more about plants and animals, they suggested that species have *not* always been the same and that new species are being formed. This is the **theory of evolution**.

Charles Darwin was one of the first scientists to explain how the process of evolution takes place.

Changing people's ideas

A five year voyage on board a ship called *HMS Beagle* took Darwin all around the world. During this long voyage Darwin kept careful records of his many observations and collected hundreds of specimens.

After studying all his evidence and discussing his ideas with other scientists, Darwin suggested that new species can be formed by a process called **natural selection**.

Darwin was so concerned about how other scientists would react to his ideas that he did not publish his findings for many years. Most people still believed that species were created and did not evolve. To suggest that species evolve went against what many people understood from the Bible to be the 'truth'.

When Darwin's ideas were first presented to a group of well-known scientists, the audience remained in total silence at the end the talk.

Darwin finally published his ideas in 1859, but his findings were rejected by some scientists for over 50 years afterwards.

Natural selection

The process of natural selection is summarised in the diagram on the right.

a **Look at the diagram. Why do varieties with poor camouflage have less chance of passing on their genes to the next generation?**

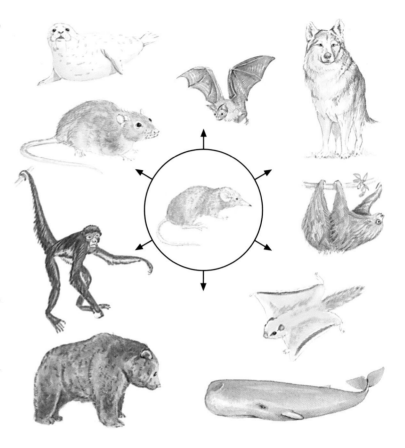

Species gradually change over many generations. This is evolution.

1 Organisms produce many offspring and have to compete for food.

2 Organisms struggle to survive. They may die from disease or be eaten by predators.

3 Members of a species may have different characteristics.

4 Characteristics that give an organism an advantage are more likely to be passed on to the next generation.

Natural selection means that helpful characteristics are inherited by more offspring.

Different varieties

On his voyage Darwin visited a group of islands near South America called the Galapagos Islands. He made many recordings of the features of birds on the islands called finches.

When he returned to England, Darwin continued to study his recordings. He realised that many of the birds he had seen were different varieties of the same species of finch. One of the characteristics of each variety was the shape and length of its beak. The shape of its beak enabled each variety to feed on a particular type of food.

Darwin suggested that each of the different varieties was descended from one variety of finch. The diagram shows how different varieties evolved by natural selection.

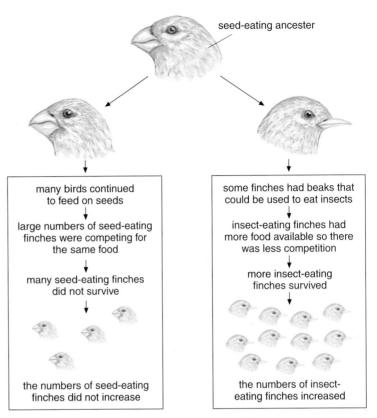

seed-eating ancestor

many birds continued to feed on seeds	some finches had beaks that could be used to eat insects
large numbers of seed-eating finches were competing for the same food	insect-eating finches had more food available so there was less competition
many seed-eating finches did not survive	more insect-eating finches survived
the numbers of seed-eating finches did not increase	the numbers of insect-eating finches increased

Some finches had slightly narrower beaks, good for eating insects. These birds got more food than the others, lived longer and had more offspring.

Questions

1 The following boxes summarise how species may change by natural selection. Place the boxes in the right order to show how this process takes place.

> organisms that survive and breed will pass their genes on to the next generation

> individual organisms may have different characteristics

> organisms with characteristics most suited to the environment are more likely to survive and breed

> organisms may die because of predation, disease and competition

2 Charles Darwin suggested that the different varieties of finch on the Galapagos islands had evolved from one variety of finch that came from South America.

   a Name the process that may have resulted in the evolution of different varieties.

   b The finch that came from South America probably had a thick beak. Suggest why birds with thinner beaks that can reach insects in tree bark survived better.

Darwin was a young man when he set out on *HMS Beagle*.

Summary

• All species have evolved from simpler organisms.

• Species may evolve by a process of natural selection.

• The theory of natural selection was first suggested by Charles Darwin.

• It took many years before Darwin's ideas were accepted.

4:14 Evidence about the past

The first organisms

There is evidence that all species have evolved from simple organisms that lived on the Earth more than three billion years ago. These simple organisms evolved to form larger more complex organisms.

Evolution usually occurs as a result of very small changes taking place over a long period of time. This is why scientists investigate changes in evolution taking place over millions of years.

Evidence from the past

Evidence of the way organisms have changed can be seen in fossils. Fossils are the remains of plants and animals that are found in rocks.

Fossils can be formed from:

◆ the hard parts of animals, which do not decay easily

◆ parts of animals and plants that have not decayed because the conditions for decay were not present

◆ parts of plants and animals that are replaced by other materials as they decay

◆ preserved traces of plants and animals such as footprints and traces of plant roots.

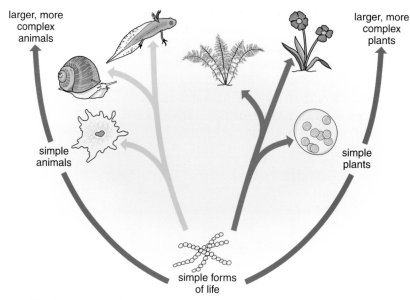

Simpler forms of life evolved to form larger and more complex organisms.

If remains can't decay (because there is no water or because it is too cold, for example) then they may form fossils.

Dinosaur footprints at Hanover Point on the Isle of Wight.

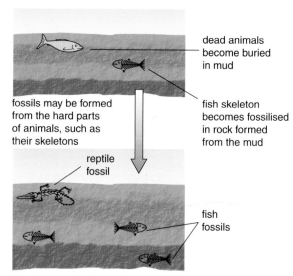

dead animals become buried in mud

fish skeleton becomes fossilised in rock formed from the mud

fossils may be formed from the hard parts of animals, such as their skeletons

reptile fossil

fish fossils

more layers of rock are formed on top of the older rock

Fossils can show us what plants and animals looked like millions of years ago.

28   Inheritance and selection ◆ Paper 1

Fossil records

The bones, shells, leaves and other remains found in rocks give some idea of what animals and plants looked like when they were alive, perhaps millions of years ago.

The position of a fossil also provides evidence of its age. The deepest rocks are likely to contain the oldest fossils. This means that fossils provide a record that shows how plants and animals have changed over a long period of time.

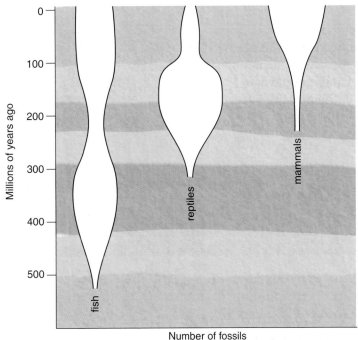

rocks appear as bands (strata)

younger

older

different types of fossils appear in each band of rock

The fossil record gives us vital information about how organisms have evolved.

Extinct species

The fossil record shows that some species lived in the past but are no longer living – they have become **extinct**. For example, about 100 million years ago there were many more species of reptiles on the Earth than there are today, including many species of dinosaur.

Species may become extinct because:

♦ the environment they need to survive changes

♦ new predators or diseases kill them

♦ they cannot compete with other species.

Using the fossil record

By studying the numbers and types of fossils found in different layers of rock scientists can build up a record of how living things evolved. The diagram shows the fossils found in layers of rock.

Millions of years ago

0

100

200

300

400

500

fish

reptiles

mammals

Number of fossils
(the wider the band, the more fossils present)

In this diagram, the wider the bands, the more fossils there are present in that rock layer.

Questions

Look at the diagram showing the numbers and types of fossils found in different rock layers. Use it to answer the following questions.

1 The colours in the diagram represent each layer of rock. Which colour represents the oldest rock?

2 How does the fossil record show that there were more fish on Earth 300 million years ago than there were 200 million years ago?

3 About 200 million years ago the Earth was dominated by dinosaurs. This started a period in evolution called 'the age of dinosaurs'.

   a How long ago did dinosaurs become extinct?

   b Explain how the record shows this.

Summary

• Fossils are the remains of organisms from many years ago.

• Fossils can be formed in various ways.

• Fossils show how much different organisms have changed since life developed on Earth.

• Fossils show that some species have become extinct.

4:15 Changing genes

Mutation

Your cells contain a gene that controls the production of a substance called **melanin**. Melanin gives your skin its colour, and it can even give you a suntan.

The photograph shows a blackbird that cannot make melanin. Animals that cannot make melanin and have no pigment in their skin are called **albinos**.

Albinos cannot make melanin because the gene that controls its production has changed. A change in a gene is called a **mutation**.

Not all blackbirds are black! This is an albino blackbird.

Increasing mutations

Mutations occur by chance. Some things, such as ionising radiation and some chemicals, can increase the chance of mutations occurring.

Ionising radiation includes UV light, X-rays, and radiation from radioactive substances.

Chemicals that can increase the chance of mutations occurring include benzene and the hydrocarbons in tobacco smoke.

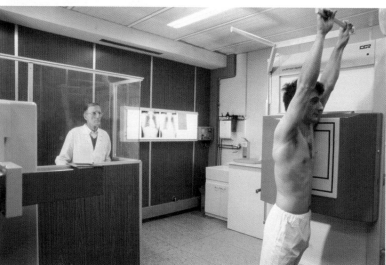

X-rays increase the chance of genes becoming damaged, or mutated.

Harmful mutations

Some forms of cancer are due to gene mutation. For example, mutations in skin cells may lead to cells growing in an uncontrolled way. This is **skin cancer**.

Being exposed to the sun's harmful UV radiation can cause skin cancer. People who spend hours sunbathing to get a tan are increasing the chances that they will also get skin cancer. This is why doctors advise people to follow the sun safety code.

a Why do black or brown skinned people rarely get skin cancer?

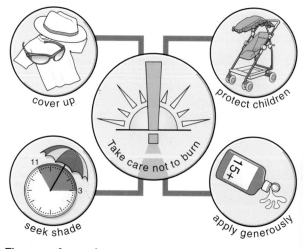

cover up

protect children

Take care not to burn

seek shade

apply generously

The sun safety code.

Investigating the effects of radiation

Yeast cells are single-celled organisms that can be grown in the laboratory on nutrient gel. When yeast cells grow they form colonies that can be seen on the surface of the gel. Some gene mutations make the yeast colonies look different.

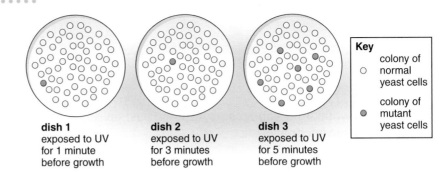

dish 1
exposed to UV
for 1 minute
before growth

dish 2
exposed to UV
for 3 minutes
before growth

dish 3
exposed to UV
for 5 minutes
before growth

Key

○ colony of normal yeast cells

● colony of mutant yeast cells

The diagram shows the effect of putting yeast cells in UV light for different amounts of time.

b What is the effect of increasing the amount of UV light on yeast cells?

The UV light increases the chances of mutations occurring in the yeast cells.

The Chernobyl disaster

In April 1986, a nuclear power station exploded in Chernobyl, in Ukraine. The explosion was a major disaster.

The explosion released a radioactive cloud, which spread from Chernobyl across Europe. Heavy rain washed radioactive materials from the clouds into fields in Wales and other parts of the UK.

Sheep feeding in fields ate grass contaminated with radioactive materials. The sale of lamb from contaminated areas was banned. Even now, more than fifteen years after the explosion, some lambs in these areas are found to have high levels of radiation in their bodies.

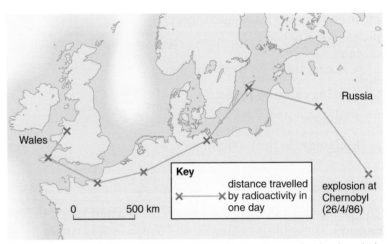

Russia

Wales

Key

✕—✕ distance travelled by radioactivity in one day

✕ explosion at Chernobyl (26/4/86)

0   500 km

Radioactive material from the Chernobyl explosion was carried by the wind for hundreds of miles.

Questions

1 a How long did it take for the radioactivity from Chernobyl to reach Wales?

b Suggest why lamb from contaminated areas was banned from being sold.

2 a Copy and then complete the table by counting the number of normal yeast colonies and mutant yeast colonies in the dishes shown above.

	Number of normal colonies	Number of mutant colonies
Dish 1		
Dish 2		
Dish 3		

b Describe the effect of increasing the amount of time for which yeast cells are exposed to UV light.

3 Explain why doctors advise parents to keep babies out of the sun completely.

Summary

- New forms of genes result from changes in existing genes.

- Changes in genes are called mutations.

- Mutations occur by chance.

- Ionising radiations and some chemicals increase the chance that mutations will occur.

Changing with the times

Some species of animals and plants from the past do not now exist. They have become extinct.

Some animals and plants that are present today did not exist long ago.

Through evolution, species change in response to their environment. They **adapt** to the conditions around them. **Adaptations** help organisms to survive and reproduce.

To survive and reproduce, organisms also have to **compete** with other organisms for food and space.

Factors that affect an organism's chances of surviving include:

♦ competition for food and space

♦ being eaten by predators

♦ disease

♦ changes in the environment.

Organisms can be adapted to their environment in different ways. How are these organisms adapted to survive in their environments?

Becoming extinct

The photograph shows a Kakapo, which is a bird found in New Zealand. These birds cannot fly and live in forests where they feed on berries and leaves.

When the first European settlers arrived in New Zealand, they cleared forests to provide grassland to graze their sheep. They also released deer into the forests where they fed on berries and leaves.

Rats, and even the ships' cats, escaped into the forests and started to breed. The rats ate the Kakapos' eggs and the cats easily caught the flightless birds.

a Kakapos used to be very common in New Zealand but now they are facing extinction.

Using the information above give one example of

 i predation

 ii competition

 iii change in the environment

to explain why Kakapos are facing extinction.

Kakapos are facing extinction.

Super bugs

Bacteria can cause skin infections such as boils. Doctors can treat patients with these infections with **antibiotics**.

The bar charts, on the opposite page, show the effect of using an antibiotic to treat skin infections in a hospital.

When the antibiotic was first used, most of the infections cleared up because the bacteria were killed. A small number of infections did not clear up because some bacteria were **resistant** to the antibiotic. The antibiotic failed to kill them. The resistant bacteria carry a gene that makes them resistant to the antibiotic.

After several years of using the antibiotic in the hospital, the number of infections caused by resistant bacteria increased.

Resistant and non-resistant bacteria compete for food. During the time the antibiotic was used, the resistant bacteria survived and reproduced. They passed the resistant gene on to the next generation of bacteria. At the same time, the non-resistant bacteria were killed and could not pass on their genes.

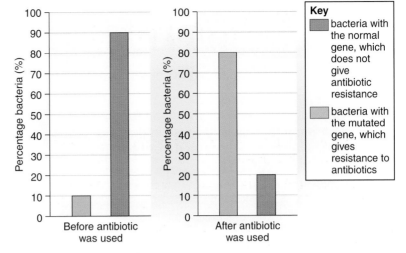

Key
- bacteria with the normal gene, which does not give antibiotic resistance
- bacteria with the mutated gene, which gives resistance to antibiotics

The long-term use of antibiotics can lead to the evolution of 'super bugs' – antibiotic-resistant bacteria.

b Look at the bar charts.

  i What percentage of the bacteria present were resistant when the antibiotic was first used?

  ii What percentage of the bacteria present were resistant after the use of antibiotics?

  iii Explain why the number of resistant bacteria increased during the time the antibiotic was used.

Changing environments

There are two types of peppered moth – a pale form and a dark form. The moths feed at night and rest on tree bark during the day.

In environments where the air is clean, tree bark is covered by a type of plant called **lichen**.

Air pollution kills the lichen. In polluted environments tree bark has no lichen covering it and is very dark.

The photographs shows the two types of moth on tree bark in a clean environment.

Two forms of the peppered moth.

Questions

The bar chart shows the numbers of each type of peppered moth in two environments.

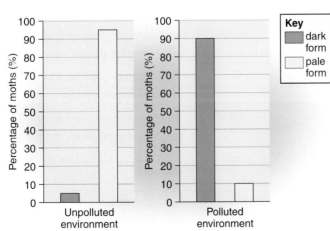

Key
- dark form
- pale form

1 Describe how pollution affects the environment of the moth.

2 Which type of moth is most common in the unpolluted environment?

3 Explain why there are more dark moths in the polluted environment.

Summary

- Organisms best adapted to their environment are more likely to survive and reproduce.

- Organisms may die because of competition for food and space, predation and disease.

- Organisms need to be able to survive changes in their environment.

- Over-use of antibiotics can lead to the evolution of resistant bacteria.

End of module questions

1 These young kittens have the same fur colour as their parents. This is because information about characteristics is passed from parents to their young.

Choose words from this list to complete the sentences.

alleles   chromosomes   genes   nucleus

The _____ of a cell contains thread-like strands called _____ . Characteristics that are inherited are controlled by _____ , which may exist in different forms called _____ .

2 Geraniums produce flowers with many different colours.

A gardener wants to grow geranium plants. She decides to grow them from cuttings from one plant.

2.1 Give one condition that cuttings need to grow well.

2.2 Give two advantages of growing the geraniums from cuttings.

3 The diagram below shows some of the parts of a woman's reproductive system.

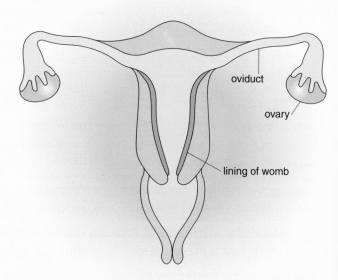

During each month, the thickness of the lining of the womb changes and an egg is released. This is called the monthly menstrual cycle.

3.1 Which part of the reproductive system shown in the diagram produces hormones?

3.2 Which part of the reproductive system releases eggs?

If a woman's reproductive system is not able to release eggs, she can be given fertility drugs to make this happen.

3.3 What do fertility drugs contain?

3.4 Describe a problem that may be caused by using fertility drugs in this way.

4 Huntington's disease is an inherited disease. It is due to a faulty dominant allele. People with the disease have the dominant allele H. People who do not have the disease have the recessive allele h.

4.1 What are the possible pairings of the alleles H and h for people who have Huntington's disease?

4.2 What system in the body is affected by Huntington's disease?

4.3 People do not show the effects of having Huntington's disease until they are over 30 years old. Explain how this affects how the disease can be passed on to children.

4.4 A child can inherit Huntington's disease if only one parent suffers from the disease. Explain how this can happen.

5 The strawberries that you see in supermarkets remain ripe for several days.

Strawberries used to rot very quickly after ripening. A small number of strawberry plants produced strawberries that were disease-resistant and did not rot quickly.

5.1 Copy and place these sentences in the correct order, to show how to develop more disease-resistant strawberry plants.

- Grow the seeds into new plants.
- Repeat this for many generations of plants.
- Breed plants together to produce seeds.
- Select plants producing strawberries that do not rot quickly.

5.2 Breeding plants to produce seeds involves the fusion of male and female gametes. What type of reproduction involves gametes?

New strawberry plants can also be grown from runners.

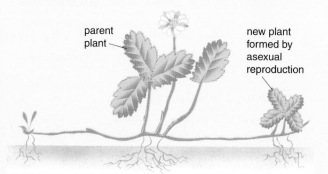

parent plant

new plant formed by asexual reproduction

5.3 All the new plants grown from the original plant form a clone. Explain why these plants form a clone.

5.4 One strawberry plant produced pink flowers instead of the usual white flowers. The growers thought this was because of mutation. Explain what 'mutation' means.

6 Kakapos are a species of bird found in New Zealand. They cannot fly, and they live in forests. They make their nests close to the ground.

Rats from visiting ships escaped into the forests and ate birds' eggs. Cats also escaped into the forests. Large areas of forests were cleared to make fields to graze sheep.

A few years ago, there was only a very small number of kakapos remaining.

6.1 Kakapos faced extinction. Explain what is meant by an extinct species.

6.2 Use the information given to suggest reasons why kakapos faced extinction.

7 The diagram below shows some fossils in layers of rock. The rock was formed from mud.

7.1 When animals die bacteria make them decay. Warmth, water and oxygen are needed for decay. Explain why the rocks in the diagram contain fossils.

7.2 Explain why the fossils are of bones but not of soft tissues such as skin.

7.3 Explain how the position of a fossil in the layers of rock shows the age of the fossil compared to fossils in other layers.

8 Cystic fibrosis is an inherited disease caused by a faulty gene.

8.1 Explain how a child can inherit this disease even if neither parent suffers from it.

8.2 The faulty gene was caused by the normal gene changing. What are changes to genes called?

8.3 Give three factors that may cause genes to change.

9 Diabetes can be treated using insulin produced by genetically engineered bacteria.

9.1 Describe how bacteria are changed to produce human proteins.

9.2 Insulin is made by cloned bacterial cells. Explain what we mean by a clone.

10 The photograph shows two forms of the same species of moth, resting on the bark of a tree growing in the country. In cities the air is more polluted, making the bark of trees darker.

A group of students counted the numbers of moths resting on five trees in the countryside. Their results are shown in the table below.

10.1 Copy and then complete the table by filling in the total numbers.

Tree	Dark moths	Light moths
1	1	12
2	2	10
3	3	8
4	0	11
5	2	7
Total		

10.2 Explain why light moths are more common than dark forms in the countryside.

10.3 Explain why the light moths are more likely to survive and breed in this environment.

Module 8 – Structures and bonding

Everything in the world is made of chemicals. There are millions of different kinds of chemicals, so how can we possibly know what is going on? Fortunately, we can all benefit from the work of great scientists. Over the last 200 years they have helped to unravel the mysteries of chemistry. They have discovered that all this complexity can be explained by the relatively simple rules that govern the behaviour of just a few different kinds of atoms and sub-atomic particles. In this module you will learn the basic rules that underlie the material world.

You will learn:

◆ what controls the properties of the different elements;

◆ how the elements are arranged in the periodic table;

◆ how the periodic table gives a summary of atomic structure;

◆ how atoms combine to form compounds;

◆ why different types of materials have different properties that depend on their structure;

◆ how to work out chemical formulae and balance chemical equations.

Before you start, check what you remember about the structures and bonding of elements and compounds.

1 What happens to the particles in a solid when you heat it (without melting)? What effect does this have on the volume of the solid?

2 The particles in liquids and gases are both free to move, but what is the difference between the way the particles are arranged?

3 What is the difference between an element and a compound?

4 Roughly how many different elements are there (10, 50, 100, 500)?

5 Which elemental gas is used to kill germs?

6 Which gas is used to fill modern lighter-than-air balloons?

Everything is made of particles. Water is made of water particles, iron is made of iron particles, and so on.

But ice, water and steam are all made of the same particles. Why is ice a solid, water a liquid and steam a gas?

a Why can you pour a liquid but not a solid?

b Why can you squash a gas but not a liquid?

The answer is that it all depends on:

◆ how the particles are arranged;

◆ how big the forces of attraction are between the particles; and

◆ how much movement energy the particles have.

	Properties	Particle arrangement	Forces of attraction compared to movement energy
Solid	Fixed shape and fixed volume	regular close-packed	The particles vibrate but the forces of attraction are strong enough to hold them together
Liquid	No fixed shape but fixed volume	irregular close-packed (some gaps)	The particles vibrate more. Clumps of particles break free and can move about
Gas	No fixed shape and no fixed volume	few, spaced out, random	The forces of attraction have been overcome. The particles spread out and whiz about at high speed

Solid ice, liquid water or gaseous steam? It all depends on the temperature.

The amount of movement energy the particles have depends on the temperature.

c Do particles move faster or slower as the temperature goes up?

The energy link

The particles in ice have enough energy to vibrate. They cannot break away from each other because they are held in place by strong forces.

When you heat ice, you give the particles more energy. This makes them vibrate more. The more you heat the particles, the more violently they vibrate. Eventually, the particles have enough vibration energy to overcome some of the forces that hold them together. As the solid melts, clumps of particles become free to move. For water, this happens when the temperature reaches 0 °C. This is the **melting point** of water.

d Iron melts at 1540 °C. Are the forces between iron particles stronger or weaker than the forces between water particles?

If you keep heating liquid water, the particles can move around faster and faster because they get more energy. Some of the particles at the surface get enough energy to break free and escape into the air. This is called **evaporation**.

Evaporation happens more and more as the liquid gets hotter and hotter. This is because the particles get more and more energy.

If you keep heating, the particles will eventually get enough energy to completely overcome the forces that were holding them together. The liquid starts to boil and it turns into a gas. This gas is called **water vapour**. For water, this happens when the temperature reaches 100 °C. This is the **boiling point** of water.

It's reversible

The changes from solid to liquid and from liquid to gas are called physical changes. Physical changes are easily reversed.

If you cool water vapour back down to 100 °C, it will **condense** to form liquid water. The particles lose energy and clump back together. If you continue to cool the water it will **freeze** back to solid ice again at 0 °C.

Questions

1 Copy and complete the following sentences. Choose from:

   boiling   gas   liquid   melting   vibrate

   If a solid is heated the particles _____ more. When the _____ point is reached, some of the particles break loose and are able to move about as a _____. If the _____ point is reached, the particles start to break free completely and whiz about at high speed as a _____.

2 **a** Water boils at 100 °C. How does washing on a washing line dry when the temperature is only 15 °C?

   b Why does washing dry faster on a hot day?

3 How do the particles in a gas keep so far apart?

Data analysis

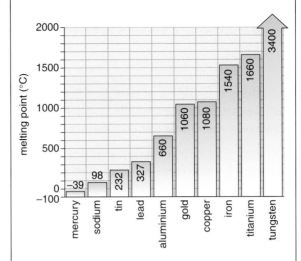

e The filament in a light bulb has to get 'white hot' – over 2000 °C. Why can't a filament be made of iron?

f A house has been burnt down. In the kitchen the fire got so hot that the aluminium saucepans melted but the copper electrical wires did not. Which of these temperatures might have been reached? 600 °C, 900 °C or 1200 °C?

g In a Siberian winter the temperature drops below –50 °C. Why can't mercury thermometers be used in Siberia?

Summary

- The particles in solids are close together and vibrate but are held in place by forces.

- The particles in liquids are still close together but are free to move about.

- The particles in gases have broken free and are whizzing about at high speed.

- The higher the temperature, the more energy the particles have and the faster they move.

Naming the pieces

Everything is made up of particles. For most substances, these particles are built from smaller particles called **atoms**. Groups of two or more atoms joined together are called **molecules**.

There are about 100 different kinds of atoms on Earth. Substances made from only one type of atom are called **elements**. As there are 100 different types of atom, there are 100 different elements.

Many elements, such as oxygen and sulphur, form molecules containing just one type of atom.

a How many atoms of oxygen are there in an oxygen molecule?

Compounds

When *different* elements combine they form **compounds**. The 100 different atoms can combine to give an enormous number of different compounds. However, the same compounds are always formed in the same way.

b Which elements combine together to make water molecules? Which elements combine together to make methane?

Dalton and the atom

About 200 years ago, John Dalton was studying the way elements combined to form compounds. By careful experimentation, he found that the simple compounds he made always contained the same elements in the same proportions.

Dalton explained his results by the idea that elements were made of tiny particles that could not be broken – atoms. This was quite surprising to many scientists at the time, but it was not a new idea. The idea of atoms was first thought up by the Ancient Greeks, 2000 years ago. The Greeks had no experimental evidence to support their idea, so the idea went out of favour!

c What evidence did Dalton use to convince other scientists that everything was made of atoms?

Using symbols for elements

Each of the 100 elements has a unique, internationally recognised symbol of one or two letters. Most of these symbols are 'sensible' choices from the name. Some seem odd, because they refer to older names that are no longer used.

atoms

hydrogen   helium   carbon   oxygen

molecules

hydrogen   water   methane   oxygen

elements

hydrogen   helium   carbon   oxygen

compounds

water   methane   carbon dioxide

John Dalton (1766–1844).

Symbols for compounds

For compounds, the symbols of the elements that they are made from are simply listed one after another.

So iron sulphide, which has one iron atom joined to one sulphur atom, is written as FeS.

If there is more than one atom of a particular element in a compound, this is shown by a small subscript number after its symbol.

So water, which has two hydrogen atoms joined to one oxygen atom, is written as H_2O.

In this way, each chemical compound has its own list of symbols and numbers to describe how the compound is made. This is called its **chemical formula**.

Remember that each chemical compound always has the same formula. If the formula is different, it is a different compound, with different properties.

◆ CO_2 is carbon dioxide, the harmless gas that you breathe out and plants take in.

◆ CO is carbon monoxide, a deadly poisonous gas.

d How many of each type of atom are there in the compound sulphuric acid, H_2SO_4?

e Why can't sodium use the symbol 'S'?

Spelling it out

It is easy to get confused when thinking about atoms and compounds. Here is a model that might help.

◆ Atoms are like the letters of the alphabet.

◆ Compounds are like words.

Think how many different words you can make from just 26 letters. Now you can understand just how many different compounds can be made from 100 atoms!

Questions

1 What are the chemical symbols for gold, silver, iron, copper and potassium?

2 a What atoms make up a glucose molecule ($C_6H_{12}O_6$)?

b How many of each type of atom are there?

3 Ammonia is a compound made from one nitrogen atom joined to three hydrogen atoms. What is the chemical formula of ammonia?

Some elements and their symbols

Single letters (always capital)	Double letters (first letter capital)
H = hydrogen	He = helium
C = carbon	Mg = magnesium
N = nitrogen	Al = aluminium
O = oxygen	Si = silicon
S = sulphur	Cl = chlorine
I = iodine	Br = bromine
	Ca = calcium
	Zn = zinc

Some 'oddities'

Na = sodium, from the Latin name *natrium*

K = potassium, from the Latin name *kalium*

Fe = iron, iron and steel are the *ferrous* metals

Cu = copper

Pb = lead, *plumbers* used to work with lead pipes

Ag = silver, *argent* is French for coins – 'silver'

Au = gold, from the Latin name *aurium*

Hg = mercury, from the Latin name *hydrargyrum*, which means liquid silver

---

Summary

• All substances are made of atoms.

• There are about 100 different types of atoms.

• A substance which contains only one type of atom is called an element.

• Each element has its own symbol.

• A substance made from different types of atoms joined together is called a compound.

8:3 Formulae and equations

Working out the formula

A chemical formula tells you how many of each type of atom there is in a compound. But why do the compounds form in the way that they do?

For example, why is there:

◆ only one chlorine atom in sodium chloride (NaCl);

◆ but two chlorine atoms in magnesium chloride ($MgCl_2$)?

The answer is that the atoms of different elements can make different number of chemical bonds. It is as if the atoms had different numbers of 'arms' that they could use to join up with 'handshake' bonds. To make a compound, you must use up all of the 'arms'.

Sodium and chlorine have just one 'arm' each, so they join in a simple one to one compound. Magnesium has two 'arms', so one magnesium atom can hold on to two chlorine atoms.

a Calcium chloride is $CaCl_2$. How many 'bond arms' must calcium have?

Oxygen also has two 'arms'. Magnesium oxide is just MgO as the atoms join with a 'double handshake'. But oxygen can hold onto two sodium atoms, so sodium oxide is Na_2O.

b Potassium oxide is K_2O. How many 'bond arms' must potassium have?

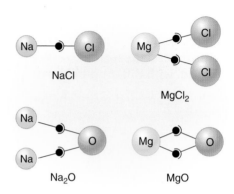

The simple 'handshake' model for bonding can help you work out the formulae of some compounds.

Charge it!

Atoms do not have arms, of course. The way that metals and non-metals form compounds is by becoming charged particles called **ions**.

◆ Metals such as sodium and magnesium form **positive ions**.

◆ Non-metals such as oxygen and chlorine form **negative ions**.

These opposite charges are attracted to one another, to form an **ionic bond** (see page 50).

In a compound, the charges must balance out.

The 2+ charge on a magnesium ion could be balanced out by:

◆ one 2– oxygen ion (in MgO); or

◆ two 1– chlorine ions (in $MgCl_2$).

So the charge on the ion is the same as the 'number of arms' in the simple 'handshake' model.

c Use the figures in the tables to work out the formulae of silver chloride, zinc oxide and zinc chloride.

1+
sodium (Na^+)   potassium (K^+)
silver (Ag^+)

2+
magnesium (Mg^{2+})   calcium (Ca^{2+})
lead (Pb^{2+})   iron(II) (Fe^{2+})
copper(II) (Cu^{2+})   zinc (Zn^{2+})

3+
aluminium (Al^{3+})   iron(III) (Fe^{3+})

Some metal ions.

1–
chlorine (Cl^-)   bromine (Br^-)
iodine (I^-)

2–
oxygen (O^{2-})   sulphur (S^{2-})

Some non-metal ions.

Chemical reactions and equations

When chemical reactions occur, new compounds are formed as atoms are combined in different ways.

These reactions can be written as **word equations**, to show what is happening.

The chemicals you start with are written on the left. These are the **reactants**.

The chemicals that form are written on the right. These are the **products**.

reactants → products

For example, when the metal magnesium burns in air, magnesium atoms and oxygen atoms are the reactants. They combine to form the new compound magnesium oxide, which is the only product in this reaction. So:

magnesium + oxygen → magnesium oxide

Burning magnesium gives off light and heat as the chemical reaction takes place.

d Iron reacts with sulphur to form iron sulphide. Write this as a word equation.

Symbol equations

You can get even more information about the chemical reaction if you use symbols and formulae.

Here is the symbol equation for the magnesium/oxygen reaction:

$2Mg(s) + O_2(g) \rightarrow 2MgO(s)$

This shows that two magnesium atoms react with one oxygen molecule to form two lots of magnesium oxide. One oxygen molecule contains two atoms of oxygen.

The symbols in brackets tell you that magnesium and magnesium oxide are solids (s), while oxygen is a gas (g).

These symbols are:

◆ (s) solid;   ◆ (g) gas;   ◆ (l) liquid;

◆ (aq) aqueous solution (a solution in water).

Questions

1 Carbon (C) burns in oxygen (O_2) to form carbon dioxide gas (CO_2).

   a Write this as a word equation.

   b Use the symbols to write a symbol equation.

   c Add the 'state symbols' to complete the equation.

2 Use either the 'bond arms' model or the idea of ionic bonds. Work out the formulae of the following compounds:

   a potassium chloride   b silver oxide

   c aluminium chloride

Summary

• You can work out the formula of a simple compound if you know how many bonds each element can make.

• For metal/non-metal compounds you can work out the formula if you know the charge on each ion.

• Chemical reactions can be shown as word equations or symbol equations.

8:4 Balancing equations

Keeping in balance

Hydrochloric acid and sodium hydroxide react to make sodium chloride and water.

hydrochloric acid	+	sodium hydroxide	→	sodium chloride	+	water
HCl	+	NaOH	→	NaCl	+	H_2O

Look at the chemical equation and the simple diagram of the particles involved. You can see that there are the same number of each type of atom on each side.

Equations like this are called **balanced equations**.

a There are two hydrogen atoms in water. Where did these hydrogen atoms come from in this reaction?

Mass too

If you weigh the hydrochloric acid and sodium hydroxide before and after they have been mixed, you will find that there is no change in the mass. This follows a fundamental rule of chemistry:

mass of reactant(s) = mass of product(s)

This makes sense, because you still have the same number of atoms – you have just rearranged them!

b 20 g of sodium hydroxide and hydrochloric acid produced 15 g of salt. How much water was formed?

Going up?

Reactions involving gases sometimes seem to show a change of mass. For example, when magnesium burns in air, the magnesium oxide formed weighs more than the magnesium metal you started with.

But, if you look at the equation, you will see that this is not surprising. The magnesium has joined with extra oxygen atoms that have come from the air. If these atoms are taken into account, the mass does not change.

magnesium + oxygen → magnesium oxide

2Mg + O_2 → 2MgO

c 2.4 g of magnesium produced 4 g of magnesium oxide. How much oxygen did it react with?

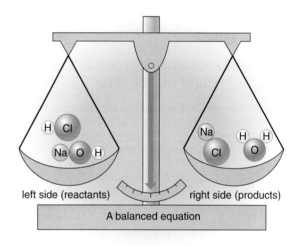

left side (reactants)   right side (products)

A balanced equation

Making salt and water from acid and alkali – it's just a case of rearrangement!

Balancing equations

To write a balanced chemical equation, you need to follow a series of steps in the correct order. How many steps it takes depends on the reaction. For some reactions, this can be quite simple.

For example, calcium carbonate breaks down when it is heated to give calcium oxide and carbon dioxide.

Step 1: Write a word equation

    calcium carbonate → calcium oxide + carbon dioxide

Step 2: Find out (or work out) the formulae for the reactants and products. Write a symbol equation.

    $CaCO_3 \rightarrow CaO + CO_2$

Step 3: Count the atoms on each side. Do they balance?

    $1 \times Ca, 1 \times C, 3 \times O \rightarrow 1 \times Ca, 1 \times C, 3 \times O$

The answer is yes!

d Where does the carbon dioxide go?

e 10 g of calcium carbonate gave only 5.6 g of calcium oxide. What mass of carbon dioxide was produced?

Calcium carbonate breaks down when it is heated.

What if it doesn't balance?

Not all equations balance quite so easily.

For example, sulphuric acid reacts with sodium hydroxide, making sodium sulphate and water.

    sulphuric acid + sodium hydroxide → sodium sulphate + water

Step 1: If you put in the formulae for these chemicals, the numbers do not add up.

$$H_2SO_4 + NaOH \rightarrow Na_2SO_4 + H_2O$$

Step 2: There are two sodium atoms on the right, but just one on the left. You need two lots of sodium hydroxide to start with. Put a large 2 in front of the formula for NaOH.

$$H_2SO_4 + \mathbf{2}NaOH \rightarrow Na_2SO_4 + H_2O$$

Step 3: Now there are four hydrogens on the left but only two on the right. Two molecules of water balances the equation!

$$H_2SO_4 + 2NaOH \rightarrow Na_2SO_4 + \mathbf{2}H_2O$$

This equation is now balanced!

Questions

1 Copy and complete the following sentences. Choose from:

    atoms   chemical   equals   reactants   rearranged

    In a _____ reaction, the mass of the products _____ the mass of the _____. This is not surprising as you have the same _____. They have just been _____.

2 Balance these equations.

    a $CaO + HCl \rightarrow CaCl_2 + H_2O$

    b $N_2 + H_2 \rightarrow 2NH_3$

    c $Zn + HCl \rightarrow ZnCl_2 + H_2$

Summary

- In a chemical reaction, the mass of the products equals the mass of the reactants.

- In a balanced equation, you must have the same number of each type of atom on each side.

8:5 Inside the atom

There are millions of different kinds of chemicals in the world. All these chemicals are made from just the 100 different kinds of atoms. To make so many different chemicals, the atoms are arranged in different ways.

To understand how these atoms join together to make all these different chemicals, you will need to know how the atoms themselves are made.

Sub-atomic particles

Atoms are made from just three types of particles, arranged in a particular way. These sub-atomic particles are called **protons**, **neutrons** and **electrons**.

a What form of energy involves the flow of electrons along wires?

At the very centre of an atom is the **nucleus**. The nucleus contains the protons and the neutrons. The protons carry a positive electrical charge. The neutrons are electrically neutral.

The nucleus is very small compared to an atom, so how does the atom get its shape? Whizzing around the nucleus are even smaller particles, the electrons. Electrons carry a negative electrical charge.

When you look at a TV picture, there is just a moving dot of light, but it moves so fast that you see a complete picture. In a similar way, the electrons are moving so fast around the proton that they make an outer shell for the atom. This outer shell gives the atom its shape. But, surprising as it may seem, most of every atom is just empty space!

b In 1911 a scientist called Rutherford fired tiny radioactive particles at a thin sheet of gold. He was very surprised to find that most of the particles passed straight through! How could this happen?

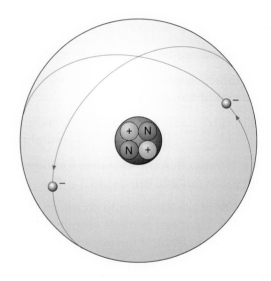

An atom of helium has two negatively charged electrons whizzing around a nucleus. The nucleus is made of two positively charged protons and two neutrons.

More about sub-atomic particles

The sub-atomic particles have different electrical charges. They also have different masses. The masses of the sub-atomic particles are too small to usefully measure in grams. The masses are simply compared to the mass of a hydrogen atom. On this model, protons and neutrons both have a mass of 1, but electrons are so light that their mass is usually ignored!

c What is the mass of a helium atom?

Atoms of the same element always have the same number of protons in the nucleus. If the number of protons is different then it is a different element!

	Mass	Charge
proton	1	positive
neutron	1	neutral
electron	0	negative

Putting atoms in order

The number of protons an element has is called its **proton number** or **atomic number**. We use the symbol **Z** for the atomic number.

◆ Hydrogen is the simplest atom, with just one proton, so it is atomic number 1.

◆ Helium has two protons, so it is atomic number 2.

◆ Uranium has ninety-two protons, so it is atomic number 92.

The more protons there are in the nucleus, the more neutrons are needed. So the higher the atomic number, the bigger the mass of the atom compared to hydrogen. You can find this **relative atomic mass** (symbol: A_r) by adding the number of protons and neutrons together.

d Sodium has 11 protons and 12 neutrons. What is its A_r?

Remember, the atomic number (Z) tells you the number of protons, while the relative atomic mass (A_r) tells you the overall mass. To find the number of neutrons you must take the smaller number from the bigger one!

Finally, remember that atoms are neutral overall. So the number of electrons whizzing around an atom is equal to the number of protons in its nucleus.

Example: Helium

relative atomic mass (A_r) = 4; atomic number (Z) = 2

Helium has two protons (Z), two electrons (= Z) and two neutrons ($A_r - Z$).

e For carbon, sulphur and copper, state how many protons, neutrons and electrons there are in an atom.

Isotopes

For atoms of most elements, the number of neutrons in all the atoms is usually the same. Some elements, however, have different numbers of neutrons. These alternative versions are called **isotopes**.

For example, chlorine always has 17 protons. But chlorine atoms can have either 18 or 20 neutrons. As the '18' isotope is three times as common as the '20' isotope, the average relative atomic mass comes out as 35.5!

f Most carbon has an A_r of 12. But carbon has another isotope, with an A_r of 14. In what way is this similar to and different from the carbon in the photograph above?

Questions

1 Copy and complete the following sentences. Choose from:

An electron   A neutron   A proton

_____ has the mass of a hydrogen atom and has no charge.
_____ has almost no mass, but has a negative charge.
_____ has the mass of a hydrogen atom and a positive charge.

2 Lithium has three protons and four neutrons. What is the atomic number and relative atomic mass of lithium?

The atomic number and relative atomic mass of some common elements.

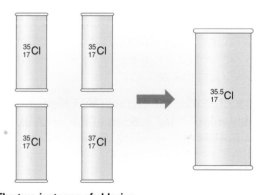

The two isotopes of chlorine.

Summary

• Atoms are made from three sub-atomic particles: protons, neutrons and electrons.

• Protons (positive) and neutrons (neutral) are found in the nucleus.

• Electrons (negative) whiz around the nucleus.

• Isotopes are versions of the same element, with different numbers of neutrons.

8:6 Electrons rule chemistry

Energy levels (electron shells)

The electrons whiz round the nucleus of an atom forming an 'electron cloud'. This electron cloud gives the atom its shape. But the electron cloud is not haphazard. The electrons can only fit into certain zones. These zones are called **energy levels** or **electron shells**.

In a neutral atom the number of electrons is the same as the number of protons. These electrons normally fit into levels closest to the nucleus. For the first 20 elements, the pattern is a simple one:

◆ level one: 1 or 2 electrons only;

◆ level two: up to 8 electrons;

◆ level three: up to 8 electrons;

◆ level four: 1 or 2 electrons fit in, then the pattern becomes more complicated.

If you know the number of electrons in an atom, you can work out how the electrons are arranged in the levels.

a How many electrons does an atom of magnesium have ($Z = 12$)? How many electrons will fit in each energy level?

This is called the **electronic structure** of the atom. It can be drawn on a 'flat' version of the atom like this, or written as the numbers in each level, in turn.

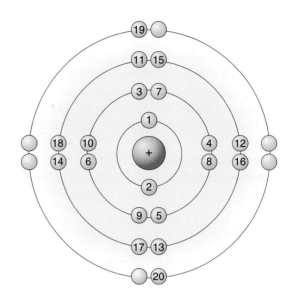

How the first 20 electrons fit in the energy levels. You can mark a cross (×) to show the position of an electron.

Filling them up

◆ Hydrogen's single electron fits in the first level.

◆ Helium's two electrons fill up the first level completely.

◆ At number 3, lithium's third electron must start a new level.

◆ Carbon is number 6, so it half-fills the second level.

◆ Neon has ten electrons, which fill up levels one and two.

◆ Sodium starts a third level for its 11th electron.

◆ Elements number 12 to 18 fill up level three.

◆ Calcium, at number 20, is the last element to show this simple pattern. Its last two electrons are found in the fourth level.

b Draw the electron structures of fluorine ($Z = 9$), aluminium ($Z = 13$) and sulphur ($Z = 16$).

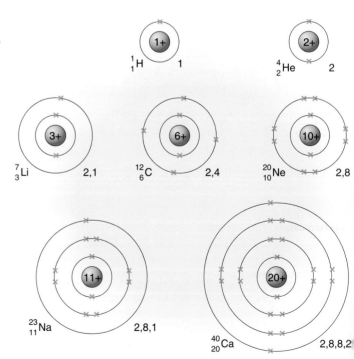

Electrons usually fit into the lowest available energy levels.

Making compounds

Most substances are compounds. It is the electrons in the outer energy levels of the atoms that decide how a compound is formed.

◆ A compound made of metals and non-metals is usually made by a process of 'give and take'.

◆ A compound made of just non-metals has to make do with sharing.

Give and take

Sodium is a metal. Sodium ($Z = 11$) has just one electron in its outer shell. If it loses this electron, sodium becomes an ion with a single positive charge. The sodium ion has a single positive charge because it has 11 protons but only 10 electrons. This ion is smaller than the atom, as it has one fewer electron shells.

c Explain why a sodium ion has an overall positive charge.

Chlorine is a non-metal. Chlorine ($Z = 17$) has seven electrons in its outer shell. Chlorine can gain an extra electron to form an ion with a single negative charge. The chlorine ion has 17 protons but now has 18 electrons.

d Explain why a chlorine ion has a negative charge.

All metals are able to lose electrons and form positive ions. Reactive non-metals can gain electrons and form negative ions.

Oppositely charged ions will attract each other. They can join together to form **ionic compounds**, such as sodium chloride.

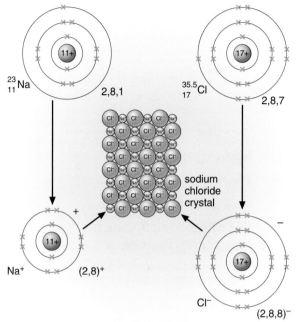

Sodium chloride (common salt) is built from ions.

Sharing

Non-metals can form compounds on their own by sharing outer electrons rather than making ions. These compounds are called **covalent compounds**.

Sodium chloride is an ionic compound.
Water is a covalent compound.

Many covalent compounds form small particles called molecules.

e Is carbon dioxide likely to be an ionic compound or a covalent compound? Explain your answer.

Question

1 Copy and complete the following sentences. Choose from:

compounds   electrons   energy   nucleus   outer

Electrons fill the _____ levels around the _____ from the bottom up. The number of _____ there are in the _____ level controls the way the atom forms _____.

Summary

• Electrons are arranged in energy levels (electron shells) around the nucleus.

• The way the electrons are arranged controls the way an atom reacts to form compounds.

• Metals form ionic compounds with non-metals after a 'give and take' of electrons.

• Non-metals share electrons to form covalent compounds.

8:7 More about ionic compounds

Happiness is a full energy level

Helium ($Z = 2$), neon ($Z = 10$) and argon ($Z = 18$) belong to a family of elements called the **noble gases**. They have this name because they keep to themselves. They do not join in chemical reactions at all. What is it that makes them so stable and unreactive?

The answer is that they all have a full outer energy level.

A full outer energy level appears to be a very stable arrangement, which is not easy to upset. Or, to put it in a less scientific way, if you are an atom, 'happiness is a full outer energy level'!

a Atoms of the element krypton have eight electrons in their outer energy level. Will krypton be reactive or unreactive? Explain your answer.

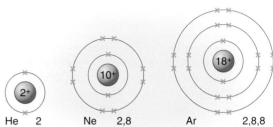

He 2   Ne 2,8   Ar 2,8,8

The full outer energy levels of the noble gases makes them very unreactive.

Why form ions?

Metallic elements usually have just one or two electrons in their outer energy level. These electrons are quite 'loose' and are easily lost. When these electrons are lost, the atom becomes an ion with one less energy level. Ions like this have the electronic structure of a noble gas, so they are very stable. But, unlike the noble gases:

◆ their electric charges are not balanced;

◆ they have an overall positive charge.

b Atoms of zinc have two electrons in their outer energy level. Is zinc a metal or non-metal? What sort of ion does zinc form?

Many non-metallic elements have five, six or seven electrons in their outer energy level. They can capture extra electrons to fill the energy level and so form an ion. These ions also have the electronic structure of a noble gas, so they are very stable. However:

◆ their electric charges are not balanced;

◆ they have an overall negative charge.

c Atoms of iodine have seven electrons in their outer energy level. Is iodine a metal or non-metal? What sort of ion does iodine form?

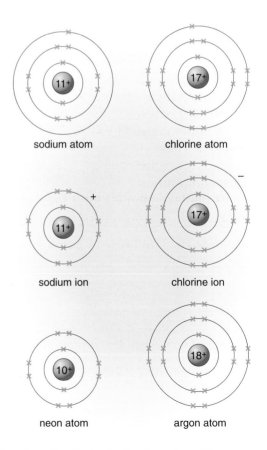

sodium atom   chlorine atom

sodium ion   chlorine ion

neon atom   argon atom

Ions have the electronic structure of a noble gas.

The atomic dating agency

You may have spotted the obvious connection. Metallic atoms want to lose electrons. Non-metallic elements want to gain electrons. They are made for each other!

The oppositely charged ions then attract one another to form a strong **ionic bond**.

d How many iodine ions could be made by one zinc atom?

Charges in balance

The overall charges in an ionic compound must balance out.

One sodium ion (Na⁺) joins with just one chlorine ion (Cl⁻) in NaCl.

However, magnesium ($Z = 12$) loses two electrons and so forms a double positive ion (Mg^{2+}). This can balance out two single negative chlorine ions to form magnesium chloride, $MgCl_2$.

e Draw energy level diagrams to show how magnesium chloride forms.

Oxygen ($Z = 8$) has six electrons in its outer energy level. It can gain two electrons to form an ion with a double negative charge.

When magnesium and oxygen form a compound, you only need one oxygen ion for every magnesium ion. The formula of magnesium oxide is MgO.

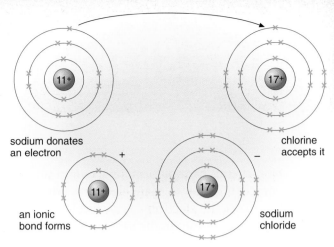

sodium donates an electron

chlorine accepts it

an ionic bond forms

sodium chloride

The electric charges on ions make ionic bonds.

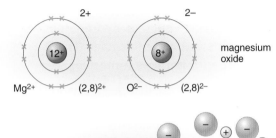

magnesium oxide

Mg^{2+} $(2,8)^{2+}$ O^{2-} $(2,8)^{2-}$

Giant ionic structures

Ionic compounds such as sodium chloride stack up in a regular way to form a **giant ionic structure** (an ionic lattice). Every ion is held in place by strong electrostatic forces from its neighbours. These strong forces are called ionic bonds. Ionic compounds:

◆ have high melting points and high boiling points;

◆ are quite hard but brittle, so they shatter easily;

◆ only conduct electricity when molten or in solution.

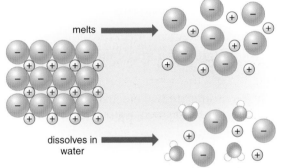

melts

dissolves in water

Metals

Metal atoms can also stack up in a regular way to make a giant structure.

All metal atoms have 'loose electrons' in their outermost electron energy levels. These loose electrons form a 'cloud' of electrons that binds the structure together. Metals are strong but flexible. Metals:

◆ have high melting points and high boiling points;

◆ are hard but also flexible and easily shaped;

◆ conduct electricity even when solid.

f How could you tell a metal from an ionic compound using a hammer?

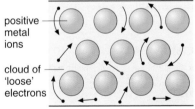

positive metal ions

cloud of 'loose' electrons

Metals have their special properties because of their cloud of electrons.

Question

1 Copy and complete the following sentences. Choose from:

full   **ions**   **noble**   **stable**   **unreactive**

_____ gas atoms have a _____ outer energy level. This makes them _____. Other atoms form _____ by losing or gaining electrons to reach this _____ state.

Summary

• A full outer electron energy level gives stability.

• Ions form when atoms lose or gain electrons to reach this stable state.

• Ionic compounds often form giant structures.

• Metals are held together by electron clouds.

8:8 Share and share alike

Fair shares

Non-metals cannot form ionic compounds on their own, but they can get together to share electrons. When non-metals share electrons, the electron energy levels join together. The electron energy levels join in the same way that bubbles sometimes join up in groups of two or three.

When the electron energy levels join, the two atoms form a strong chemical bond called a **covalent bond**. This is how molecules form.

a Many gases such as hydrogen and oxygen usually exist as 'double bubble' molecules (H_2, O_2). What kind of bonding is there within these molecules?

Chlorine atoms are just one electron short of a full outer energy level, so they need to share just one pair of electrons to form Cl_2 molecules. This is a **single covalent bond**.

b Draw an electron structure diagram for an H_2 molecule. (Remember, the first energy level can only take two electrons.)

Oxygen atoms are two electrons short of a full energy level, so they share two electron pairs. The O_2 molecule has a **double covalent bond**.

The bonds in molecules can be shown in different ways. You can show how the outer energy level electrons are shared, or simply show the bonds as linking bars.

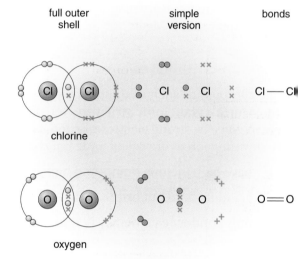

Chlorine and oxygen molecules shown in different ways. Electrons are shown as 'dots' from one atom and 'crosses' from the other.

Covalent compounds

Atoms of different non-metallic elements can also join together to make compounds.

◆ Chlorine can form a single covalent bond with hydrogen to make hydrogen chloride (HCl).

◆ Oxygen needs to share two electrons and so can join with two hydrogen atoms to make hydrogen oxide. You know this as water (H_2O).

c Draw an electron structure diagram for an HCl molecule.

Nitrogen is three electrons short of a full outer energy level. It can share a pair of electrons with each of three hydrogen atoms to make an ammonia molecule (NH_3).

Carbon is four electrons short of a full outer energy level. It can share a pair of electrons with each of four hydrogen atoms to make a methane molecule (CH_4).

d Carbon can also combine with two oxygen atoms, forming two double covalent bonds. Draw an electron structure diagram for a CO_2 molecule.

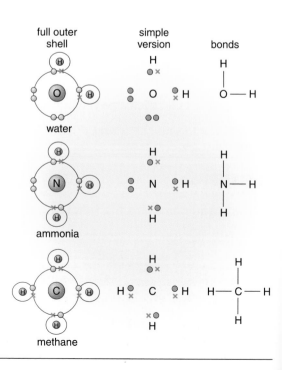

Data Analysis – materials

Different types of substances have different properties because of differences in the forces between their particles.

The stronger the forces between the particles:

◆ the harder the material;

◆ the higher its melting point.

Type of material	Example	Forces between particles	Melting points and boiling points	Does it conduct electricity?	Hardness	Flexibility	
Ionic compound	common salt	strong ionic bonds	high	only when molten or in solution	high	low	
Metal	iron	strong electrostatic forces	high	yes – as both solid and liquid	high	high	
Molecular covalent	oxygen	only very weak forces	very low – gas at room temperature	no	–	–	
Giant covalent	diamond	strong covalent bonds	very high	no	very hard	low	

e   Why is oxygen a gas at room temperature?

f   Why are diamonds so hard?

g   Solid vanadium conducts electricity. What type of material is it?

h   Solid lead bromide does not conduct electricity, but molten lead bromide does. What kind of structure does lead bromide have?

i   Sand (silicon dioxide) has a very high melting point but does not conduct electricity even when molten. What kind of structure does it have?

j   Oxygen molecules are made of two atoms. Petrol molecules are made of more than 20 atoms and wax molecules are made of more than 200 atoms. What is the relationship between the size of a molecule and melting/boiling points?

Questions

1   Copy and complete the following sentences. Choose from

   covalent   molecules   non-metals   sharing   strong

   Atoms of _____ can 'fill' their outer energy levels by _____ electron pairs. This is how _____ covalent bonds form. _____ form when atoms join together with _____ bonds.

2   Draw a structural diagram to show how the covalent compound hydrogen fluoride (HF) forms. (Fluorine: $Z = 9$)

Summary

• Atoms of non-metals can combine by sharing electrons in covalent bonds.

• Molecules are made from covalently bonded atoms.

8:9 Ordering the elements

Looking for patterns

a What pattern can you see in this jumble of black and white?

When you first turned this page, the black and white picture probably appeared to be a complete jumble. It is, in fact, a picture of dalmatians in the snow. Now that you know that, it probably looks obvious!

Early chemists faced an even worse problem as they tried to find a pattern in the properties of the elements.

◆ They did not know how many elements were still undiscovered.

◆ They had no idea about atomic structure.

It is only thanks to their work that you now know what to look for!

Ordering the elements

A few elements, such as gold and copper, have been known for thousands of years. However, most of the elements were only discovered 100 or so years ago. Some early chemists found that elements could be grouped in families. An example of a family is the reactive non-metals chlorine, bromine and iodine.

But it was only when it became possible to arrange the elements in order of increasing relative atomic mass (A_r) that real progress was made. Once chemists did this, a pattern started to emerge.

b What pattern can you see in this list of elements?

Z	A_r	Element	Properties
1	1	hydrogen	very reactive gas
2	4	helium	unreactive gas
3	7	lithium	very reactive metal
4	9	beryllium	reactive metal
5	11	boron	non-metal
6	12	carbon	non-metal
7	14	nitrogen	non-metal
8	16	oxygen	reactive gas
9	19	fluorine	very reactive gas
10	20	neon	unreactive gas
11	23	sodium	very reactive metal
12	24	magnesium	reactive metal
13	27	aluminium	metal
14	28	silicon	non-metal
15	31	phosphorus	non-metal
16	32	sulphur	reactive non-metal
17	35.5	chlorine	very reactive gas
18	40	argon	unreactive gas
19	39	potassium	very reactive metal
20	40	calcium	reactive metal

The first 20 elements.

The first 20

When the first 20 elements are listed in order of their relative atomic mass, they show a repeating pattern. This pattern was first spotted by the British chemist John Newlands in 1864. He compared this to the repetition of notes on a musical scale and called it the 'law of octaves'.

The chart clearly shows this repetition, particularly in the very reactive gas/unreactive gas/very reactive metal sequence that appears three times (1/2/3, 9/10/11, 17/18/19).

c Newlands did not know about three of these elements, so his list of 17 elements repeated exactly like a musical scale. Which elements were missing from Newland's scale (shown right)?

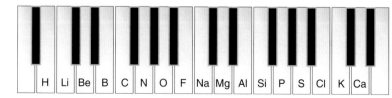

Mendeleev's table

The simple pattern described above breaks down after the first 20 elements. Because of this, Newlands' ideas were not taken up immediately by other scientists. But just 5 years later, in 1869, the Russian chemist Dimitri Mendeleev extended these ideas. He arranged the similar elements in vertical groups on a table.

Mendeleev's table also had its problems. He needed to put iodine out of position compared to its relative atomic mass in order to keep it in the same group as chlorine. Many scientists did not like this.

d Look at the Z and A_r figures towards the bottom of the 'first 20' table. Which elements are the wrong way around according to their relative atomic masses?

But Mendeleev had realised that some elements were missing. He thought they had not yet been discovered. So he left gaps in his table. He was so confident that he even used his table to predict the properties of these 'unknowns'. When some of the missing elements were discovered, the accuracy of his predictions gave great support to his ideas.

Dimitri Mendeleev (1834–1907).

Introducing the periodic table

A modern table of the first 20 elements arranged in columns clearly shows the repeating (or periodic) pattern. It is called the **periodic table** of the elements. Now that we understand the sub-atomic structure of the elements, they are arranged according to their proton number (Z).

The numbered rows across the table are called **periods**. They are numbered using Arabic numerals, from 1 to 4. The main vertical columns are called **groups**. They are also numbered using Arabic numerals, from 1 to 7, then 0 (sometimes Roman numerals are used: I to VII, then 0).

e Which group is aluminium (Al) in?

f Name an element in the same period as aluminium.

A simple periodic table for the first 20 elements.

Questions

1 Give elements with similar properties to:

   a lithium (Li)

   b fluorine (F)

   c beryllium (Be)

2 a How many metals and how many non-metals are there in the first 20 elements?

   b How are metals and non-metals grouped in the simple version of the periodic table?

3 In the full periodic table, krypton is below argon. Predict the properties of krypton.

Summary

• If the elements are arranged in order of relative atomic mass, a repeating pattern of properties can be seen.

• The modern periodic table arranges the elements into eight groups with similar properties, based on their proton number.

8:10 The periodic table

Here is the modern periodic table. This periodic table is ordered by proton number (Z). Beyond the first 20 elements, the simple pattern of vertical groups and horizontal periods is wedged apart by a block of metals with similar properties (the transition metals). The additional blocks that wedge in after elements 57 and 89 have been left out, including element 92, uranium.

Example: uranium

relative atomic mass —— (A_r) 238 **U**
atomic number —— (Z) 92

a Which element is in group 4, period 2?

The electron link

The pattern of the periodic table links in precisely with the way the electrons are arranged around the atoms of each element. This was, of course, unknown to Mendeleev.

◆ The period number tells you how many energy levels the element has.

◆ The group number tells you how many electrons an element has in its outer energy level.

For example, all the elements in period 2 have two energy levels.

b How many electrons does iodine (I) have in its outer energy level?

c Which element has two electrons in its fifth energy level?

Period

| 1 |
| 2 |
| 3 |
| 4 |
| 5 |
| 6 |
| 7 |

1 2

1	2							
7 **Li** 3 lithium	9 **Be** 4 beryllium							
23 **Na** 11 sodium	24 **Mg** 12 magnesium							
39 **K** 19 potassium	40 **Ca** 20 calcium	45 **Sc** 21 scandium	48 **Ti** 22 titanium	51 **V** 23 vanadium	52 **Cr** 24 chromium	55 **Mn** 25 manganese	56 **Fe** 26 iron	59 **C** 27 cob
85.5 **Rb** 37 rubidium	88 **Sr** 38 strontium	89 **Y** 39 yttrium	91 **Zr** 40 zirconium	93 **Nb** 41 niobium	96 **Mo** 42 molybdenum	**Tc** 43 technetium	101 **Ru** 44 ruthenium	103 **R** 45 rhod
133 **Cs** 55 caesium	137 **Ba** 56 barium	139 **La** 57 lanthanum	178 **Hf** 72 hafnium	181 **Ta** 73 tantalum	184 **W** 74 tungsten	186 **Re** 75 rhenium	190 **Os** 76 osmium	192 **I** 77 irid
Fr 87 francium	**Ra** 88 radium	**Ac** 89 actinium						

1 **H** 1 hydrogen

The power of the periodic table is the way it can be used to predict the chemical properties of elements, which are governed by their electronic structure.

Metals

More than three-quarters of the elements are metals. Metals are found in the middle and on the left of the full periodic table.

Groups 1 and 2 contain very reactive but quite soft metals with low melting points. Examples are sodium (group 1) and calcium (group 2).

The block of metals that wedges in between groups 2 and 3 in period 4 is called the **transition metals**. This block contains the typical 'everyday' metals such as iron and copper. They are not as reactive as those in groups 1 and 2 but they are harder and stronger and have higher melting points.

d What kind of a metal is nickel (Ni)?

Element	Group	Electrons in outer level
lithium	1	1
beryllium	2	2
boron	3	3
carbon	4	4
nitrogen	5	5
oxygen	6	6
fluorine	7	7
neon	0	0 (8 in the full level beneath)

Non-metals

Less than a quarter of the elements are non-metals. All the non-metals are found to the right of the periodic table.

Groups 6 and 7 contain reactive non-metals. Examples are oxygen (group 6) and chlorine (group 7).

Elements in these groups are gases at the top of the groups but solids further down.

Group 0 contains the noble gases, a family of completely unreactive non-metals.

e Is fluorine a solid, a liquid or a gas?

Hydrogen is unique and stands alone.

Helium is put in group 0 because its outer shell is full.

	0
Group	4 **He** 2 helium

3	4	5	6	7	
11 **B** 5 boron	12 **C** 6 carbon	14 **N** 7 nitrogen	16 **O** 8 oxygen	19 **F** 9 fluorine	20 **Ne** 10 neon
27 **Al** 13 aluminium	28 **Si** 14 silicon	31 **P** 15 phosphorus	32 **S** 16 sulphur	35.5 **Cl** 17 chlorine	40 **Ar** 18 argon

	63.5 **Cu** 29 copper	65 **Zn** 30 zinc	70 **Ga** 31 gallium	73 **Ge** 32 germanium	75 **As** 33 arsenic	79 **Se** 34 selenium	80 **Br** 35 bromine	84 **Kr** 36 krypton
Ni nickel	108 **Ag** 47 silver	112 **Cd** 48 cadmium	115 **In** 49 indium	119 **Sn** 50 tin	122 **Sb** 51 antimony	128 **Te** 52 tellurium	127 **I** 53 iodine	131 **Xe** 54 xenon
Pt tinum	197 **Au** 79 gold	201 **Hg** 80 mercury	204 **Tl** 81 thallium	207 **Pb** 82 lead	209 **Bi** 83 bismuth	**Po** 84 polonium	**At** 85 astatine	**Rn** 86 radon

Groups 3 to 5 have less clear-cut properties. Elements in these groups are non-metals at the top of the groups, but grade into metals down the group.

Questions

1 Are the following elements metals or non-metals?

   a lithium (3)   b nitrogen (6)   c calcium (20)

   d titanium (22)   e palladium (46)   f iodine (53)

2 How many electrons are there in the outer energy level of:

   a barium (56)   b bromine (35)   c lead (82)

   d selenium (34)   e radon (86)   f caesium (55)

3 Describe the likely chemical properties of:

   a xenon (54)   b strontium (38)   c cobalt (27)

   d fluorine (9)   e rubidium (37)

4 Why is helium put in group 0, even though it only has two electrons in its electron shell?

Summary

- The periodic table has the elements arranged in groups according to their proton number.

- The pattern follows the arrangement of the electron structure of the atoms.

- Elements in the same group have similar properties.

- The periodic table is a powerful tool for predicting how elements react.

Group 0 (sometimes called group 8) of the periodic table is the **noble gas** family. These are typical non-metals in many ways as:

◆ they have very low melting points and low boiling points;

◆ when solid they are soft and crumbly;

◆ they do not conduct electricity.

But, unlike most non-metals, they are spectacularly unreactive.

You may think that such unreactive gases will not be of much use. However, sometimes their very inactivity is just what is required.

a How many electrons do group 0 atoms have in their outer energy level (not counting helium)?

Group 0

| 4 He 2 helium |
| 20 Ne 10 neon |
| 40 Ar 18 argon |
| 84 Kr 36 krypton |

Introducing the noble gases

Helium is not very soluble in water, even under pressure. This makes it an excellent substitute for nitrogen in the 'air' that deep-sea divers breathe. Nitrogen bubbling out of the blood can cause divers to suffer from 'the bends' when they return to the surface. Helium doesn't do this. But it does have the side-effect of making you sound like Donald Duck when you talk!

Neon is most commonly used for another reason. Neon glows if an electric current is passed through it. Neon tubes can be coloured, making them ideal for flashy neon signs!

Argon is the cheapest of the noble gases to produce. This is because it makes up 1% of air. Argon is used inside ordinary light bulbs, to stop the filament from burning. Argon is also used to give an unreactive atmosphere for welding. Welding can be dangerous in air.

Krypton is used in lasers.

b Where do you use noble gases at home?

Single atoms

Because the noble gases are so unreactive they do not combine to form molecules. Instead they exist as single atoms.

c Spot the noble gas in this close-up picture of air. (How can you tell?)

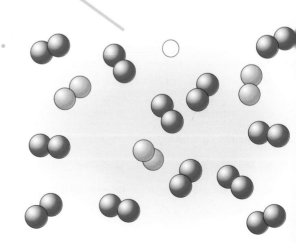

Helium and hydrogen

One other useful property of helium is that it has a very low density. The density of helium is much less than that of air. This makes helium a safe alternative to hydrogen for modern airships, and party balloons.

The explosive property of hydrogen is used as a test for hydrogen gas. If you put a lighted splint next to a tube of hydrogen, it will burn with a squeaky pop.

d Why is helium a better gas than hydrogen to use in airships?

This photograph of the Hindenburg disaster may help you answer question d.

Discovering the noble gases

Air is approximately 20% oxygen (which is reactive) and 80% nitrogen (which is unreactive). But what was unsuspected until 100 years ago was that, hidden within air, there was about 1% of truly unreactive gas – what we now know as a noble gas.

In 1892, scientists discovered that nitrogen from the air was denser than nitrogen produced experimentally. They also found that they could react nitrogen with hot magnesium. When this reaction was performed with the 'nitrogen' from the air, about 1% of the gas would not react. That 1% was identified as other gases, which became known as the 'noble gases' because they were so unreactive.

e How much neon is there in the air? More than 1%, 1%, 0.1% or less than 0.1%?

f Why did it take so long to discover the noble gases?

g What was the clue that suggested that nitrogen from the air had something 'hidden' in it?

h What reaction finally left the noble gases on their own?

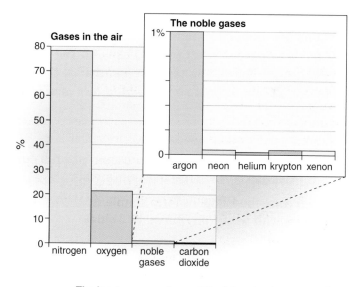

The inert gases make up 1% of the air – but most of that is argon.

Questions

1 Copy and complete the following. Choose from:

    argon   **atoms**   **noble**   **periodic**   **unreactive**

Air contains 1% of a gas called _____. This is in the form of single _____. Argon gas is very _____. It is one of the _____ gases from group 0 of the _____ table.

2 a What would happen to a light bulb when it was switched on if the bulb were filled with air rather than argon?

  b Why is argon used rather than helium?

3 Peter had a test-tube full of hydrogen and another full of helium. How could he tell them apart?

Summary

- Group 0 contains the unreactive noble gases.
- These gases exist as single atoms.
- The noble gases have other properties that make them useful.
- Hydrogen gas 'pops' with a lighted splint.

8:12 The halogens

Group 7 of the periodic table contains a family of very reactive non-metals called the **halogens**. This group includes chlorine, bromine and iodine. Like other non-metals they have low melting points and low boiling points, form soft crumbly solids (if cooled down enough) and do not conduct electricity at all.

Chlorine is a green gas. It was used as a poison gas in World War I. Today it is used to kill germs in swimming baths and drinking water.

Bromine is a brown liquid that vaporises easily to form a brown gas.

Iodine is a soft, purple-black solid that gives off a purple vapour. Iodine stains the skin brown because it dissolves in skin oils. This reaction is used to develop fingerprints on paper.

a Consider iodine, bromine and chlorine. Are they solids, liquids or gases? What pattern can you see as you go up the group? Fluorine is the first member of the group. Is fluorine likely to be a solid, a liquid or a gas?

How they react

All the halogens are just one electron short of a full outer shell. This is what makes them reactive non-metals.

On their own, the halogens form simple molecules with two atoms joined by a single covalent bond.

The halogens can also share electrons in covalent bonds with other non-metals. For example, chlorine forms carbon tetrachloride with carbon.

b What type of bond would form between oxygen and chlorine atoms? Explain your answer.

With metals, however, the halogens can capture electrons to form single negative ions. The halogens can form ionic compounds such as sodium chloride, Na^+Cl^-.

Note how the name of a halogen changes as it forms an ion:

♦ chlori**ne** forms chlori**de** (Cl^-) ions;

♦ bromi**ne** forms bromi**de** (Br^-) ions;

♦ iodi**ne** forms iodi**de** (I^-) ions.

c What is the ion that will form from fluorine?

Group 7

19	**F**
9	fluorine
35.5	**Cl**
17	chlorine
80	**Br**
35	bromine
127	**I**
53	iodine

fluorine   chlorine   bromine   iodine

The halogens form coloured gases.

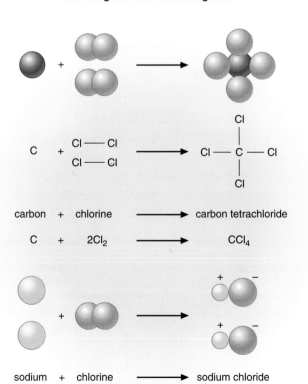

$$C + \begin{array}{c} Cl—Cl \\ Cl—Cl \end{array} \longrightarrow \begin{array}{c} Cl \\ | \\ Cl—C—Cl \\ | \\ Cl \end{array}$$

carbon + chlorine $\longrightarrow$ carbon tetrachloride

C + $2Cl_2$ $\longrightarrow$ CCl_4

sodium + chlorine $\longrightarrow$ sodium chloride

2Na + Cl_2 $\longrightarrow$ 2NaCl

The halogens form covalent compounds with non-metals, but form ionic compounds with metals.

What's the trend?

The melting points and boiling points of the halogens get higher as you go down the group. That is why chlorine is a gas, bromine is a liquid and iodine is a solid at room temperature.

The halogens get less reactive as you go down the group. For example:

- chlorine and hydrogen explode together in sunlight;
- bromine and hydrogen only react if heated;
- iodine and hydrogen only partially react even if heated.

d Do you think it would be wise to mix fluorine and hydrogen?

Because of this difference in reactivity, chlorine can displace bromine and iodine from solutions of their compounds. For example:

chlorine + sodium bromide → bromine + sodium chloride
(green)   (colourless)   (brown)   (colourless)
$$Cl_2 + 2NaBr \rightarrow Br_2 + 2NaCl$$

e Why do you need to have 2NaBr in this balanced equation?

f Why is bromine able to displace iodine from sodium iodide?

g Could iodine displace chlorine from sodium chloride? Explain your answer.

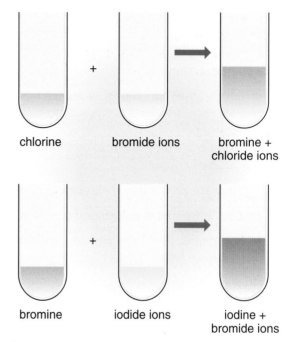

chlorine   bromide ions   bromine + chloride ions

bromine   iodide ions   iodine + bromide ions

Halogen displacement reactions. Iodine can form a dark brown solution in water.

Questions

1 Copy and complete the following sentences. Choose from:

coloured   down   gases   halogens   reactive

Group 7 contains a family of very _____ non-metals called the _____ . These are _____ at the top of the group but change to liquid then solid as you go _____ the group. They all have _____ vapours.

2 What type of bonding would you expect to find in the following compounds:

  a calcium bromide ($CaBr_2$)

  b nitrogen tri-iodide (NI_3)

Explain your answers.

3 Sea water contains bromide ions. Bromine is made by bubbling chlorine gas through sea water. Explain what happens and why.

4 The element astatine (At) appears below iodine in group 7.

  a Is astatine likely to be a solid, a liquid or a gas?

  b Will astatine be able to displace iodine from iodine compounds?

Summary

- Group 7 contains a family of very reactive non-metals with coloured vapours.

- As you go down the group, the elements change from gases, through a liquid to a solid.

- As you go down the group, the elements become less reactive.

8:13 The alkali metals

The metals in group 1

Group 1 of the periodic table contains a family of very reactive metals. This group includes lithium, sodium and potassium.

Like all metals they:

◆ have a shiny metallic appearance when fresh;

◆ are good conductors of heat and electricity.

But in other ways they are unlike ordinary 'everyday' metals such as iron or copper.

◆ They are very soft and can be cut easily with a knife.

◆ They have low densities and can float on water.

◆ For metals, they have very low melting points and low boiling points.

a Give two physical differences between lithium and iron.

Group 1 metals are very soft. Because they are so reactive they have to be stored under oil.

Positive ions

When group 1 metals react, each atom loses an electron to form a single charged positive ion. These ions can then form ionic compounds with non-metals. For example, lithium forms Li^+ ions when it reacts with oxygen:

lithium + oxygen → lithium oxide
$$4Li(s) + O_2(g) → 2Li_2O(s)$$

b What do the symbols (s) and (g) mean?

c Oxygen ions are O^{2-}. Explain why there must be two lithium ions (Li^+) for every oxygen ion in lithium oxide.

The alkali metals

The elements in group 1 react with water. They form soluble metal hydroxides which give strongly alkaline solutions. Because of this, group 1 metals are also called the **alkali metals**. Hydrogen gas is given off during this reaction.

For example, with sodium:

sodium + water → sodium hydroxide + hydrogen

d What colour would pH paper turn in sodium hydroxide solution?

e What test would show that the gas is hydrogen?

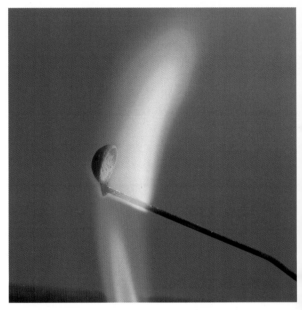

Lithium burns in air with a bright red flame.

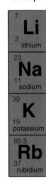

Group 1

7	
Li	
3	
lithium	

| 23 |
| **Na** |
| 11 |
| sodium |

| 39 |
| **K** |
| 19 |
| potassium |

| 85.5 |
| **Rb** |
| 37 |
| rubidium |

What's the trend?

The alkali metals become softer and have lower melting points and lower boiling points down the group. They also get more and more reactive down the group. This is seen in the reaction with water.

Lithium fizzes steadily.

Sodium reacts so rapidly that the heat given out by the reaction melts the metal. The metal whizzes around the surface of the water. The hydrogen gas may catch fire, giving a yellow flame (because of the sodium).

Potassium reacts even more violently. The hydrogen catches fire instantly and burns with a lilac-coloured flame (because of the potassium).

f What do you think would happen if you put rubidium (Rb) in water?

Group 1 physical properties

Look at the table of information about the group 1 metals.

g How hard or soft do you think rubidium will be?

h In the desert the temperature can get as high as 40 °C. Which metal might melt in the desert?

i Describe in words how the melting point varies down group 1.

j Water has a density of 1 g/cm³. Will rubidium float or sink in water? Explain your answer.

k In general, the metals get denser down the group. Which metal is the 'odd one out' of this trend?

Group 1 metal	Density (g/cm^3)	Melting point (°C)	Hardness
lithium	0.53	180	soft
sodium	0.97	98	very soft
potassium	0.86	64	even softer
rubidium	1.53	38	

Questions

1 Copy and complete the following sentences. Choose from:

    alkaline   densities   electricity   hydrogen   reactive

The metals in group 1 conduct heat and _____. They are unusually soft and have low _____. They are very _____ and fizz in water, giving off _____ gas and leaving an _____ solution.

2 In what way are group 1 metals 'typical metals'? In what ways are they unusual?

3 What is the charge on a potassium ion?

Summary

- Group 1 contains soft but very reactive metals called the alkali metals.
- Group 1 metals react with water to give strongly alkaline solutions.
- Group 1 metals form single positive ions.
- Group 1 metals get more reactive down the group.

8:14 Metal halides

Making salt

Sodium is an alkali metal. It is dangerously reactive, fizzing violently in water, leaving a strongly alkaline solution.

a   What gas is given off in this reaction?

Chlorine is a halogen. It is a dangerously reactive and deadly poisonous gas. If you put damp litmus paper in chlorine it turns red then bleaches to white as the chlorine reacts with the dye.

If you put hot sodium into a jar of chlorine you get a violent reaction as the two elements combine to form an ionic compound. A great amount of heat is given out.

b   Is this reaction exothermic or endothermic?

So what is the result of combining these two dangerously reactive chemicals? You get a white crystalline solid which dissolves in water to give a neutral solution. It is *sodium chloride* – common salt. You need it in your diet and you sprinkle it on your chips to improve the flavour...

Useful chemicals from salt

Salt occurs naturally in solution in the sea (**brine**) and in large beds of rock underground (**rock salt**).

When salt is dissolved in water, its splits up into its ions (Na^+ and Cl^-). These ions are free to move about. Because the ions can move about, brine conducts electricity.

This is used in industry to split the brine apart by the process of **electrolysis**. The electrolysis of brine makes three useful products.

◆ *Chlorine gas* forms at the positive electrode. Chlorine is used to kill bacteria in swimming pools and drinking water. Chlorine can also be used to make disinfectants, bleach and plastics such as PVC.

◆ *Hydrogen gas* forms at the negative electrode. Hydrogen is used to make ammonia for fertilisers. Hydrogen also changes oils into fats for margarine and chocolate.

◆ *Sodium hydroxide* is left in solution. This strong alkali (caustic soda) is used to make soap, paper and ceramics. It is also used to clean ovens!

$$\text{sodium chloride} + \text{water} \xrightarrow{\text{electrolysis}} \text{chlorine} + \text{hydrogen} + \text{sodium hydroxide}$$

c   Why do the chloride ions go to the positive electrode?

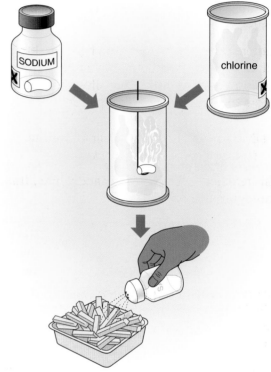

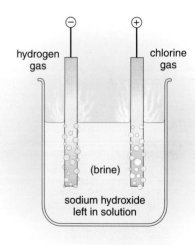

Salt can be made by combining the reactive elements sodium and chlorine.

Three useful products are made by the electrolysis of brine.

Metal halides

Compounds of metals with halogens are called **halides**.

Sodium is a very reactive metal, so sodium halides are stable compounds that can only be broken apart by electrolysis.

Silver is an unreactive metal. Silver forms halides such as silver chloride, silver bromide and silver iodide. These compounds are much weaker than sodium chloride and can be split up easily.

Radioactivity, X-rays and even light can break up these silver halides. If you shine light onto a film containing a silver halide, the compound is reduced to silver. This leaves a dark spot where the light fell. For example:

$$\text{silver bromide} \xrightarrow{\text{light}} \text{silver} + \text{bromine}$$
$$\text{(colourless)} \qquad\qquad \text{(black)}$$

This reaction is used in black and white films and photographic papers.

d Why is it a waste to throw old X-ray photographs away?

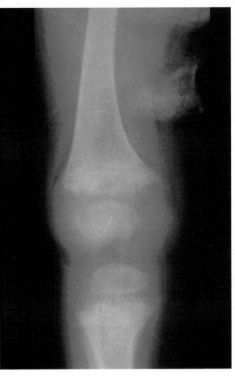

Silver halide films give a negative image with light – or with X-rays!

Hydrogen halides

Halogens react with hydrogen to form covalent molecules called the *hydrogen halides*. The hydrogen halides are colourless gases which are very soluble in water and give acidic solutions.

Hydrogen burns in chlorine to give hydrogen chloride, a colourless gas. Hydrogen chloride dissolves in water to give hydrochloric acid.

$$\text{hydrogen} + \text{chlorine} \rightarrow \text{hydrogen chloride}$$
$$\text{H}_2 \quad + \quad \text{Cl}_2 \quad \rightarrow \qquad 2\text{HCl}$$

e How could you tell chlorine gas from hydrogen chloride gas using damp pH paper?

Hydrochloric acid is made by dissolving hydrogen chloride gas in water.

Questions

1 Copy and complete the following sentences. Choose from:

   chlorine   compound   poisonous   sodium   unreactive

   _____ is a dangerous and very reactive metal. _____ is a very reactive and highly _____ gas. Yet they combine to make a safe, stable and _____ ionic _____, sodium chloride.

2 Explain how sea water can help to kill germs, make chocolate and clean ovens.

3 Iodine is much less reactive than chlorine. Which compound would be easier to split apart, silver chloride or silver iodide? Explain your answer.

Summary

* Halogens react with metals to form ionic compounds called halides.

* Three useful products can be made by the electrolysis of sodium chloride: chlorine, hydrogen and sodium hydroxide.

* Silver halides are used in photography.

* Hydrogen halides form acid solutions.

End of module questions

1 The first part of the periodic table is shown here, with 8 elements marked in.

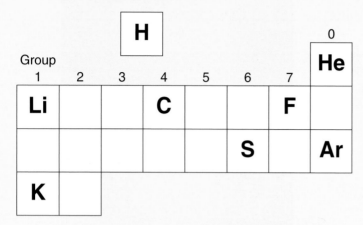

a Put the symbol for sodium (Na) in the correct box.

b What is the symbol for an unreactive gas?

c What is the symbol for the most reactive metal shown?

2 a Copy and complete the table below.

	Atomic number	Mass number	Number of protons	Number of neutrons
Carbon $^{12}_{6}C$	6	12	6	
Nitrogen $^{14}_{7}N$	7		7	7

b Which sub-atomic particle has a positive charge?

c What is the atomic number of an isotope $^{14}_{6}X$?

d Is X an isotope of carbon or nitrogen?

3 The electron structure of fluorine is shown.

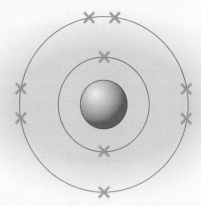

a Copy and complete the electron structure for chlorine.

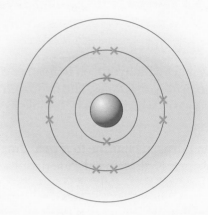

b The electron structure for fluorine can be written as (2,7). Fluorine forms a negative ion by gaining one electron. What is the electron structure of a fluoride ion (F^-)?

c The electron structure of a sodium atom can be written as (2,8,1). Sodium forms a positive ion by losing an electron. What is the electron structure of a sodium ion (Na^+)?

4 Water can be broken up into its component elements by passing electricity through it.

a What is the name of this process?

b Copy and complete the table.

Substance	Test for the substance
water	turns white anhydrous copper sulphate blue
hydrogen	
oxygen	

c State one important product that is made from hydrogen.

5 **a** Copy and complete this table, showing some non-metals and their compounds.

Element	Symbol	Electron structure	Formula of compound with hydrogen
carbon	C	(2,4)	
nitrogen	N	(2,5)	NH_3
oxygen	O	(2,6)	H_2O
fluorine	F	(2,7)	

b What type of bonding holds all these compounds together?

6 About 200 years ago, John Dalton was studying the way elements combined to form compounds. By careful experimentation, he found that the simple compounds he made always contained the elements in the same proportions. Dalton explained his results by the idea that elements were made of tiny particles that could not be broken – atoms.

Some students burnt magnesium in air (oxygen) and worked out how much of each element reacted to form magnesium oxide. Here are their results.

Student	Weighed mass of magnesium (g)	Weighed mass of magnesium oxide (g)	Calculated mass of oxygen (g)	Mg:O ratio
Derek	2.4	4.0	1.6	3:2
Jasmin	1.2	2.0	0.8	3:2
Petra	1.5	2.5	1.0	3:2

Show how Derek, Jasmin and Petra's results support Dalton's findings and explain how this leads on to the idea of atoms.

To gain full marks in this question you should write your ideas in good English. Put your ideas into a sensible order and use the correct scientific words.

7 Iron is a solid element. Oxygen is a gaseous element that has diatomic molecules. Sodium chloride is a compound. Which of these diagrams is which? Give reasons for your answers.

a

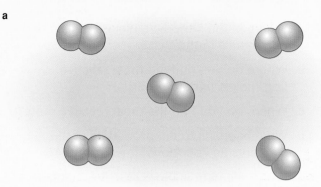

b

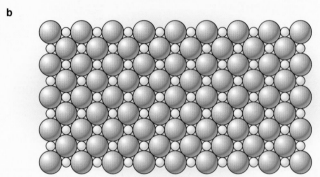

c

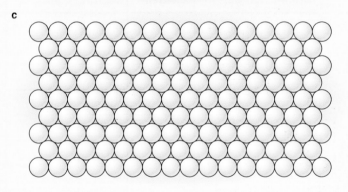

8 **a** Draw the electronic structure of sulphur ($Z = 16$).

b How many electrons does sulphur need to fill its outer shell?

c What is the charge on a sulphur ion when it fills its outer shell?

d Which noble gas has the same electronic structure as the sulphur ion in part **c**?

e Draw the electronic structure of beryllium ($Z = 4$).

f How many electrons does beryllium need to lose to empty its outer shell?

g What is the charge on a beryllium ion when it has emptied its outer shell?

h Which noble gas has the same electronic structure as the beryllium ion in part **g**?

i What type of compound could beryllium and sulphur form?

j What would the formula be for the compound in part **i**?

9 **a** Where in the periodic table are metals and non-metals found?

b Where do you find the most reactive non-metals (ignore group 0)?

c Where do you find the most reactive metals?

d What happens to the properties of the elements as you move down group 4?

e Which element is more reactive, sulphur or oxygen?

f Which metal is more reactive, strontium ($Z = 38$) or barium ($Z = 56$)?

g Which metal is more likely to be used in construction, vanadium ($Z = 23$) or rubidium ($Z = 37$)?

10 The table below shows the melting points of the first 20 elements.

Atomic number (Z)	Element	Melting point (°C)
1	H	−259
2	He	−272
3	Li	181
4	Be	1278
5	B	2300
6	C	3652
7	N	−210
8	O	−218
9	F	−220
10	Ne	−248
11	Na	98
12	Mg	649
13	Al	660
14	Si	1410
15	P	44
16	S	119
17	Cl	−101
18	Ar	−189
19	K	63
20	Ca	839

a By hand or using a computer, plot a graph of melting point against atomic number.

b Describe the pattern you see.

c How many elements are solid at room temperature (25 °C)?

11 For each of the following elements, give the atomic number (proton number, Z) and the mass number (A).

a Lithium (Li) has 3 protons, 4 neutrons and 3 electrons.

b Oxygen (O) has 8 protons, 8 neutrons and 8 electrons.

c Phosphorus (P) has 15 protons, 16 neutrons and 15 electrons.

d Uranium has 92 protons, 146 neutrons and 92 electrons.

12 **a** Copy and complete this table:

Atomic number (Z)	Metal or non-metal?	Atom	Atom electron structure	Ion	Ion electron structure
8	i ____	O	2,6	O^{2-}	ii ____
11	iii ____	Na	2,8,1	Na^+	iv ____
12	metal	Mg	2,8,2	Mg^{2+}	2,8
17	non-metal	Cl	2,8,7	Cl^-	2,8,8
20	v ____	Ca	vi ____	Ca^{2+}	vii ____

b What do you notice about the electron structure of:

  i O, Na and Mg ions?

  ii Cl and Ca ions?

c What is different about the ions in part **b**?

d From the table, explain why:

  i sodium chloride is NaCl but magnesium chloride is M_gCl_2.

  ii calcium oxide is CaO, but sodium oxide is Na_2O.

Module 12 – Waves and radiation

In this module, you will be finding out more about two topics you have studied before – light and sound. You have probably heard people talking about light waves and sound waves. But why do we picture these things as waves?

We will look at waves on water and on springs and ropes, as a way of understanding how waves behave. Then we will see how the same ideas apply to light and sound.

In this module, you will also learn more about many different types of radiation. You may think that anything called 'radiation' must be dangerous. This isn't necessarily so. The radio waves used by mobile phones and the infrared radiation coming from a heater are both forms of radiation which we need not fear. And by learning about the more hazardous forms of radiation, including X-rays and gamma rays, we can understand how to use them safely and avoid any harm they might do us.

We are surrounded by radioactive substances – fortunately, usually only in small quantities, so that their radiation is quite weak. When radioactivity was first discovered, a little over a hundred years ago, it gave scientists a new way of looking at atoms. By using alpha radiation, Ernest Rutherford was able to show that every atom has a tiny nucleus at its centre.

Waves carry energy. These giant breakers carry vast amounts of energy, but not quite enough to knock down the lighthouse.

Before you start this module, check that you can recall the answers to the following questions about sound and light.

1 What do we call a sound which is reflected back to us from a hard surface?

2 The *frequency* of a sound is the number of complete vibrations each second. What are its units?

3 If you increase the *amplitude* of a sound, how does the sound change?

4 When a ray of light travels from one material into another, it may be *refracted*. What does this mean?

5 When white light passes through a prism, it may be split up to form – what?

Waves are a disturbance travelling across the surface of the sea.

Scientists talk about light waves and sound waves. But if you see light or listen to sounds, you won't notice anything very wavy about them. So why do we call them waves?

To answer this, we have to think about waves on water. The photograph shows waves on the surface of the sea. On a calm day the surface of the sea is flat and undisturbed. On a rough day, the waves travel across the surface, making the boat go up and down.

Measuring waves

Water waves are a disturbance which moves across the surface of the water. The diagram shows how we can represent waves. It is like a cross-section of the surface of the water. There are two quantities we can measure on this diagram:

The **amplitude** of the wave: This is the maximum amount by which the surface of the water moves upwards from its undisturbed position.

The **wavelength** of the wave: This is the distance from the crest of one wave to the crest of the next.

(The small diagram shows that there are other ways to measure the wavelength: from one trough to the next, or from any point on one wave to the same point on the next wave.)

The amplitude and wavelength of a water wave are both measured in metres (m).

a Look at the diagram of the wave. Which is greater, its amplitude or its wavelength?

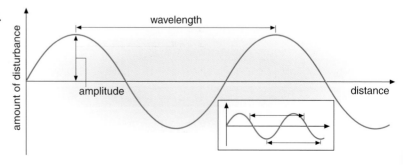

Take care! The amplitude of a water wave is measured from the undisturbed level of the surface.

Making waves

You can see waves on the surface of water using a ripple tank. A straight bar vibrates up and down, disturbing the surface of the water so that waves travel across it. An image of the waves is projected onto the floor, or onto a screen. To find the wavelength, measure across several waves.

In the picture, there is 20 cm between wave 1 and wave 11. There are 10 waves in this distance. So:

wavelength = 20 cm/10 = 2 cm.

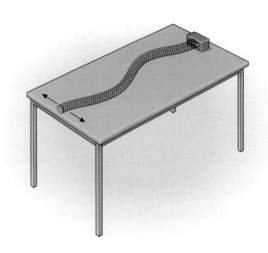

Stretching strings and springs

Fix one end of a long spring, and move the other from side to side. A wave travels along the spring. (You can do this with a string or rope, too.)

By moving your hand from side to side more rapidly, you will make more waves each second. You have increased the frequency of the wave.

The **frequency** of a wave is the number of waves which pass a point each second. It is measured in hertz (Hz). One hertz (1 Hz) means one wave per second.

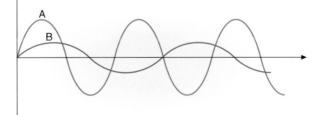

b If you move the end of the spring from side to side twice each second, what is the frequency of the waves produced?

Questions

Quantity	Unit
amplitude	
wavelength	
frequency	

1 Copy the table. Fill in the correct units in the second column. Choose from hertz (Hz) and metres (m).

2 Look at the diagram of the two waves, A and B.

  a Which has the greater amplitude?

  b Which has the greater wavelength?

3 Look at the diagram of a wave below.

  a What is its amplitude, in cm?

  b What is its wavelength, in cm?

4 Jo is making waves travel along a stretched length of rope. She moves her hand up and down 30 times in 10 s.

  a How many waves does she make in 1 s?

  b What is the frequency of the waves?

Summary
- Waves can travel across the surface of water, and along strings and springs.
- Waves can be measured to find their amplitude, wavelength and frequency.

Imagine that you are sitting in a small boat on the open sea. It is a windy day, and waves are travelling across the surface of the sea. As the waves pass under the boat, you move up and down.

This shows that a wave on water is a disturbance which makes the surface of the water move up and down. The wave itself moves along horizontally.

Making transverse waves

You can make a similar wave on a stretched spring by moving your hand up and down. The wave travels horizontally along the spring, while your hand moves vertically. This is an example of a **transverse wave**.

In a transverse wave, the disturbance is at right angles to the direction in which the waves themselves are travelling.

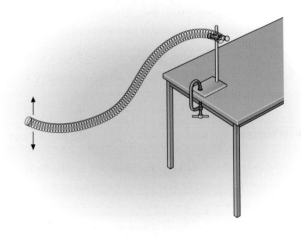

a Using the spring in the picture, you could make a wave along the spring by moving your hand from side to side, instead of up and down. Would this wave be transverse?

Making longitudinal waves

There is another way of making a wave on a stretched spring. Push the end back and forth, along the length of the spring. The wave looks different from a transverse wave. A region of squashed-up spring travels along, followed by a region of stretched-out spring. This is an example of a **longitudinal wave**.

In a longitudinal wave, the disturbance is back and forth, along the direction in which the waves themselves are travelling.

b Water waves travel horizontally, while the surface of the water moves up and down. Are these transverse waves or longitudinal waves?

The speed of waves

Some waves travel quickly; others travel more slowly. Waves on the sea move at a few metres per second; the water in a ripple tank is much shallower, and the waves travel more slowly.

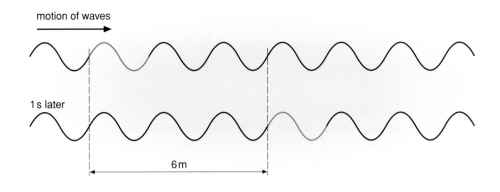

The diagram shows a line of waves. After 1 s, the red wave has moved 6 m to the right. The speed of the waves is 6 m/s.

Here is how we can calculate the speed of a wave from its frequency and wavelength:

Wave speed (m/s) = frequency (Hz) × wavelength (m)

Worked example

Some waves on the sea have a wavelength of 20 m and a frequency of 0.2 Hz. What is their speed?

Wave speed = frequency × wavelength
= 0.2 Hz × 20 m
= 4 m/s

c Some waves are travelling along a spring. Their wavelength is 1 m and their frequency is 2 Hz. What is their speed?

A surfer can ride along on the top of a breaking wave. It can be quite a fast ride!

Questions

1 Copy the table. Write **transverse wave** or **longitudinal wave** in the first column.

Type of wave	Description
	disturbance in same direction as wave moves
	disturbance at right angles to direction in which wave moves

2 Describe how you would make a longitudinal wave travel along a horizontal stretched spring.

3 Copy the correct equation which links wave speed, frequency and wavelength:

wave speed = frequency × wavelength

wave speed = frequency/wavelength

4 A vibrating motor sends waves along a stretched string. It produces 20 waves each second, and their wavelength is 0.5 m.

a What is the frequency of the waves?

b What is their speed?

DIGGING DEEPER
It is easiest to think of waves on the sea as transverse. However, they are really a mixture of transverse and longitudinal. As waves pass beneath a small boat, it goes both up and down and back and forth, so that it moves around in a vertical circle.

Summary
- Waves may be transverse or longitudinal.
- Wave speed = frequency × wavelength

Waves on the sea are whipped up by the wind. The wind transfers energy to the water, and the waves carry the energy across the sea. The energy of waves can cause a lot of damage when they strike the shore.

If you make waves on a stretched spring, you are transferring energy to the spring. The energy is carried along the spring by the waves, though the spring itself does not move along.

All waves transfer energy from their source to other places, without any matter being transferred.

The high winds of a hurricane transfer a lot of energy to waves on the sea.

Bouncing off barriers

If you send a single wave along a stretched spring, you will see it bounce off the fixed end and come back towards you. This is an example of **reflection**.

You can see waves on water being reflected by a barrier in a ripple tank. In the diagram, ripples are travelling from the left. The reflected ripples are travelling upwards.

a What happens when waves on the sea hit a harbour wall?

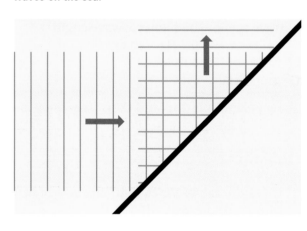

Refraction of ripples

By placing a sheet of glass in the water in a ripple tank, you can make it shallower. The ripples travel more slowly in shallow water because they drag on the bottom. How do the waves change when they move more slowly?

Ripples changing direction is an example of **refraction**. Refraction happens when waves change their speed. You should recall that light can be refracted, too. This suggests that light changes speed when it enters glass. The diagrams will remind you about what happens when a ray of light enters glass.

b Look at the diagram of the light ray entering glass at an angle to the normal. Does it bend towards the normal, or away from it?

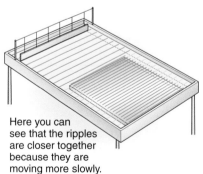

Here you can see that the ripples are closer together because they are moving more slowly.

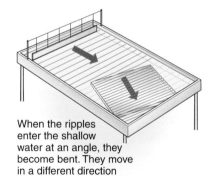

When the ripples enter the shallow water at an angle, they become bent. They move in a different direction

Sound and light

Sounds can be reflected – an echo is a reflected sound. Sound can also be refracted.

Light can be reflected, for example, by a mirror. It can also be refracted when it travels from one material to another.

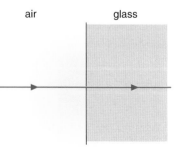

A ray travelling along the normal is not refracted.

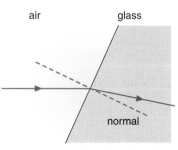

A ray at an angle to the normal is refracted.

This suggests that both sound and light travel as waves. That is why scientists talk about **sound waves** and **light waves**.

It also suggests that sound and light travel at different speeds in different substances. Scientists have made measurements and found that this is true.

Longitudinal or transverse?

The cone of a loudspeaker moves back and forth to make a sound. It pushes the particles of the air back and forth, making a longitudinal wave in the air. This is just like a longitudinal wave you make on a spring by pushing the end back and forth. Sound waves can travel through solids, liquids and gases.

Light is a form of **electromagnetic radiation**. Light waves are transverse waves. They do not need a material to travel through – they can pass through a vacuum.

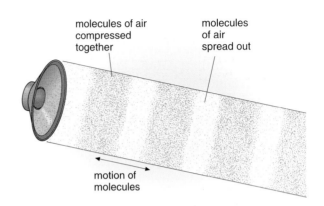

molecules of air compressed together

molecules of air spread out

motion of molecules

c How do we know that sound waves can travel through air?

d How do we know that light waves can travel through a vacuum (empty space)?

Questions

1 Copy the table and write **transverse** or **longitudinal** in the second column.

Type of wave	Transverse or longitudinal?
Water wave	
Sound wave	
Light wave	

2 Copy the sentences below. Choose the correct word from each pair.

Ripples travel more quickly/slowly when they enter shallower water.

This can cause them to be reflected/refracted.

3 What do we call a sound that has been reflected?

4 Which of the following statements are true, and which are false?

a Light waves can be reflected. TRUE/FALSE

b Light waves can be refracted. TRUE/FALSE

c Light waves can travel through a vacuum. TRUE/FALSE

5 Which of the following statements are true, and which are false?

When you listen to the radio:

a Sound waves travel from the loudspeaker to your ear. TRUE/FALSE

b Sound energy travels from the loudspeaker to your ear. TRUE/FALSE

c Air particles travel from the loudspeaker to your ear. TRUE/FALSE

DIGGING DEEPER
Some whales and dolphins have a large block of wax in their heads. This acts as a lens to refract and focus sound waves; they have a sort of sonar for finding their prey in dark waters.

Summary

- Waves transfer energy without any matter being transferred.

- Waves on water can be reflected and refracted.

- Because light and sound can also be reflected and refracted, this suggests that they travel as waves.

A harbour can provide protection from big waves on the open sea. The photograph shows what happens when waves enter a harbour. They spread out as they enter the harbour mouth into the space beyond, so that boats in the furthest corners are rocked up and down.

You can make a model of this using a ripple tank. Straight ripples approach a gap in a barrier, just like the mouth of the harbour. As they pass through the gap, they spread out into the space beyond.

In a similar way, ripples spread around the corner as they pass an obstacle, to fill the space behind it.

This spreading out of waves as they pass through a gap or around an obstacle is known as **diffraction**.

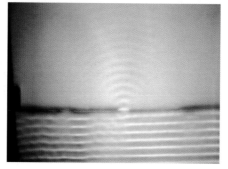 

Longer wavelengths

The diagrams show how waves of different wavelengths are diffracted as they pass through a gap. Waves with a longer wavelength are diffracted more strongly.

a Look at the first diagram of ripples being diffracted. What do you think would happen if the gap was made narrower? Would the ripples be diffracted more, or less?

Diffracting sound and radio waves

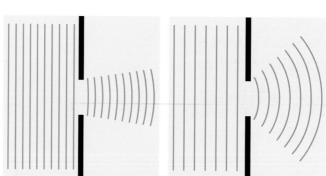

short wavelength (ripples close together): very little diffraction

longer wavelength: more diffraction

longest wavelength: strongest diffraction

If you are in the next room to someone who is speaking to you, you may be able to hear them even though you cannot see them. The sound waves of the voice are diffracted as they come through the doorway and spread out around the room you are in.

Because sounds can be diffracted, this supports the idea that sound travels as waves.

Radio waves are a form of electromagnetic radiation (like light). They have long wavelengths. There may be a hill between you and the transmitter, but the waves are diffracted round the hill so that you can still pick up the signal.

Because electromagnetic radiation can be diffracted, we believe it travels as waves.

b Which radio waves are more likely to reach the radio aerial, ones with long wavelengths or ones with short wavelengths? Explain your answer.

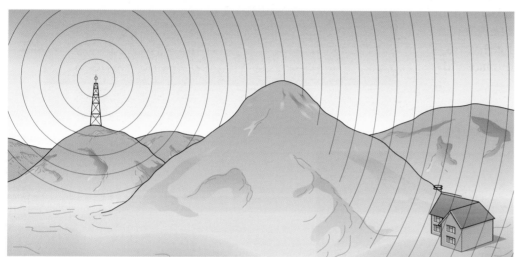

Questions

1 Copy and complete this table. Use words from the list to fill the first column.

refraction   diffraction   reflection

	Waves change direction when they bounce off a surface.
	Waves change direction when they change speed.
	Waves spread out when they pass through a gap.

2 **a** Draw a diagram to show how straight, parallel ripples are diffracted when they pass through a narrow gap.

 b Write a sentence to say how your diagram would be altered if the ripples had a longer wavelength.

3 You are standing at your friend's front door. Explain how you can hear someone mowing the lawn in the back garden.

4 You receive radio signals from a transmitter a few kilometres away. Explain how your radio set can pick up these signals even though there may be a block of flats in the way.

DIGGING DEEPER
Light can be diffracted by mist on a window or car windscreen. That's why we sometimes see a halo of light around streetlamps on a foggy night.

Summary
- Waves spread out when they go through a gap or past an object. This is diffraction.
- The longer the wavelength, the more strongly the waves are diffracted.

12:5 The electromagnetic spectrum

When you are listening to the radio, you can tune it into different stations. When you turn the dial, you are changing the frequency of the radio waves you are tuning in to. On the FM scale, the frequencies range from about 88 MHz to about 107 MHz. They make up a **spectrum** of frequencies from which you can select the frequency of the station you want to hear.

You can make a spectrum of light by passing white light through a prism or diffraction grating. The light is broken up into different colours, from red to violet. The light waves of each colour have a different frequency and wavelength.

a Which colour of light has the longest wavelength? Which colour has the shortest wavelength?

long wavelength   short wavelength

More waves

Light and radio waves are just two types of electromagnetic wave. There are several others, and together they make up the **electromagnetic spectrum**. The spectrum shows all types of electromagnetic radiation, arranged in order of their wavelengths and frequencies.

You will have heard of each of these types of radiation, but you may not have realised that they all belong to one big family of electromagnetic waves.

b Which type of electromagnetic wave has the longest wavelength? Which has the shortest wavelength?

highest frequency   lowest frequency

gamma rays	X-rays	ultraviolet rays	visible light	infrared rays	microwaves	radio waves

shortest wavelength   longest wavelength

Top speed

Light waves travel very fast. So do all other types of electromagnetic wave. They travel fastest in empty space, where there is nothing to slow them down. In empty space, they all travel at the same speed:

Speed of electromagnetic waves in space = 300 000 000 m/s

That's 300 million metres per second, or over 7 times round the Earth in one second. Most scientists think that nothing can travel faster than this – it's the speed limit of the Universe.

Getting warm

If you lie in the sun, three types of electromagnetic radiation fall on your skin: light, infrared rays and ultraviolet rays. You can tell that these are all absorbed by your skin – you can feel yourself getting warmer. The energy carried by the waves is transferred to your body.

All electromagnetic waves carry energy, and when they are absorbed their energy makes the substance which absorbs them get warmer.

We have another way of absorbing radio waves. We use a metal aerial. The waves make an electric current flow up and down in the aerial. This is an alternating current (because it flows back and forth), and it has the same frequency as the radio waves.

c Sometimes we use microwaves to heat things up. Give an example of this.

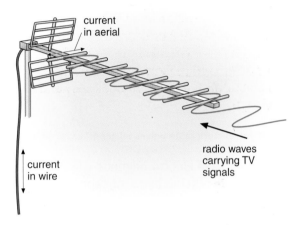

Television signals are carried by high frequency radio waves. They make an alternating current flow in the aerial, and this flows down a wire to the TV set.

Questions

1 Put the following types of electromagnetic radiation in order, starting with the ones with the longest wavelength:

light	radio waves	infrared rays	ultraviolet rays	X-rays	gamma rays	microwaves

2 Which have a higher frequency, gamma rays or ultraviolet rays?

3 A mobile phone uses radio waves to receive and transmit messages. There is a danger that your brain will be heated when you use such a phone. Explain why this is.

4 a How fast do radio waves travel in empty space?

b If a spacecraft sent radio waves and microwaves through space to Earth, which would get there first?

Summary

- Electromagnetic waves all travel through space at the same speed.

- They form a continuous spectrum:
  highest frequency
  shortest wavelength
    gamma rays
    X-rays
    ultraviolet rays
    light
    infrared rays
    microwaves
    radio waves
  lowest frequency
  longest wavelength

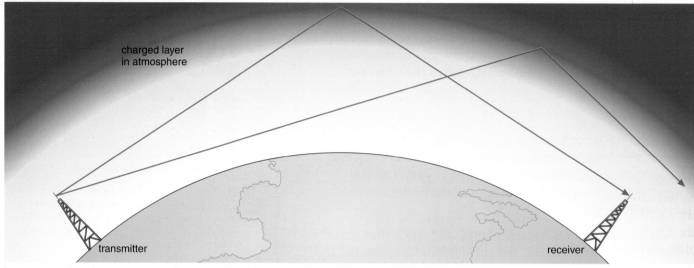

Longer wavelength radio waves reflect off an electrically charged layer in the upper atmosphere.

charged layer in atmosphere

transmitter

receiver

We make use of electromagnetic waves every day. By knowing how they are reflected and absorbed, we can discover new ways of using them.

Guglielmo Marconi was the first person to send messages using radio waves. In 1901, he sent the first radio message across the Atlantic. Many people thought his signal would travel straight out into space, because the Earth is curved. However, he was lucky. Radio waves are reflected by the upper atmosphere, and so they can be sent between distant points on the Earth's surface.

Radio stations use long-wavelength radio waves to broadcast over large areas. On holiday, you might be able to pick up a station from your home country even if you are thousands of kilometres away. Television stations use much shorter wavelength radio waves which do not travel so far.

Using microwaves

A microwave oven uses microwaves, of course. They have a wavelength which is easily absorbed by water molecules. Since most foods contain water, this is a good way to transfer energy to food. China plates and plastic containers do not absorb the microwaves.

Microwaves are also used by mobile phone networks to transmit messages over long distances. Radio waves from a mobile phone are picked up at a base station. The signal is then carried by microwaves to another distant base station, close to the receiving phone. Then it is sent by radio waves to the phone.

Some wavelengths of microwaves can pass easily through the atmosphere. They are not reflected (unlike radio waves). This

Marconi sent the first transatlantic radio messages. One of his signals helped catch Dr Crippen, a murderer who had escaped from England on a liner. Detectives were ready to arrest him when he arrived in New York.

DIGGING DEEPER
Astronomers look at radio waves coming from space. Radio and TV broadcasts can interfere with this. There are some wavelengths which broadcasters are not allowed to use, so that astronomers can have a clearer view of space.

means that they are useful for sending messages up to satellites which are orbiting high above the atmosphere. Satellites can also use microwaves to send signals back down to Earth.

a In a microwave oven, a plastic plate remains cool even while the food is being heated. Explain why this is so.

Infrared radiation

Infrared radiation is given out by warm objects. The hotter they are, the more radiation they give out. The glowing element in an electric toaster is very hot, and it gives out intense infrared radiation. This is absorbed by the bread which is being toasted, so that it becomes hot and burns gently. Grills and radiant heaters also emit infrared radiation.

We cannot see infrared radiation. It is used in remote controls for TVs and video recorders. When you press a button, an invisible infrared signal is flashed to the appliance. Some security keys for cars also use infrared; others use radio waves.

b Some stoves are fitted with electric grills. You can see them glowing as they cook the food. What type of electromagnetic radiation do you see? What other type of electromagnetic radiation does a grill produce?

These 'dishes' are microwave aerials; masts like this are usually found on hilltops. They form part of a mobile phone network. The dishes send microwave signals horizontally to other dishes many kilometres away.

This satellite is in orbit far above the Earth. It receives microwave signals sent up from Earth, and broadcasts television programmes back down to Earth.

The element in this toaster is hot – about 700 °C. It emits two types of electromagnetic radiation – light and infrared.

Questions

1 For each of the following types of electromagnetic radiation, state whether its wavelength is longer or shorter than that of light:

   radio waves   microwaves   infrared

2 Draw a diagram to show how radio waves can travel around the Earth, despite the fact that the Earth is curved.

3 a How might microwaves be used in the kitchen?

   b How might infrared radiation be used in the living room?

4 a How do satellites orbiting high above the Earth make use of microwaves?

   b Why can we not use radio waves to communicate with satellites?

Summary
- Radio waves and microwaves are used for communications systems.
- Microwaves and infrared radiation are used in cooking.
- Remote controls use infrared radiation.

The ozone layer in the atmosphere protects us from the Sun's most harmful rays, but there is a man-made hole in it. Even if you have dark skin, you need to take care to avoid being exposed to too much ultraviolet radiation. Some people use sunbeds to give themselves a tan, but it isn't very sensible to increase the amount of ultraviolet radiation to which you are exposed.

Suntan lotion contains chemicals which absorb ultraviolet radiation.

Short wavelengths

Ultraviolet radiation is like light, but with shorter wavelengths. It is invisible to the human eye (though some other creatures can see it). Fluorescent lamps produce ultraviolet radiation; it is absorbed by the white coating inside the tube, and then re-emitted as visible light.

a Explain why a special lamp is needed to show up the security marking on the banknote in the photo.

X-radiation is very penetrating. It can pass easily through flesh, but not so readily through bone or metal. People who work with X-rays use lead shields and even lead aprons to protect themselves from the radiation.

b Explain how X-rays would be useful if a small child swallowed a coin.

This banknote has a security marking which only shows up under ultraviolet (UV) radiation. The marking (lamb at lower left) absorbs the UV and re-emits it as visible light.

Damaging cells

The more radiation you are exposed to, the more harm it may do you.

- Low doses of ultraviolet, X-radiation and gamma radiation can damage normal cells so that they become cancerous.

- Higher doses of these types of radiation can kill normal cells.

Sometimes we want to kill cells. Some foods are exposed to radiation to kill harmful bacteria. The food can then be safely given to seriously ill people or taken on space flights. In the same way, surgical instruments and sanitary towels and tampons are sterilised using gamma radiation.

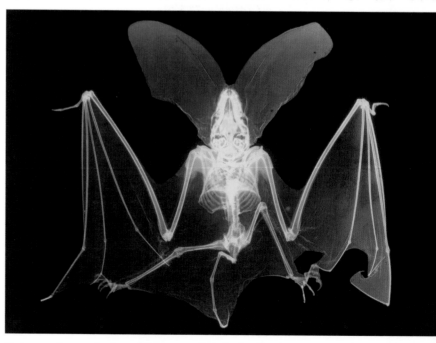

X-rays produce a shadow picture, revealing the bones of creatures such as this bat.

The paler your skin, the deeper ultra violet radiation can penetrate, and the greater the chance that a cancer may be caused.

c Why is it important to sterilise surgical instruments before use?

Other types of radiation can affect living tissue:

◆ All living cells contain water, and this can absorb microwaves. The cells are heated and may die.

◆ Infra red is absorbed by the skin; you feel warm. Intense infrared can cause burns.

Gamma radiation has been used to sterilise these plastic syringes inside their packaging.

Questions

1 Copy the sentences below; use words from the list to fill the gaps.

   killed   absorbed   cancerous

   When radiation penetrates living tissue, it may be _____ or it may pass straight through.

   A low dose may cause cells to become _____ , while cells may be _____ by a higher dose.

2 Copy the table; use words from the list to complete the first column.

   microwaves   ultraviolet   X-radiation
   gamma   radiation

Type of radiation	Effect
	causes tanning of skin
	produces shadow picture of bones in flesh
	kills harmful bacteria
	absorbed by water in cells; causes heating

3 When a dentist takes an X-ray of a patient's teeth, she stands outside the room, or behind a protective metal screen.

   a Why might she leave the room?

   b Why should the protective screen be made of metal?

4 Describe what happens when:

   a infrared radiation lands on your skin;

   b ultraviolet radiation lands on your skin.

DIGGING DEEPER
Permission has been given for some irradiated foods, particularly spices, to be sold in the UK. They have to be labelled to indicate that they have been irradiated.

Summary
• Radiation may be absorbed by living tissue, or it may pass through.

• When radiation is absorbed by cells, they may be killed by it; lower doses may cause the cells to become cancerous.

12:8 Total internal reflection

A doctor may use an instrument called an endoscope to look inside a patient. To see inside the patient's stomach, a long, flexible device is passed down their throat. This contains a bundle of **optical fibres**. Light rays which enter one end of a fibre bounce along inside it until they emerge at the other end.

Some of the fibres in an endoscope carry light downwards, to provide illumination; others carry light rays back upwards to show an image of the stomach.

a What scientific term could be used for the 'bouncing' of light rays as they travel along an optical fibre?

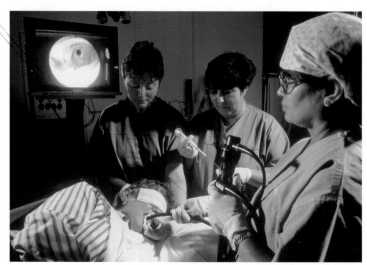

The image of the patient's insides appears on a monitor screen, so that all of the medical team can see it.

Inside glass

Optical fibres are made of very pure glass. They are quite flexible, so that they can be bent into a curved shape. The diagram shows how a ray of light is reflected when it strikes the inside surface of the fibre. The good thing about this reflection is that it is *total*; that is, 100% of the light is reflected. The inside surface of the fibre behaves like a perfect mirror.

optical fibre

This type of reflection is known as **total internal reflection (TIR)**. It is called *internal* because it happens *inside* the glass.

b Why is it called total?

The diagrams show what happens when a ray of light travels from glass (or Perspex or water) into air.

TIR occurs when the angle between the ray and the normal is greater than a certain angle called the **critical angle**.

c Look at the first of the two diagrams. What happens when the angle between the ray and the normal is less than the critical angle?

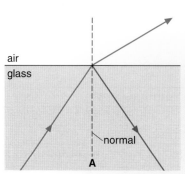

The ray of light strikes the surface of the glass at a narrow angle. Some of the light is refracted as it passes through; some is reflected.

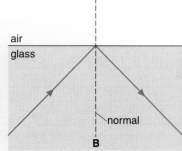

Here the ray strikes the surface at a greater angle. There is no refracted ray; all of the light is reflected.

Up and over

A periscope allows the user to see over an obstacle in front. Some periscopes are made with two mirrors; others use two glass prisms to reflect the light. The light is totally internally reflected inside each prism.

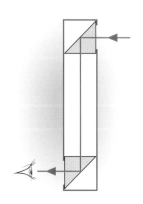

Getting the picture

Today, many houses are connected to a cable TV network which also provides a telephone system. Optical fibres are used to transmit television, radio and telephone signals to the user. The signals are carried by rays of light. This is better than using electrical signals in cables (wires):

◆ Light rays in a thin fibre can carry much more information than electrical signals in a cable of the same thickness.

◆ The light signals can travel much further than electrical signals before they become too weak to detect.

This technician is adjusting an array of optical fibres.

Questions

1 Copy and complete the two diagrams which show what happens when a ray of light strikes the inside of a Perspex block.

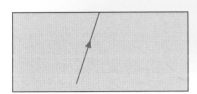 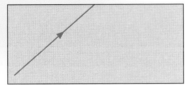

2 List three uses of total internal reflection.

3 Why would you expect to see a brighter image using a periscope which contains two prisms, rather than one with two mirrors?

4 Copy the sentences below, which explain why cable TV systems use optical fibres instead of electrical cables. Use the words **more** or **less** to fill the gaps.

An electrical cable can carry _____ information than an optical fibre of the same thickness.

There is _____ weakening of the signal in an electrical cable than in an optical fibre.

Summary

• When a light ray strikes the inside surface of glass (or another transparent material), it is partly reflected and partly refracted, provided the angle between the ray and the normal is small.

• If the angle is greater than the critical angle, it is totally internally reflected.

• Total internal reflection occurs in optical fibres, which are used in endoscopes and periscopes, and for transmitting information over long distances.

Today, we are surrounded by information – pictures, speech, music, text, data. It reaches our eyes and ears in the form of light waves and sound waves.

Information travels around in many forms – it may be carried by radio waves or microwaves through the air, as electrical signals along wires and cables, or as light or infrared signals along optical fibres.

a **What type of electromagnetic waves are used to transmit television signals through the air?**

A computer with Internet access can connect you to many sources of information, including text, data, images and music.

Waves of information

Information is transferred as a signal; signals can have two forms, **analogue** or **digital**. An analogue signal varies like a wave, to carry the information. The amplitude or the frequency of the wave changes continuously, like a sound wave. The diagrams show two forms of analogue signal.

A loudspeaker makes use of analogue signals. An electric current in the wires varies up and down. It flows through the loudspeaker, and makes the cone move backwards and forwards. This pushes the air back and forth to make a sound wave.

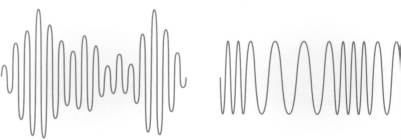

The analogue signal on the left has a varying amplitude. The one on the right has a varying frequency.

Dot dash dot

A digital signal is similar to Morse code. The information is coded as a series of pulses (on and off). A source of light or infrared radiation, such as a laser, is flashed on and off to send the signal down an optical fibre. Later it must be converted back to sounds and pictures which we can understand.

b **Look at the diagram of the digital signal. How many 'on's are there? How many 'off's?**

A digital signal is a series of on–off pulses.

Digital quality

In many ways, digital signals are a better way of transmitting information than analogue signals.

- ◆ Digital signals are of higher quality, because they do not get distorted as easily as analogue signals. They retain their information better as they are transmitted from place to place.

◆ Digital signals can carry more information than analogue signals. A single optical fibre can carry over a hundred TV channels as digital signals, many more than a similar analogue system. This is why much of television and radio broadcasting is changing to make use of digital signals.

c A digital signal can be carried along an optical fibre by light waves. What other form of electromagnetic radiation can be used?

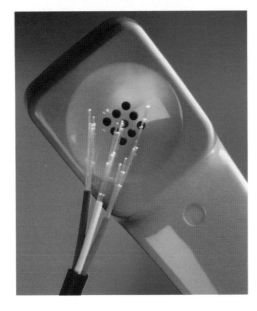

A conventional telephone wire can carry just one conversation, in the form of an analogue signal. If it is replaced by an optical fibre, hundreds of conversations can be carried simultaneously. This photograph shows how fine individual optical fibres are.

Questions

1 Copy the table. Write **analogue** or **digital** in the first column.

Type of signal	Description
	a series of on–off pulses
	a wave whose frequency or amplitude varies

2 Computers can send information to one another along cables. Which can transfer information more rapidly, analogue or digital signals?

3 Look at the diagrams.

   a Which represents an analogue signal?

   b Which represents a digital signal?

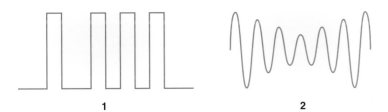

1   2

4 One advantage which digital signals have is that they can transfer large amounts of information more quickly than analogue signals. State one other advantage of transferring information in digital form.

DIGGING DEEPER
An analogy is when we say one thing is like another, so an analogue signal is one which has some of the same characteristics as the original information it carries. For instance, in a loudspeaker the current in the wires gets bigger or smaller to make a louder or quieter volume of sound. Digital is to do with fingers (digits). We count on our fingers; each finger is a unit or whole number. So a digital signal is one which consists only of whole numbers.

Summary
• Information can be transferred in the form of a signal. Signals can be carried by varying electric currents, by electromagnetic waves, or by light or infrared waves along optical fibres.

• Signals can be digital (on-off pulses) or analogue (varying amplitude or frequency).

12:10 Alpha, beta, gamma

There are radioactive substances all around us, and they give out radiation all the time. We can't see the radiation that they give out. That's why it took scientists a long time to discover radioactivity.

The first person to observe the radiation coming from a radioactive substance was a French scientist called Henri Becquerel, in 1896. He was studying rocks which contained uranium. Some of these rocks glow in the dark. He noticed that they made a photograpic film go dark, even when the film was wrapped in black paper to stop light getting at it. Some kind of radiation was getting through the paper.

Becquerel discovered that uranium gives out radiation at the same rate even if you heat it or cool it, or change its chemical form. There is no way to switch on or off the radiation from a radioactive substance.

I hope you all enjoyed our visit to the nuclear power station

a People are often very nervous about radioactive substances. Suggest why this is.

Detecting radiation

In the lab, your teacher can show you some radioactive sources. Remember that these give out radiation all the time, even when they are not in use. That is why they must be stored securely – there is no on–off switch.

One way to detect the radiation emitted by a radioactive source is to use a Geiger counter. The detector is a Geiger tube; a counter shows how much radiation has been detected. If the tube is moved further away from the source, the reading on the counter goes up more slowly. This shows that the radiation spreads out from the source; it is weaker further away from the source.

b How will the reading on the counter change if the tube is moved towards the source? Give a reason for your answer.

The teacher is using a Geiger counter to detect the radiation from a radioactive source.

Absorbing radiation

Henri Becquerel discovered that he could make the radiation from uranium weaker by putting a metal coin in the way. Some of the radiation was absorbed by the metal. The thicker the metal, the greater the absorption.

With experiments like this, it was possible to show that radioactive substances emit three types of radiation:

◆ alpha (α) radiation – stopped by a thin sheet of paper, or a few centimetres of air;

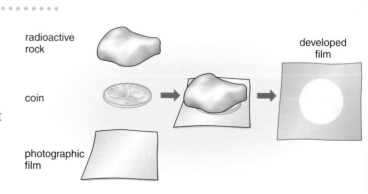

radioactive rock

coin

photographic film

developed film

◆ beta (β) radiation – passes easily through air or paper, but stopped by a few millimetres of metal;

◆ gamma (γ) radiation – needs many centimetres of lead, or metres of concrete, to absorb it.

This is summarised in the diagram.

c Which type of radiation is the most penetrating? Which is the least penetrating?

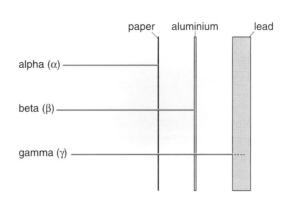

Monitoring thickness

Many factories make use of radiation to check the thickness of materials they are producing. For example, beta radiation can be used to check the thickness of plastic sheeting.

◆ If the sheeting is too thick, less beta radiation passes through it. The machine goes faster to make the sheeting thinner.

◆ If the sheeting is too thin, more beta radiation gets through to the detector. This tells the machine to go slower.

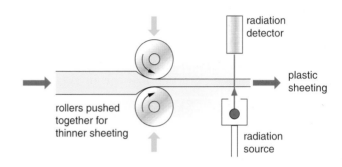

d The thickness of metal sheeting can be monitored in the same way. Explain why gamma radiation must be used instead of beta radiation.

Questions

1 Copy the diagram; add the following labels:

radioactive source   **radiation**   **absorber**
detector   **counter**

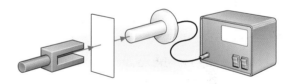

2 Copy the table.

a In the spaces in the first column, write **most** or **least**.

b Complete the last column by writing the correct symbols for beta and gamma radiation.

_____ easily absorbed	alpha radiation	α
	beta radiation	
_____ penetrating	gamma radiation	

3 Which types of radiation are being described here? Choose from alpha, beta and gamma.

a Absorbed by a few millimetres of aluminium

b Passes easily through air and through a centimetre of metal

c Absorbed by a thin sheet of paper

Summary

• Radioactive substances give out radiation all the time, no matter what is done to them.

• Radioactive substances emit three types of radiation:

— alpha (most easily absorbed, least penetrating)

— beta

— gamma (most penetrating, least easily absorbed)

12:11 Radiation around us

There are radioactive substances all around us. This means that we are exposed to a low level of radiation all the time. This is called **background radiation**. The diagram shows the sources of background radiation.

Cosmic rays come from sources far out in space. They are mostly absorbed by the atmosphere, but they are a serious problem for astronauts.

The food we eat contains small amounts of radioactive substances.

The air around us contains radon and other radioactive gases. In some parts of the country, people have fans under their floors to blow out the radon as it seeps up from underground.

Building materials (stone and brick) contain radioactive substances such as uranium. The radiation from these substances adds to background radiation

a Make a list of the sources of background radiation mentioned above.

Cell damage

It is right to be cautious about radiation. It can cause cancer. The more radiation you are exposed to, the greater the chance that you will get cancer. Here is how it does it.

◆ Radiation is energetic and fast-moving. When radiation smashes into neutral (uncharged) atoms or molecules, they may be left in a charged state – they are **ionised** (they have become ions).

◆ If radiation damages a molecule in a living cell, the cell may go out of control and start to divide over and over again. This is how a tumour (a cancer) develops.

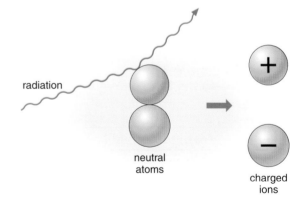

b What is the difference between a neutral atom and an ion?

Radiation protection

Because we understand radiation, we can find ways to protect ourselves from its effects. We can understand which are the most dangerous radioactive substances.

When a source of radiation is *outside* our bodies, we are safe from alpha radiation. It cannot penetrate the layer of dead skin cells which covers us. Beta and gamma radiation are more dangerous because they can penetrate the skin. Then they may damage the cells of organs within our bodies.

A source of alpha radiation is much more dangerous when it is *inside* our bodies. Then we are not protected by dead skin cells. The alpha radiation can easily damage cells and trigger the development of cancer.

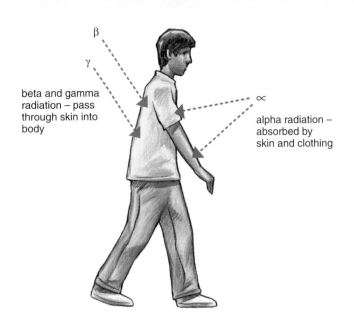

β

γ

beta and gamma radiation – pass through skin into body

∝

alpha radiation – absorbed by skin and clothing

c   Our skin is covered with a layer of dead cells. Which type of radiation does this protect us from? Why does it not protect us from the other two types?

Questions

1   Copy the sentences which follow; use words from the list to fill the gaps.

    cancer   ions   background   neutral

We are constantly exposed to _____ radiation.

Radiation can damage _____ atoms and molecules, so that they become charged _____ .

If a molecule within a living cell is damaged, this may cause _____ .

2   We are exposed to background radiation from many different sources. The pie chart shows the contributions which different sources make to background radiation in the UK. Put them in order, from biggest contributor to smallest.

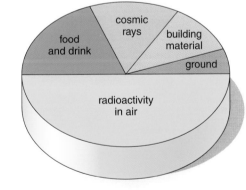

cosmic rays

food and drink

building material

ground

radioactivity in air

3   Explain why a source of alpha radiation is dangerous when it is inside us, but not dangerous when it is outside us.

4   The air contains a radioactive gas called radon. Radon is a source of alpha radiation. In some parts of the country, there is a lot of radon in the air. Explain why people in these areas are more likely to develop lung cancer.

Summary

• We are always exposed to background radiation from radioactive substances around us.

• If radiation damages molecules inside our cells, a cancer may start to develop.

12:12 Radioactive decay

Radioactive substances don't stay radioactive forever. As they give out their radiation, they gradually **decay**. At first, they give out radiation at a high rate. Then the rate gradually declines.

Some of the radioactive sources used in school labs decay quite quickly. After a few years, new ones have to be ordered because the old ones are giving out radiation at a very slow rate. Others give out radiation at a rate which decreases only very slowly, so they never have to be replaced.

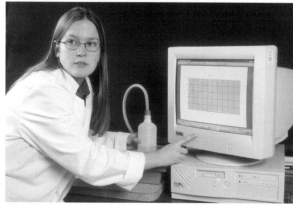

This teacher is demonstrating how the amount of radiation coming from a particular radioactive substance decreases quickly.

Representing radiaoctive decay

The **count rate** tells us the amount of radiation which is detected coming from a radioactive substance. As the substance decays, the count rate gets less.

We can show the pattern of radioactive decay as a graph. From the graph you can see:

- ◆ at first, the count rate is high;
- ◆ after a while, the count rate is less;
- ◆ the count rate gradually gets closer and closer to zero as the substance decays away.

a Look at the graph. Does the count rate decrease steadily to zero?

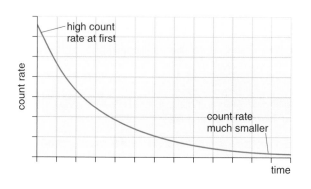

Half-life

When the Earth formed, about four and a half billion years ago, it contained more uranium than it does now. Uranium is radioactive, and about half of it has decayed away.

Other radioactive substances decay much more quickly than uranium. To describe how quickly they decay, we give their half-life. The meaning of this is illustrated by the graph.

The **half-life** of a radioactive substance is the time it takes for half of the original substance to decay away.

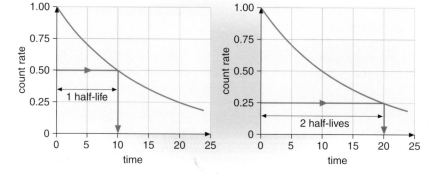

The second graph shows that, after twice this length of time, one quarter of the original substance will still remain. (We cannot say when all of the substance will have decayed.)

b A scientist measures the count rate for a sample of a radioactive substance. At first it is 40 counts per second. After 5 minutes, the count rate is 20 counts per second. How long is the half-life of the substance?

Radioactive decay and atoms

It is useful to picture the atoms in a radioactive substance. When an individual atom decays, it gives out a tiny burst of radiation. Now it has become an atom of a different substance.

◆ The original atoms are called **parent atoms**.

◆ The atoms which remain when the parent atoms decay are called **daughter atoms**.

The diagram shows what happens when we start with 100 parent atoms (shown in green). After one half-life, the number of parent atoms has halved.

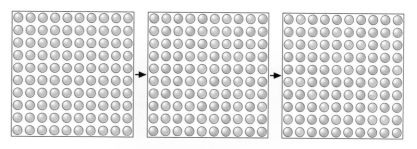

Key
○ parent atom (undecayed) ○ daughter atom (decayed)

c How many daughter atoms (red) are there after one half-life?

Questions

1 Only one of the graphs shows correctly the pattern of radioactive decay. Copy the correct graph.

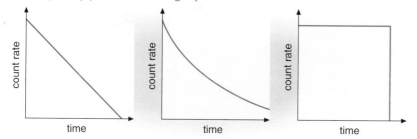

2 Copy out the sentences which follow, choosing the correct word from each pair.

The half-life of a radioactive substance is the time taken for the number of parent/daughter atoms in the substance to fall to half/zero.

The half-life of a radioactive substance is the time taken for the count rate from the original substance to fall to half its original/final value.

3 A sample of a radioactive substance initially contained 100 000 parent atoms. How many of these would remain after one half-life?

4 The table shows the count rate measured for a radioactive substance.

Count rate in counts per second	300	240	190	150	120
Time in minutes	0	20	40	60	80

a What was the initial count rate?

b How can you tell from the table that the substance was decaying?

c After how long had the count rate fallen to half its initial value? What is the half-life of the radioactive substance?

DIGGING DEEPER
One of the radioactive sources used in school laboratories is americium. This is element number 95, beyond uranium (element 92) in the Periodic Table. Elements beyond uranium are not found naturally, and must be made in nuclear reactors. Americium is also used in smoke detectors, such as you may have at home.

Summary

• The count rate for a sample of a radioactive substance decreases rapidly at first, then more and more slowly.

• The half-life is the time taken for the count rate to halve; after this time, half of the parent atoms have decayed.

Many people have to use radioactive substances at work. They must know how to use them safely, and how to check that they haven't been exposed to too much radiation.

Radiation badges

People who work with radioactive substances often wear a special badge. This does not protect them from radiation, but it does measure how much radiation they are exposed to.

The badge contains a small piece of photographic film. Radiation affects the film inside the badge. When the film is developed, it is grey or black. The more radiation the worker has been exposed to, the darker the film appears. If someone is exposed to a high level of radiation, they may have to stop working with radioactive substances.

a Why is it important to check that workers are not exposed to too much radiation?

These people are handling dangerous radioactive substances. They use robot arms; the glass they look through contains lead to absorb the radiation.

752145

The film is contained inside the blue plastic holder. The darker the developed film, the greater the amount of radiation to which the wearer has been exposed.

Killing microbes, destroying cancer

The medical equipment in the photo is going to be sterilised using gamma radiation from an intense source. Hospitals need to be sure that their equipment is not contaminated with

Gamma radiation is used to sterilise hospital equipment.

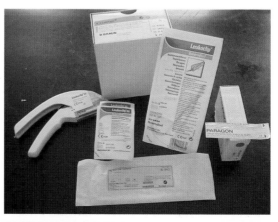

Veterinary equipment is also sterilised using gamma rays.

microorganisms which might harm their patients. When the equipment is exposed to strong radiation, any microorganisms are killed.

Other items, such as tampons, can be sterilised in this way. Some food is also sterilised; this is useful for some hospital patients, and for astronauts.

b Explain why alpha radiation would be no good for sterilising the syringes. Why is gamma radiation a good choice?

Radiation may cause cancer, but it can also be used to cure it. When a patient has cancer, their tumour may be given a high dose of radiation to kill the cancer cells.

A look inside

Just as we can use X-rays to look inside a person's body, we can use gamma radiation to see inside solid objects. A bridge made of concrete and steel can easily be checked for cracks or other damage if it is photographed using gamma radiation. This is because gamma radiation passes more easily through concrete than through steel.

c Why is gamma radiation a good choice for looking inside the solid bridge?

Questions

1 Look at the photo at the top of the opposite page. In what two ways are the people protected from dangerous levels of radiation?

2 Copy out the following sentence, adding the correct ending:

People who work with radioactive substances often wear a radiation badge ...

a ... to absorb any dangerous radiation.

b ... to see how much radiation they are exposed to.

c ... to warn others that they may be radioactive.

3 Explain how radiation from radioactive substances:

a can cause cancer;

b can help to cure cancer.

4 a Give an example of an item which may be sterilised using gamma radiation.

b Explain what the word *sterilised* means here.

DIGGING DEEPER
People who work in nuclear power stations now rarely wear film badges. Instead, they carry small solid state detectors. These register their exposure to radiation, and the information can be downloaded directly into a computer which keeps a running check on each individual's exposure.

Summary
- A radiation badge can show how much radiation the wearer has been exposed to.
- High doses of radiation can be used to kill harmful microorganisms and cancer cells.

12:14 Inside the atom

To understand more about radioactivity, we need to have a picture of the particles which make up an atom. Like all scientific ideas, our idea of the structure of atoms has changed over the years. Experiments have revealed more and more about the world of the atom.

The drawings show two different pictures, or **models** of the atom. One is old and out of date; the other is still useful.

The model on the left is called the **plum pudding model** of the atom. Scientists knew that atoms were made up of positive and negative charge. They thought that an atom might be made up of a sphere of positive charge (the 'pudding'), with negatively charged electrons dotted around inside it (the 'plums').

This model was replaced by the model on the right, the **nuclear model**. The atom has a tiny, positively charged **nucleus** at its centre. The electrons orbit around outside the nucleus.

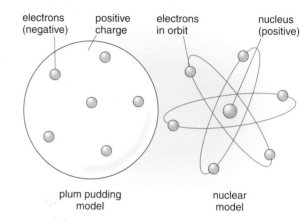

a In the plum pudding model, what charge has the pudding, positive or negative? What charge have the 'plums'?

b In the nuclear model, what charge has the nucleus? What particles orbit the nucleus?

Rutherford's experiment

To understand why scientists changed their minds about the model of the atom, we need to study a famous experiment. It was thought up by Ernest Rutherford, and carried out by his assistants Geiger and Marsden, at Manchester University, in 1905.

They directed a beam of alpha radiation from a piece of radioactive material at a thin gold foil. The foil was so thin that most of the radiation went straight through it. However, Geiger and Marsden found a most surprising thing: some of the alpha radiation was reflected back towards the source. It appeared to be bouncing off something in the foil – this 'something' was the atomic nucleus.

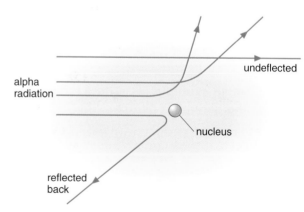

Rutherford argued that the energetic alpha radiation would pass straight through plum pudding atoms. He realised that the alpha radiation, which has positive electric charge, must be being repelled by the positive charge of the atom, concentrated in a tiny nucleus.

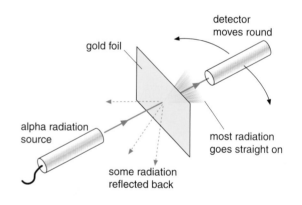

Today's picture

Rutherford's idea of the atom was soon accepted. Other experiments followed which supported his idea, and he used his model to explain what happens during radioactive decay.

Today, we know much more about atoms than was known 100 years ago. We picture each atom as being made up of three types of particles, protons and neutrons (in the nucleus), and electrons (orbiting outside the nucleus). The table gives details of these particles.

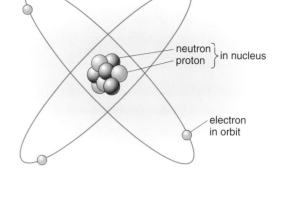

Particle	Mass	Charge	Position
proton	1	+1	in nucleus
neutron	1	0	in nucleus
electron	negligible	−1	outside nucleus

c Which particle has the smallest mass?

d Which particle has no electric charge?

Neutral atoms

An atom has equal numbers of protons and electrons. This means that it has equal amounts of positive and negative charge, so it has no overall charge – it is neutral.

Questions

1 Copy and complete the following sentences; use words from the list to fill the gaps.

   neutral   positive   negative   electrons
   neutrons   protons   nucleus

   The _____ of an atom contains _____ and _____ . It has a _____ charge.

   Around this orbit the _____ . These have a _____ charge.

   Because the amounts of positive and negative charge balance, an atom is _____ .

2 a Which has a greater mass, a proton or an electron?

   b Which two particles, found within every atom, have equal but opposite charges?

3 Explain why most of the mass of an atom is concentrated in its nucleus. (Use the table above to help you.)

4 This question is about Rutherford's experiment which showed up the existence of the nucleus.

   a What radiation did he direct at the metal foil?

   b What metal was the foil made of?

   c What happened to most of the alpha radiation?

   d What did he discover that suggested that most of the mass of the atom was concentrated at its centre?

5 Suggest two reasons why Rutherford's model of the atom rapidly replaced the earlier plum pudding model.

Summary

• Rutherford's alpha particle-scattering experiment revealed that the atom has a nucleus at its centre.

• We can picture an atom as having a positively charged nucleus, with negatively charged electrons orbiting it. The nucleus consists of protons and neutrons, and contains most of the mass of the atom.

12:15 Atoms, elements, isotopes

If you could look very closely at an atom, how could you tell which element it was? Simple: count the number of protons in its nucleus.

◆ An atom with 1 proton in its nucleus is an atom of hydrogen.

◆ An atom with 2 protons in its nucleus is an atom of helium.

◆ An atom with 6 protons in its nucleus is an atom of carbon.

◆ An atom with 92 protons in its nucleus is an atom of uranium.

And so on. (If you look at the Periodic Table, you will see that hydrogen is element number 1, helium is number 2, and so on.)

Every atom of a particular element has the same number of protons.

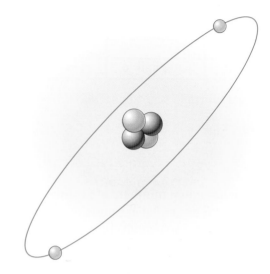

This atom has 2 protons in its nucleus; it is an atom of helium. (It also has two neutrons.)

a A neutral atom has 6 electrons orbiting its nucleus. How many protons has it in its nucleus? Of what element is it an atom? (Look in the list above.)

Isotopes

All carbon atoms have 6 protons in the nucleus. However, they are not all identical. Some have 6 neutrons, some have 7, and some have 8. The illustration shows these atoms. They are known as **isotopes** of carbon.

You can work out the **nucleon number** of an isotope by adding up the total number of protons and neutrons (nucleons) in its nucleus.

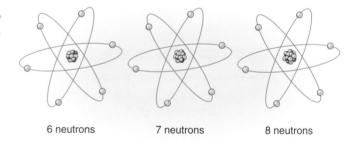

| 6 neutrons | 7 neutrons | 8 neutrons |

Atoms of three isotopes of carbon.

$$\text{Nucleon number} = \text{number of protons} + \text{number of neutrons}$$

The isotopes of an element all have:

◆ the same number of protons

◆ different nucleon numbers

b An atom of oxygen has 8 protons and 8 neutrons in its nucleus. What is its nucleon number?

c Another atom has 8 protons and 9 neutrons in its nucleus. Is it an isotope of oxygen, or a different element?

Changing elements

In radioactive decay, an atom changes from one element to another. Why is this?

Radioactive isotopes are atoms with unstable nuclei. (They are also known as *radioisotopes* or *radionuclides*.) To become more stable, the nucleus of a radioactive isotope emits radiation. The radiation carries away mass and energy, and the nucleus of the atom is lighter. It has a different number of protons, so it has become an atom of a different element.

during radioactive decay   after radioactive decay

Questions

1 Copy the table; put the words from the list in the correct places in the first column.

   radioactive isotope   nucleon number
   number of protons

	the same for all atoms of a particular element
	different for isotopes of a particular element
	an atom with an unstable nucleus

2 The atoms of two isotopes of helium contain the following particles:

   a Draw diagrams to represent these two atoms.

Isotope 1	2 protons	2 neutrons	2 electrons
Isotope 2	2 protons	1 neutron	2 electrons

   b Explain why they are both atoms of the same element.

3 The table shows the particles which are found in the nuclei of three different atoms.

   a Which two are isotopes of the same element?

   b Which two have the same nucleon number?

Atom 1	7 protons	7 neutrons
Atom 2	6 protons	7 neutrons
Atom 3	7 protons	6 neutrons

4 Some isotopes are radioisotopes; they decay by emitting radiation. Why do they do this?

Summary

- All atoms of an element have the same number of protons; isotopes of an element have different nucleon numbers.

- Radioisotopes are atoms with unstable nuclei. They decay to become atoms of a different element.

12:16 Dating using radioactivity

The Earth is about 4.5 billion years old. How do we know that? What was the clock that started as the Earth formed, and which now tells us how long has passed?

The answer lies in the radioactivity of the rocks around us. When the Earth formed, from a swirling cloud of dust and gas, there was much more radioactivity around. The rocks of the new Earth contained much more uranium, radium and other radioactive isotopes than they do today. The Earth would have been a very dangerous place to live, with high levels of background radiation.

Today, the Earth is much safer because many of the radioisotopes in the rocks around us have decayed away to become stable atoms.

This geologist is collecting rock samples. By measuring their radioactivity, he can determine the age of the rocks.

The decay of uranium

Uranium is a radioactive substance which is commonly found in rocks. Its atoms are unstable, and they decay until eventually atoms of lead are formed. These are stable atoms, and so they do not decay.

This process takes a very long time – billions of years. Even though the Earth is very old, only a fraction of the uranium in its rocks has decayed.

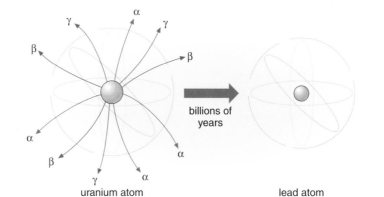

uranium atom

billions of years

lead atom

When uranium atoms decay, they eventually become stable atoms of lead.

a Which element has unstable atoms, uranium or lead? Which has stable atoms?

It is interesting to realise that most of the lead in the Earth started off as uranium. Medieval alchemists tried to turn lead into gold; we now know that the reason we find lead in the Earth is that it is a stable element, that cannot easily be changed into any other.

Now we can understand the radioactive 'clock' which allows geologists to find the age of the Earth. As time passes – billions of years – the amount of uranium in the Earth's rocks has gradually declined, and the amount of lead has increased. Geologists measure the amounts of uranium and lead in rocks. Then they can work out how old the rocks are.

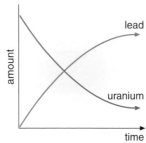

The amount of uranium in the Earth's rocks has gradually declined; the amount of lead has increased.

This meteorite is a rock from the planet Mars. Geologists have measured the amounts of different isotopes within it to find its age. It is 4.5 billion years old, the same age as the Earth.

b Which is older, a rock with a lot of uranium and a little lead, or one with a little uranium and a lot of lead?

Radiocarbon dating

Living creatures contain carbon. A small amount of this is a radioactive isotope of carbon, called carbon-14, which the plant or animal takes in from the atmosphere. After a living creature dies, the carbon-14 in it gradually decays away.

Archaeologists use this as a way of finding the age of anything which was once alive. They measure the amount of carbon-14 which remains, and this tells them how long ago it died.

This method can be used to find the age of material which died up to 50 000 years ago.

c Look at the two photos. If you took a gram of carbon from the Turin shroud, and a gram of carbon from the Iceman, which would contain more atoms of radioactive carbon-14? Explain your answer.

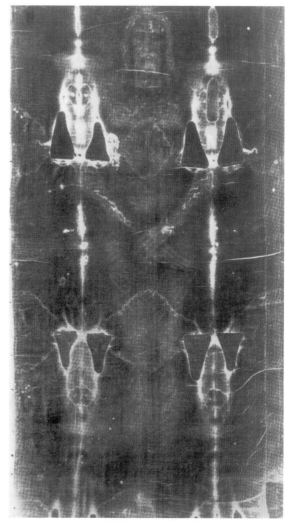

The Iceman is the body of a Bronze Age man. It was found frozen in the Alps. Radiocarbon dating showed that he lived about 5700 years ago.

Some people believe that the Turin shroud is Christ's burial shroud. Radiocarbon dating shows that the cloth it is made from was produced in the fourteenth century.

Questions

1 Why is there less background radiation today than there was when the Earth formed, 4500 million years ago?

2 The oldest rocks in the Earth contain less uranium today than when they were formed. They contain more lead.

  a Why do they contain less uranium than when they formed?

  b Why do they contain more lead?

3 The photograph shows King Arthur's Round Table, in Winchester. Its age has been found using radiocarbon dating. If you took a gram of carbon from the table, and a gram of carbon from your own body, which would contain more atoms of radioactive carbon-14? Explain your answer.

DIGGING DEEPER
An ancient 'mummy' found in Iran in 1999 was shown to be less than 10 years old, by radiocarbon dating. It was a clever fake, offered for sale on the art market for millions of dollars.

Summary
- We can find the age of rocks and other materials by measuring their radioactivity. The older the material, the less radiation it emits

12:17 Ultrasound

We cannot see sounds, but we can use an oscilloscope to show us pictures of sound waves. The microphone turns the sound into an electrical signal, and this appears as a wiggly line on the oscilloscope screen.

Oscilloscope traces allow us to compare different sounds.

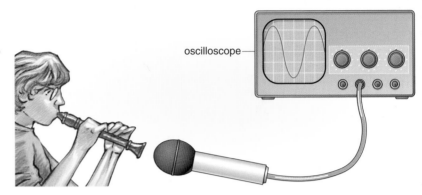

oscilloscope

a Look at the four oscilloscope traces in the diagrams on the right (red, green, blue, black). Which sound has the greatest amplitude? Which has the lowest frequency?

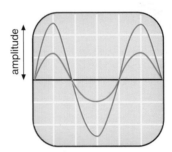

amplitude

The red trace has a greater amplitude than the green trace. It sounds louder.

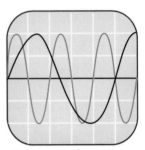

The blue trace has a higher frequency than the black trace (more waves per second). It would sound higher – it has a higher pitch.

Beyond hearing

You probably know that bats produce high-pitched squeaks, too high for us to hear. They listen for the echoes from their surroundings, and this helps them to find their way around in the dark. Any sound which is too high for us to hear is called **ultrasound**. The frequency of ultrasound is higher than the upper limit of our hearing range, which is about 20 kHz (kilohertz).

Many creatures, such as this bat, produce ultrasound. Young people can hear sounds with frequencies up to about 20 kHz.

You don't need a bat to produce ultrasound. Electronic systems can produce electrical currents which oscillate back and forth at high frequencies. When these currents flow through a device such as a tiny loudspeaker, they produce ultrasonic waves in the air.

b Which of the following frequencies could be the frequency of an ultrasound wave? 150 Hz, 15 kHz, 300 Hz, 30 kHz

DIGGING DEEPER

Small children can hear sounds with frequencies up to 30 kHz, but the upper limit of hearing drops rapidly as we grow bigger and older. Naturalists use electronic devices to allow them to hear bats. These devices reduce the frequency of the bats' calls to one-quarter of their value. It is then possible to identify different species of bats by their different calls.

Using ultrasound

Ultrasound has several uses. It is used to produce an image (a 'scan') of a baby in the womb. The operator moves the probe over the mother's stomach, and a picture appears on the screen. (The same technique can be used for other medical purposes, such as looking for gallstones in the gallbladder.) Ultrasound is better than X-rays for this purpose; there is a slight risk to mother and baby from X-rays (which can cause cancer), but there is no evidence of any risk from ultrasound.

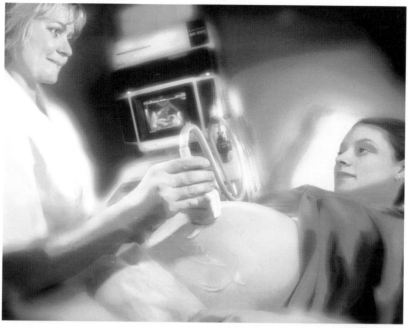

Pre-natal scanning: ultrasound waves reflect off the baby in the womb and are detected to produce an image on the screen.

In a similar way, ultrasound can be used in industry to check for flaws in solid objects. For example, ultrasound waves can show up the presence of defects in railway lines; these cannot be seen from the outside. This is known as quality control.

Ultrasound is also used for cleaning. A jeweller may place a greasy, dirty item in a bath of cleaning fluid. Ultrasound waves are then used to shake the dirt off the item, without damaging it in any way. Delicate mechanisms can be cleaned in this way, without the need to take them apart.

c Explain why it would be better to check for a defect in a car axle using ultrasound, rather than cutting it open.

Using ultrasound to check for defects in a large gear wheel.

Questions

1 Explain what is meant by **ultrasound**.

2 List two ways in which ultrasound can be useful in industry.

3 Copy the diagram below, which shows how ultrasound can be produced. Put words from the list in the gaps.

electrical oscillations   loudspeaker
electronic system   ultrasound waves

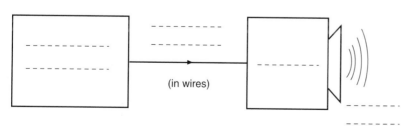

(in wires)

4 Ultrasound waves are used in pre-natal scanning.

a What does 'pre-natal' mean?

b Why is ultrasound scanning safer than using X-rays?

Summary

• Ultrasound waves are sound waves with frequencies higher than the limit of human hearing.

• Ultrasound can be used in medicine for pre-natal scanning, and in industry for quality control and for cleaning.

12:18 Inside the Earth

In the Earth materials module, you learned about the structure of the Earth. The drawing shows the important features.

◆ We live on the thin, solid crust.

◆ The mantle is made of hot rock. It extends halfway to the centre of the Earth.

◆ The core is very dense, because it is made of iron and nickel. The outer core is molten (liquid). The inner core is solid.

a **Which layer of the Earth is hottest? Which is coolest?**

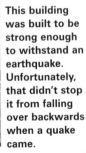

Thin crust

Outer core

Mantle

Inner core

A look inside

We can't see inside the Earth, and we can't drill down as far as the mantle. So how do we know about the structure of the Earth?

The answer is that we make use of earthquakes. An earthquake sends strong vibrations right through the Earth. A powerful earthquake can cause great damage; weaker ones may do no damage, but they can still be recorded by scientists using instruments called **seismographs**.

A seismograph produces a trace which is like a graph showing the vibrations which have travelled through the Earth. The stronger the earthquake, and the closer the seismograph is to where it happened, the greater the amplitude of the trace.

This building was built to be strong enough to withstand an earthquake. Unfortunately, that didn't stop it from falling over backwards when a quake came.

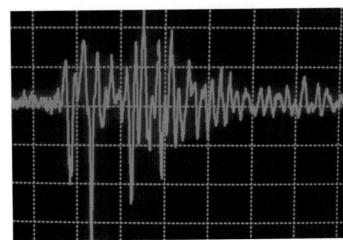

A seismograph, and the trace produced by a major earthquake.

Reflecting waves

When geologists are looking for oil, they carry out a survey of the rocks in their area of interest. They set off small explosions on the surface, and detect the shock waves which are reflected by layers of rock below. They can then drill down in likely spots to find oil.

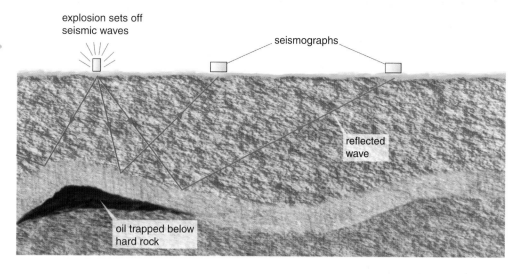

b What instrument do the geologists use to detect the reflected shock waves?

In the same way, geologists can find out about the layers of rock inside the whole Earth. They use the shock waves of an earthquake, which are known as **seismic waves**. These waves travel quickly through the Earth. When they reach the different layers inside the Earth, they are reflected and refracted. They are detected by seismographs at different points on the Earth's surface.

Geologists can use their measurements to build up a picture of the inside of the Earth, in just the same way that an ultrasound scanner builds up an image of an unborn child.

Questions

1 Give another name for the shock waves which are produced by an earthquake.

2 The diagram shows how a shock wave travels through the Earth.

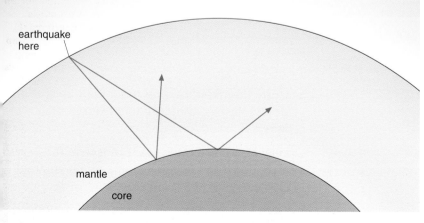

a Copy the diagram, and mark on it two places where seismographs would detect shock waves.

b Explain how scientists can use their findings to understand the inside of the Earth.

3 When astronauts visited the Moon, they left a seismograph. Later, a disused spacecraft was crashed onto the Moon's surface. Why do you think this was done?

Summary

- Earthquakes produce two types of seismic waves which can be detected using seismographs.

- By studying how seismic waves travel through the Earth, we can find out about its structure.

1 Jane has tied one end of a rope to a hook on the wall. She is moving the other end up and down, so that waves travel along the rope.

The diagram shows the waves on the rope at one instant.

12 m

a Are these waves transverse or longitudinal? Give a reason to support your answer.

b How many complete waves are there along the length of the rope?

c What is the wavelength of the waves?

2 Sound travels as waves.

a Does sound travel as transverse or longitudinal waves?

b Sound waves cannot travel through a vacuum. Give an example of a wave which does not need a medium through which to travel.

A loudspeaker produces sound waves whose frequency is 100 Hz. Their wavelength is 3 m.

c Write down an equation which connects **wave speed**, **frequency** and **wavelength**.

d Calculate the speed of the sound waves.

3 The diagram shows a wave.

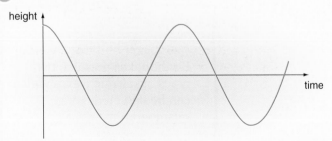

height

time

Copy the diagram. On your copy, mark the following:

a the wavelength of the wave;

b the amplitude of the wave.

4 A ripple tank is useful for looking at waves on the surface of water. In the diagram, ripples are travelling across the water. When they pass through the gap in the barrier, they spread out into the space beyond.

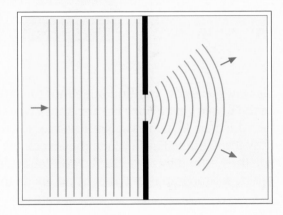

a Is this an example of reflection, refraction or diffraction?

b Radio signals also spread out when they pass through a gap. What does this suggest about radio signals?

5 The diagram shows an infrared ray travelling down an optical fibre.

optical fibre

infrared ray

a Copy the diagram, and mark with an X the points at which the ray undergoes total internal reflection.

Optical fibres are often used to transmit information such as television signals, instead of cables carrying electrical signals.

b Give two advantages of optical fibres over cables.

6 The diagram shows how a concert may be transmitted to our homes. The signal is coded as a series of pulses.

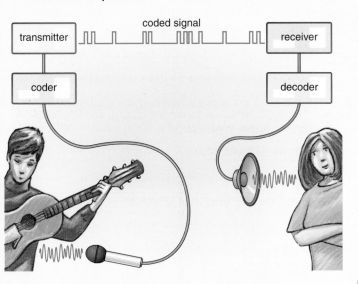

a Is this an analogue or a digital signal?

b Give two reasons why this type of signal is often preferred.

7 The radiation produced by radioactive substances can be hazardous. Put the following sentences in order to make an explanation of why this is so.

- Charged molecules are known as ions.
- Cells dividing in an uncontrolled way may result in a tumour (a cancer).
- When radiation strikes neutral molecules, it may cause them to become charged.
- Cells containing ions may divide in an uncontrolled way.

8 The graph shows how the amount of radiation coming from two samples of different radioactive substances gradually decreased.

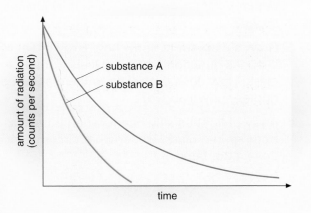

a Explain what we mean by the half-life of a radioactive substance.

b From the graph, deduce which of the two substances had the longer half-life.

9 Atoms are made of protons, neutrons and electrons.

Which of these particles:

a are found in the nucleus?

b have a negative charge?

c have a mass similar to that of a proton?

10 A helium atom is made of 2 protons, 2 neutrons and 2 electrons. What is its mass number (nucleon number)?

11 A geologist has been taking samples of granite rock from two different areas of the country. She finds that both have a similar composition, but one emits more radiation than the other. Explain what this suggests about the ages of the two rock samples.

12 Ultrasonic waves can be used for pre-natal scanning.

a Ultrasonic waves are similar to sound waves. In what way do they differ?

b What is pre-natal scanning?

c X-rays can also be used for pre-natal scanning. In what way can they be hazardous to a pregnant mother and her child?

13 An atom of a particular isotope of nitrogen contains 7 protons and 7 neutrons.

a In which part of the atom are these particles found?

b What is the nucleon number of this atom?

c How many electrons are there in a neutral atom of this isotope?

d There are other isotopes of nitrogen. How do their atoms differ from this one?

14 **a** The following sentences describe Rutherford and Marsden's experiment which allowed them to develop a new model of the atom. Complete the sentences by filling the gaps.

Rutherford and Marsden directed _____ radiation on to a thin _____ foil.

To their surprise, a small proportion of the radiation was _____.

They guessed that this radiation had been repelled by the _____ charge of the atomic nucleus.

They were able to reject the old _____ _____ model of the atom.

b Give one reason why their new model of the atom very quickly became widely accepted.

15 A teacher is showing the class the properties of radiation coming from a radioactive substance.

• She measures the radiation coming directly from the source.

• Then she repeats her measurements with various materials placed between the source and the detector.

• Finally she removes the source and measures the level of background radiation.

The table shows the results.

Absorber	Thickness	Count rate (counts in 1 minute)
none		470
paper	0.5 mm	472
aluminium	5 mm	120
lead	3 cm	114
background		119

What type of radiation did the source give out? Explain your answer as fully as you can.

16 Look at the phrases given below. Each describes either infrared waves or ultraviolet waves. Make two lists headed 'infrared waves' and 'ultraviolet waves', and copy the phrases into the correct lists.

beyond the violet end of the visible spectrum

beyond the red end of the visible spectrum

have shorter wavelengths than visible light

have longer wavelengths than visible light

waves of heat energy

given out by anything which is warm

given out by very hot objects

used in grills and ovens to cook food

used to show up security markings

carry telephone messages along optical fibres

can cause tanning and sunburn

sent out by TV and VCR remote controls

17 The diagram shows ripples in a ripple tank (viewed from above).

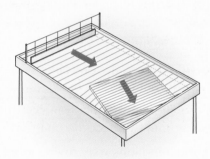

a On the right, the ripples are travelling more slowly. Why have they slowed down?

b What do we call the change in direction of ripples which can happen when they change speed?

c Draw a diagram to show how a ray of light changes direction when it travels from air into glass. How does this relate to the diagram of ripples shown above?

d A ray of light usually bends when it travels from air into glass. Under what circumstances does it not bend?

Module 1: Humans as organisms

Material included in paper 1

Breaking down food
Most of the foods you eat are made from large, insoluble molecules. These have to be broken down into small, soluble molecules which can dissolve in your blood and be carried around your body.

Your **digestive system** produces **enzymes** which breakdown large, insoluble molecules into small, soluble molecules. Each type of food needs a particular enzyme to break it down.

- **Carbohydrase** enzymes breakdown carbohydrates into sugars.

- **Protease** enzymes breakdown proteins into amino acids.

- **Lipase** enzymes breakdown fats into fatty acids and glycerol.

In addition to these enzymes **bile** is released from your liver. Bile breaks down fats into tiny fat droplets. This process is called **emulsification**.

Getting food into the body
Molecules of digested food are small enough to be absorbed through your gut wall. The wall of your small intestine is very efficient in absorbing food because:

- It contains thousands of tiny folds called villi which create a very large surface area.

- Each villus contains many blood capillaries to transport absorbed food.

- Each villus is very thin so that food molecules can easily reach the bloodstream.

Releasing and using energy
Your body is always using energy to:

- Build large molecules from smaller ones so that you can grow and repair damaged cells.

- Make muscles contract so that you can move.

- Keep your body temperature steady.

This energy comes from glucose in your blood – glucose is your body's main fuel.

Glucose and oxygen react together within body cells to release energy. This process is **aerobic respiration** and is summarised as:

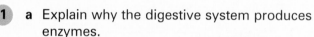

$$\text{glucose} + \text{oxygen} \rightarrow \text{carbon dioxide} + \text{water} (+\text{energy})$$

Sometimes your body cannot get enough oxygen. When this happens glucose is broken down without using oxygen. This process called **anaerobic respiration** produces lactic acid as a waste product. Anaerobic respiration is summarised as:

$$\text{Glucose} \rightarrow \text{lactic acid} (+ \text{energy})$$

Recap questions

1　**a** Explain why the digestive system produces enzymes.

　　b The diagram shows an experiment on digestion. Cellophane tubing allows small molecules to pass through but not large molecules.

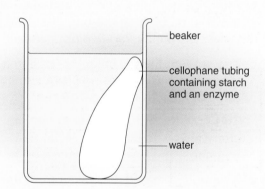

- beaker
- cellophane tubing containing starch and an enzyme
- water

The experiment was left for 30 minutes. The water and the contents of the cellophane tubing were then tested for starch and for sugar. The results are shown in the table.

	Result of starch test	Result of sugar test
Water from beaker	negative	positive
Contents of cellophane tubing	positive	positive

Explain the results shown in the table.

2 A student breathed out into an empty breathing bag 5 times.

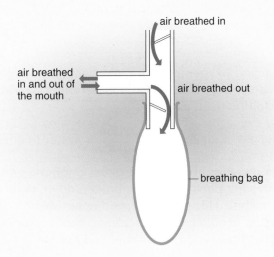

air breathed in

air breathed in and out of the mouth

air breathed out

breathing bag

a Copy and complete the sentences.

The air the student breathed out would contain more _____ than the air the student breathed in.

The air the student breathed in would contain more _____ than the air the student breathed out.

b After the student had breathed out 5 times, the volume of air in the bag was 2500 cm³. What was the average volume of each breath?

c The student then used an exercise machine. While she was exercising she again breathed out 5 times into the bag.

This time the volume of air in the bag afterwards was 8000 cm³. What does this tell you about the effect of exercise on breathing?

d A sample of blood was taken from the student before and after the exercise. The sample taken before the exercise contained no lactic acid. The sample taken after the exercise contained lactic acid. Explain the difference between the two results.

e Explain why oxygen passes from the air in the alveoli into the blood.

3 **a** Which part of the blood transports most of the:

i oxygen

ii carbon dioxide?

b The table shows the rate of supply of blood to parts of the body (cm³/min) when at rest and during exercise.

	Rate of blood supply at rest (cm³/min)	Rate of blood supply during exercise (cm³/min)
Digestive system	1350	600
Kidney	1000	550
Skin	450	1700
Brain	650	650
Arteries of heart	150	550
Muscles of skeleton	750	8000
Bone	650	450

i Copy the bar chart. Use data from the table to complete it.

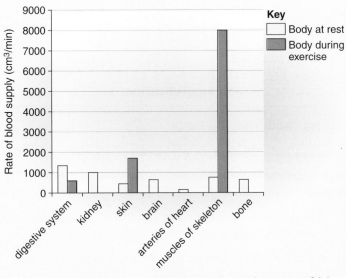

Key
☐ Body at rest
▨ Body during exercise

ii During exercise how does the rate of blood flow change in the digestive system?

iii During exercise how does the rate of blood flow change in the arteries of the heart?

iv Explain how the change in the rate of blood supply to the muscles attached to the skeleton helps the body during exercise.

Module 2: Maintenance of life

Material included in paper 1

Starch (a carbohydrate), proteins and fats are insoluble. They are broken down into insoluble substances so that they can be absorbed into the bloodstream in the wall of the small intestine. In the large intestine much of the water is absorbed into the bloodstream. The indigestible food which remains makes up the bulk of the faeces. Faeces leave the body via the anus.

The breathing system takes air into and out of the body so that oxygen from the air can diffuse into the bloodstream and carbon dioxide can pass out of the bloodstream into the air.

During vigorous exercise, muscle cells may be short of oxygen. They can then obtain energy from glucose by anaerobic respiration (respiration which does not use oxygen).

The waste product from this process is lactic acid. The body then needs oxygen to break down this lactic acid. The oxygen that is needed is called an oxygen debt.

Blood consists of a fluid called plasma in which are suspended white blood cells, platelets and red blood cells.

Plasma transports:

- carbon dioxide from the organs to the lungs;
- soluble products of digestion from the small intestine to other organs;
- urea from the liver to the kidneys.

Photosynthesis is summarised by the equation:

$$\text{carbon dioxide} + \text{water} + \text{[light energy]} \rightarrow \text{glucose} + \text{oxygen}$$

During photosynthesis:

- light energy is absorbed by a green substance called chlorophyll which is found in chloroplasts in some plant cells;
- this energy is used by converting carbon dioxide and water into sugar (glucose);
- oxygen is released as a by-product.

Waste products which have to be removed from the body include:

- carbon dioxide produced by respiration – most of this leaves the body via the lungs when we breathe out;
- urea produced in the liver by the breakdown of excess amino acids – this is removed by the kidneys in the urine; which is temporarily stored in the bladder.

Internal conditions which are controlled include:

- the water content of the body – water leaves the body via the lungs when we breathe out and via the skin when we sweat, and excess is lost via the kidneys in the urine;
- the ion content of the body – ions are lost via the skin when we sweat and excess ion is lost via the kidneys in urine;
- temperature – to maintain the temperature at which enzymes work best.

Recap questions

1 The kidneys remove waste materials from the blood plasma.

The table shows the concentration of certain substances:

- in blood plasma entering the kidneys
- in the urine.

Substance	Concentration (%)	
	in blood plasma entering the kidneys	in urine
Protein	7	0
Salt	0.35	0.5
Glucose	0.1	0
Urea	0.03	2.0

Use the data to describe what happens to blood as it flows through the kidneys.

2 The graph shows the concentration of sugars in a plant leaf during a period of 24 hours.

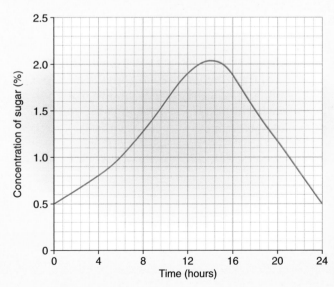

a i What was the maximum concentration of sugars in the leaf?

ii By how much did the sugar concentration change between 16 hours and 20 hours?

b Explain why the concentration of sugars rises between 0 and 14 hours.

c Explain why the concentration of sugars falls between 14 hours and 24 hours.

3 The table gives the water gains and losses for a human adult over a 24 hour period.

Water gains (cm³)	Water losses (cm³)
Drink – 1350	Urine – 1400
Food – 700	Sweat – 500
Respiration – 350	Exhaled air – 400
	Faeces – 100

a A pie chart for water gains has been drawn for you. Copy and complete the pie chart for water losses.

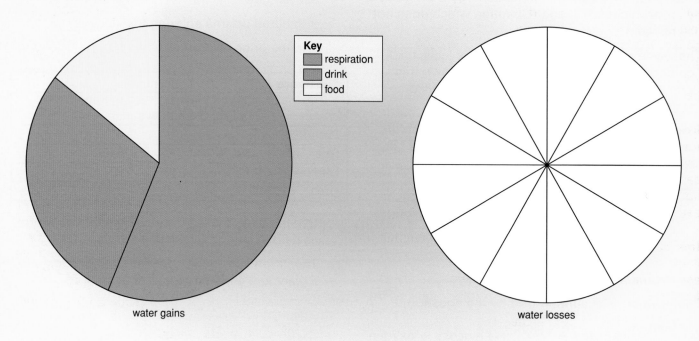

Key
- respiration
- drink
- food

water gains

water losses

b The gains and losses were measured on a cold day. What changes would you expect for the figures if the measurements were taken on a very hot day? Give reasons for your answers.

Module 05: Metals

Where do metals fit into a table of the elements?

More than three-quarters of all elements are metals. They are found to the left and centre of the periodic table.

Groups 1 and 2 are very reactive, low density metals. Group 1 (alkali) metals such as sodium react with water, giving off hydrogen and leaving an alkaline solution of the metal hydroxide. They form colourless, water-soluble, ionic compounds with non-metals.

The transition metals, such as iron and copper, are found in the middle block of the periodic table. Like all metals, these are good conductors of heat and electricity and can be easily bent or hammered into shape. Unlike the alkali metals they have high melting points (except mercury) and are hard and strong. This makes them useful as structural materials. They are less reactive and do not corrode so quickly with air and/or water. They form coloured compounds which are used in pottery glazes. The metals and their compounds are also used as catalysts.

How are metals extracted from their ores?

How a metal is obtained from its ore depends on how reactive it is. Metals can be arranged in a reactivity series, with the most reactive metals at the top. A more reactive metal can displace a less reactive metal from its compound.

How can metal compounds be made?

Metal compounds, called salts, can be made by reacting the metal hydroxide (an alkali) with an acid. Neutralisation occurs:

acid + alkai → salt + water

The salt formed depends on the metal in the alkali and the acid used.

Recap questions

1

Reactivity	Element
High	Potassium
	Sodium
	a
	Magnesium
	Aluminium
	b
	Iron
	Lead
	c
Low	Copper

The table shows the reactivity series of metals. Iron is made from iron ore by carbon reduction but aluminium cannot.

a Name a metal that could displace iron from iron sulphate solution.

b Non-metals can fit into this series. Where should carbon fit into this table (a,b or c)

c Lead slowly reacts with acid to give a salt and hydrogen gas. Copper never does this. Where should hydrogen fit into this table (a,b or c)

d Sodium is made by the electrolysis of molten sodium chloride. Explain why it cannot be made by carbon reduction.

e Iron could be made by electrolysing molten iron oxide. Instead it is made by heating iron oxide with coke (carbon) in a blast furnace. Suggest why this method is used instead of electrolysis.

f Iron can also be made by reacting iron oxide with aluminium in a thermit reaction. Suggest why this method of iron production is not used commercially.

2 Copy and complete the following sentences, using the words below to fill in the gaps. (You may use one word twice!)

electricity shiny soft alkali low reactive

The metals in Group 1 of the periodic table are called the _____ metals. They are a family of very _____ metals. They tarnish rapidly in air but are _____ when fresh. They conduct heat and _____ well but are _____, have _____ densities and _____ melting and boiling points.

3 Sodium reacts with water:

sodium + water → sodium hydroxide + hydrogen

a What would happen if you put pH paper in the water after this reaction?

b What is the name given to group 1? Why do you think it is called this?

c Lithium fizzes in water. What gas do you think is given off?

d What is the name of the alkali that forms in the water?

e Write a word equation for this reaction.

4 a What is the name of the block of metals that wedges in between calcium (Z=20) and gallium (Z=31)?

b Normally the properties of the elements changes dramatically as you move along the same period. What is unusual about this block of metals?

c Iron (Z=26) is a hard magnetic metal with a high melting point which forms coloured compounds. Nickel (Z=28) is a hard magnetic metal with a high melting point which forms coloured compounds. Predict the properties of cobalt (Z=27).

5 The table below shows the properties of some common metals. (The tensile strength of a material is a measure of how strong it is when the two ends of a piece are pulled apart.)

Metal	Density (gcm^{-2})	Melting point (°C)	Tensile strength
aluminium	2.7	660	70
copper	8.9	280	130
gold	18.9	1064	78
iron	7.9	1540	211
lead	11.3	327	16
mercury	13.6	–39	–
sodium	0.87	98	low
tungsten	19.4	3410	411

a Which metal is:

  i most dense?

  ii least dense?

  iii strongest?

b Which metal is liquid at room temperature (25 °C)?

c Why is tungsten used as the filament of electric light bulbs instead of aluminium?

d A lead weight is dropped into mercury. Does it float or sink? Explain why.

e A gold ring is dropped into mercury. Does it float or sink? Explain why.

f You can melt copper wire in a roaring Bunsen burner flame, but not iron wire. Suggest the temperature reached by a roaring flame.

g Aluminium cables are used as the conducting wires for electric pylons, but they are attached to steel cables. Why do you think that is?

h Which of these metals would float on water?

i Use the periodic table to find which of these metals are not transition metals.

6 Look again at the reactivity series shown in Q1. Zinc fits in just above iron and below carbon.

a Zinc occurs naturally as zinc sulphide ore. The first stage of zinc production is to roast this ore in air, forming zinc oxide and sulphur dioxide. Write a word equation for this reaction. (What gas in air is reacting?)

b Zinc oxide is then heated with coke (carbon) to extract the metal. Write a word equation for this reaction.

c Why is carbon able to perform this reaction?

d Why isn't electrolysis used to get the zinc?

e Zinc dissolves in sulphuric acid to give zinc sulphate. A gas is given off. What is the gas?

f This gas comes from the acid. Why is zinc able to 'push it out' of the acid?

g Write a word equation for this reaction.

7 What salt (if any) would you get if you reacted:

a Hydrochloric acid and magnesium oxide.

b Hydrochloric acid and magnesium metal.

c Sulphuric acid and copper oxide.

d Sulphuric acid and copper metal.

e Nitric acid and zinc carbonate.

f Nitric acid and sodium hydroxide.

8 For each metal described below, is it more likely to be an alkali metal or a transition metal?

A is a soft metal that has to be stored under oil.

B has a bright blue chloride.

C sinks in water and does not corrode.

D is used as a catalyst to make ammonia.

E has a colourless, water-soluble carbonate.

Module 3 – Environment

The photographs show some of the concerns that people have about the environment.

Animals can live almost anywhere, but we are destroying many of their habitats.

Forests are being cut down faster than they are being replaced.

We are polluting our environment.

Most of us are concerned about the environment. TV programmes about natural history bring animals and plants from distant parts of the world into our living rooms. But the programmes also bring news about the way we are affecting our planet. Already we are beginning to see climate changes that may bring disasters to many parts of the world. The world is not ours to use as we wish; we hold it in trust for future generations. So we must look after the Earth and its resources.

Recycling our resources is the only sustainable way forward.

This module, Environment, will help you to understand how animals and plants are adapted to live in harsh environments, and the factors that affect the sizes of their populations. You will then learn how energy from the Sun is transferred to living organisms, and how living organisms cycle natural materials. Finally, you will learn about the effects that humans have on the environment, and what we can do to preserve our world for future generations.

Climate change will make scenes like his more common.

Before you start, try these questions to check what you know about organisms and their environment.

1 **List the factors that organisms need to survive.**

2 **What is meant by a food chain?**

3 **Why are green plants called producers?**

4 **What is a pyramid of numbers?**

5 **Spraying insecticides on crops may be dangerous to other organisms. Explain why.**

In 1911, Sir Robert Scott led an expedition to reach the South Pole. Five of the team trekked to the Pole dragging their supplies of food and fuel on sledges. They reached the South Pole, but every member of the team died on the way back as the weather turned to blizzards and their supplies ran out.

a What do humans need to take with them to survive in arctic conditions?

Humans are not adapted to living in very cold places like the Antarctic, but some animals have ingenious **adaptations** that allow them to survive in freezing climates.

The emperor penguin

Emperor penguins survive long periods in the conditions that killed Scott and his team. Penguin feathers are different from the feathers of other species of birds. At the base of each feather is a fluffy tuft of 'hairs'. These fluffy tufts overlap to form a mat that covers the whole of the penguin's body. Wind and water cannot get through this mat.

b How do these special feathers help the penguins to survive in the Antarctic?

Emperor penguins spend the summer feeding on fish and become very fat. At end of summer, fat makes up about half of the body mass of the male penguin.

c Give two advantages to the male penguin of having so much fat around his body.

As winter sets in and ice begins to cover the sea, pairs of penguins begin a long trek over the ice to their breeding sites on land. This trek can be as long as 150 km. The pairs of penguins mate, and then each female lays one egg. The male takes the egg from her and places it in a fold of feather-covered skin that hangs down from his abdomen.

The female then returns to the sea to feed but the male stands, keeping the egg off the ground, for 60 days until it hatches.

When there are blizzards, the penguins huddle together.

d Explain how huddling together helps the penguins to survive blizzards.

Once hatched, the young chick stands on its father's feet, under the fold of skin to keep warm. While incubating the egg, the male loses about one third of his body mass.

e Explain why the male loses so much body mass.

By the day after the egg has hatched, the female returns from the sea bringing food for the chick. The male now makes the long trek back to the sea to feed and replenish his fat stores.

Humans need to take all kinds of special clothing and equipment to survive in freezing conditions.

Emperor penguins are adapted to survive a very cold climate. This male is incubating an egg.

The penguins huddle together on the ice.

The musk ox

Musk oxen live in the Arctic tundra. They look a lot like bison but they have wool, like sheep. Wool traps air next to the body. Air is a poor conductor of heat.

f Explain how the coat of the musk ox helps it to survive in the Arctic.

Musk oxen have long brown wool that hangs almost to their feet.

The Weddell seal

Weddell seals are mammals. They have hardly any hair, but they survive in the cold Antarctic seas. Look at the photograph of the Weddell seal.

g How is the Weddell seal adapted for surviving in cold water?

One feature that helps the seal to survive is its body shape. Animals lose heat through their body surface, so if they can reduce their body surface they can reduce the rate of heat loss.

h Think about the body shapes of a Weddell seal and a horse. Which parts of the seal are much smaller compared to the rest of its body than similar parts of a horse?

Weddell seals are adapted to live in freezing Antarctic waters.

The lemming

Lemmings are small mouse-like animals that live in the Arctic. Because it is small, the lemming's surface area is large compared to its body mass so it is liable to lose heat quickly. In winter, lemmings burrow under the snow where they feed on plant roots.

i Apart from finding food, give an advantage to the lemming of burrowing in winter.

Lemmings are smaller than many animals living in very cold climates.

The snowy owl

Snowy owls live in the Arctic. They feed on small mammals such as mice and lemmings. In summer, snowy owls are brownish with dark spots and stripes. In winter, they are completely white.

j What is the advantage to the snowy owl of being white in winter?

The snowy owl's winter plumage is white.

Questions

1 The photograph shows a polar bear. Copy and complete the sentences about the adaptations of the polar bear.

The colour of the polar bear's coat helps to _____ it. The hairs of the polar bear's coat trap a layer of _____, which insulates the bear. Polar bears also have a thick layer of _____ under the skin for insulation. Its small ears reduce _____ _____ from the polar bear's body.

2 Read about the emperor penguin. Then explain how a male emperor penguin is adapted to survive cold and blizzards.

Summary

- Animals living in freezing climates often have white coats for **camouflage**.

- Many have a thick layer of fat under the skin for **insulation**.

- Many have thick hair or feathers to trap air, which insulates the body.

- Many have small body parts to reduce the area through which heat is lost.

3:2 Living in hot places

The photograph shows part of the Sahara desert. You can't see any animals or plants – it is rare to see desert animals during the day. Desert animals need to have many specialised features in order to survive in difficult conditions.

a Why do animals find it difficult to live in the desert?

Keeping out of the sun

Not many animals can survive in deserts. Those that do come out to feed at dawn and dusk. The photographs show some of these desert animals.

Desert animals have special features to help them survive. Most desert animals are small and have sandy coloured short hair. Having short hair prevents heat being trapped around their bodies.

b How does having a sandy colour help desert animals to survive?

During the heat of the day, most desert animals sleep in a cool den or burrow, or under rocks and boulders.

c How do our bodies help us to cool down in hot weather?

Cooling down

Most mammals have body temperatures similar to humans – about 37 °C. Temperatures in hot deserts are often more than 40 °C and sometimes reach above 60 °C.

Instead of trying to conserve heat, like animals adapted to cold climates, many desert animals have adaptations for cooling down.

Big ears

The fennec, the jack rabbit and the bandicoot all have big ears. These ears act like the radiator in a car. A car radiator receives hot water from the car engine, gives out heat to the environment, then returns cooler water to the engine.

Large ears receive warm blood from the body, give out heat to the environment, then return cooler blood to the body. These animals are able to control the amount of blood flowing around their ears.

d Why do the fennec, the jack rabbit and the bandicoot need to control the amount of blood flowing around their ears?

The Sahara desert is one of the hottest environments in the world.

Bandicoot.

Fennec.

Caracal.

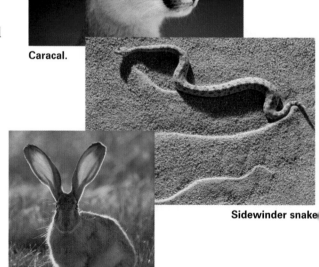
Sidewinder snake

Jack rabbit.

Panting

Desert birds have feathers like all other birds. These feathers insulate the birds' bodies so they are as good at keeping heat out as they are at keeping it in. Even so, desert birds sometimes overheat.

Birds do not have sweat glands so they have developed other methods of cooling down. Desert owls 'pant' to keep cool. They open their mouths, and then flutter their throats to evaporate water from the lining of the mouth.

e How does this cool them down?

f What is the big disadvantage of this method of cooling down for a desert bird?

The South African sand grouse has a very unusual way of getting water to its young.

Getting water

Many desert animals never get to drink water – it is always too far away. Adult sand grouse, however, will often fly up to 40 km to a pool to collect water for their young. They have special feathers on their chest that soak up water just like a sponge. When the adult gets back to the nest the young birds suck the water from the breast feathers.

Kangaroo rats make their own water.

Camels are often called the 'ships of the desert'.

Desert animals get water in the food they eat. Most of their food contains water, particularly when the food is a juicy animal!

Kangaroo rats will not drink water even if you provide it. Their diet consists mainly of dry seeds, which do not contain any water at all. These animals manufacture their own water from the food they eat.

In aerobic **respiration**, glucose from food is oxidised:

glucose + oxygen → carbon dioxide + water

Water is one of the waste products – but it is far from 'waste' for the kangaroo rat. It is its only source of water.

Questions

1 A camel can go 17 days without water – then it can drink 100 litres in one go. This water is not stored in its hump, or anywhere else in its body. The hump consists of tissues where fat is stored. The camel has a double row of long eyelashes, and hair surrounding the openings to its ears. It can also close its nostrils. The camel has very broad feet. It grows a long shaggy coat in the winter but loses this coat in the summer.

  a Explain four ways in which the camel is adapted for living where there is a lot of sand.

  b What is the advantage to the camel of shedding its coat in summer?

2 Read about the kangaroo rat again. Using this information, suggest how the camel can survive for 17 days without drinking.

Summary

- Desert animals are often active only at dawn and dusk to avoid the midday sun.

- Desert animals are usually light in colour. This helps to camouflage them and reduces the amount of heat that they absorb.

- Some desert animals have large ears. These act as radiators, increasing the surface area for losing heat.

- Many desert animals have short hair – this does not trap much heat inside the body.

3:3 Plants in dry places

Cacti

Cacti range in size from the small ones that people grow in pots on windowsills to monsters such as the one shown in the photograph. They are adapted to grow in dry places.

Look at the photograph. You will notice that the cactus has a swollen stem and no leaves.

Most cacti have swollen stems. When part of a plant becomes swollen, it is usually to store something. Cactus stems are swollen to help them store water in order to survive in very dry places.

It is not quite true to say that cacti have no leaves at all. The leaves have not been lost – they have become much reduced in size, so that they loose very little water through **evaporation**. In fact, the leaves have evolved into small spines.

a How else will having spines instead of leaves help cacti to survive?

b What is the big disadvantage to cacti in reducing the size of their leaves?

Most plants manufacture food by **photosynthesis**. Light energy is absorbed by chlorophyll and used to convert carbon dioxide into sugars. Because cacti have such small leaves, they need to use their stems to produce food.

c Cactus stems are normally green. Why is this?

Cacti have other adaptations that help them to survive in hot, dry conditions. Their roots are very long so that they can reach down to any water stored far beneath the surface. They also have a waxy layer on their stems to help reduce water loss.

Sand dune plants

Not all dry places are hot. Some plants are adapted for living on Britain's sand dunes. Though their adaptations are not quite as drastic as those of cacti, their problem is the same – water is hard to come by, so they must prevent too much water loss.

d Why is the soil on sand dunes usually dry when the dunes are so close to the sea?

Most plants have large flat leaves with **stomata** on the under surface to allow carbon dioxide to enter. Water vapour is able to diffuse out of the leaf through these stomata.

Some cacti can grow to an enormous size.

Much of the coastline of Britain consists of sand dunes.

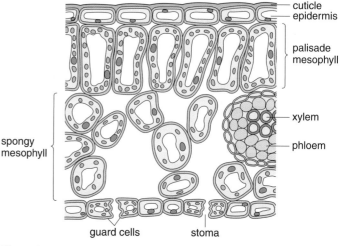
cuticle
epidermis
palisade mesophyll
xylem
phloem
spongy mesophyll
guard cells   stoma

Most plants have many stomata on the underside of each leaf.

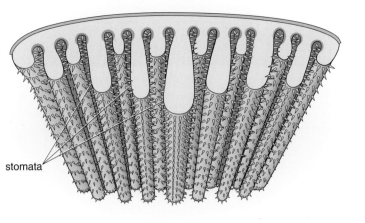

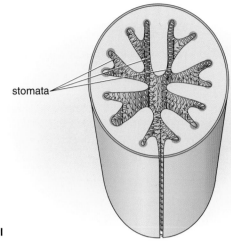

stomata

stomata

Marram grass leaves also have stomata on the underside, but the leaves roll up when there is little water available.

Marram grass is a common plant on some parts of sand dunes. In wet conditions, its leaves are flat but in dry conditions its leaves roll up.

e Explain how rolling its leaves will help marram grass to conserve water.

Questions

1 Look at the diagram below. Nerium is a shrub that lives in dry conditions. How will each of the following help Nerium to conserve water?

   a the positioning of the stomata

   b the tiny hairs

The 'living-stone' plant lives in dry, stony places in hot deserts. It is about 4 cm in height.

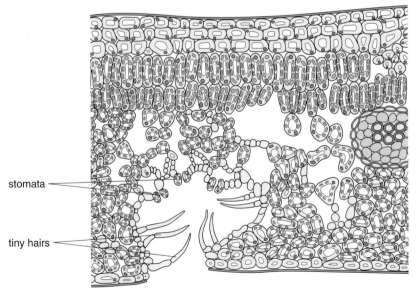

stomata

tiny hairs

Cross-section through a leaf from Nerium.

2 The photograph above shows a plant called a 'living-stone'. Read again about the adaptations of cacti. Then suggest four ways in which the 'living-stone' plant is adapted to living in a hot, stony desert.

Summary

Plants may be adapted to survive in dry conditions by:

- having very small leaves
- storing water in swollen stems
- being covered by a thick layer of wax
- having long roots
- rolling their leaves.

3:4 Plant competition

Why weed?

Farmers and gardeners get rid of weeds by digging them up, or by using chemicals called herbicides.

Farmers spend a lot of time, money and effort getting rid of weeds from their crops. To find out why, you need to think about the factors that plants need to grow.

a Copy and complete the table to show why a plant needs each factor. The first row has been done for you.

Factor	Why it is needed for plant growth
Warmth	Enzymes work best in warm conditions.
Light	
Carbon dioxide	
Water	
Nitrates	

Weeds compete with crop plants for some of these factors. Plants must adapt if they are to survive this **competition**.

b The diagram shows weeds growing in a barley field.

   i What is the advantage to the barley plants in growing taller than the weeds?

   ii What do the barley plants and the weeds compete for in the soil?

   iii How will this competition affect the barley plants?

c Look at the diagram of weeds growing in a potato field.

   i Describe the differences between the potato plants and the barley plants.

   ii There are far fewer weeds in the potato crop than in the barley crop. Use information from your answer to (i) to suggest an explanation for this.

Chemicals called **herbicides** are used to kill the weeds in the barley crop, but the weeds in the potato crop are removed by hoeing – digging them up.

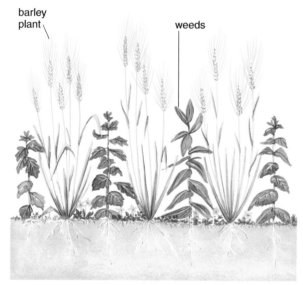

Barley is a cereal crop.

Potatoes are also grown as a food crop.

Planting seeds

Crop plants do not just compete with weeds – they compete with each other. So farmers need to know how close together they can grow crop plants so that they get the best results. Seed-planters can be programmed to sow a set number of seeds per square metre – the greater the number of seeds, the closer the plants grow to each other.

Some plants, such as cereal crops, are grown for their seeds. A farmer needs to get the highest number of seeds possible from his land. The graph shows the effect of planting different numbers of plants on the **yield** of seeds.

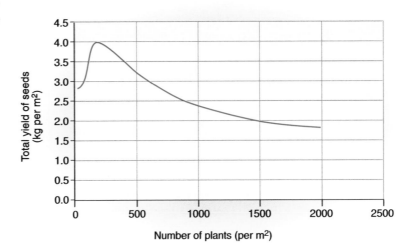

The seed yield of the crop depends on the number of plants grown per square metre.

d i What was the yield of seeds when 1000 plants were planted per m²?

ii Copy and continue the graph to find the expected yield of seeds when 2500 plants are planted per m².

iii How many plants would you advise the farmer to plant per m²?

iv Explain why the yield of seeds was greater if 1000 plants were planted per m² rather than 2000 per m².

Questions

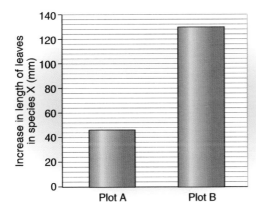

Bar chart to show how the growth of species X varied in plots A and B.

Scientists investigated competition between two related species of plant, X and Y. In plot A, small individuals of species X were planted 10 cm from large individuals of species Y. In plot B, small individuals of species X were planted at least 3 m from large individuals of Y. The graph shows the results after four weeks.

1 What effect did species Y have on species X?

2 Suggest an explanation for this effect.

3 Suggest three factors that species X and Y might be competing for.

4 Which is the stronger competitor, X or Y? Explain the reason for your answer.

Summary

• Plants compete for:

a light, which they need for photosynthesis

b water, which they need for all their living processes

c nitrates, which they need to make proteins

d space in which their roots and leaves can grow.

• Plants compete with both:

a plants of the same species

b plants of different species.

• Competition between weeds and crop plants results in a reduction in the yield of the crop plant.

3:5 Animal competition

Animals may compete with each other for food, water and space.

a Why do animals need space?

Sea birds

In the photograph, you can see part of a cliff face. Sea birds live here. The birds catch fish in the sea.

b List the factors that these sea birds compete for.

c Which birds are likely to be more successful in competing for these factors?

Tropical squirrels

The diagram shows the outlines of three different species of squirrel. All three species live in the forest on the same island in Indonesia.

d **i** How much longer is the loga than the jirit?

   ii What proportion of the total body length is the tail of the soksak?

The three species of squirrel have different diets. The bar chart shows the percentages of different foods in the diet of the three species.

e **i** Which food do all three species feed on?

   ii Which food does the jirit not feed on?

   iii What percentage of the jirit's food is bark?

   iv Explain why having different diets is an advantage to each of the three species.

   v Soksaks are rarely seen higher than 5 m up in the trees, but logas are usually seen between 5 and 30 m up. Suggest an explanation for this.

This rock face is packed with nesting birds.

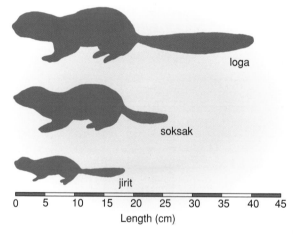

The loga, soksak and jirit are three species of Indonesian squirrel.

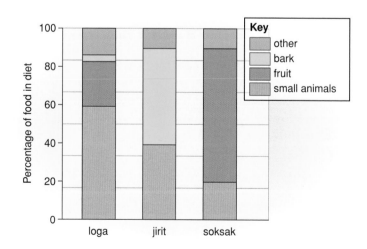

The squirrel species live in the same space, but eat different foods.

Questions

Rotifers and water fleas

Rotifers and water fleas are animals that can just be seen with the naked eye. They are sold in pet shops for feeding to goldfish. Both species can be grown in flasks in the laboratory if they are given food and oxygen.

Two flasks were set up to study competition between these two animals:

- Flask X held only rotifers
- Flask Z held both rotifers and water fleas.

Both animals feed on microscopic plants, which were added to the flasks daily. The graph shows the results of the experiment.

1 Describe what happened to the population of the rotifers:

a when living alone (flask X)

b when living with water fleas (flask Z).

2 Water fleas do not eat rotifers. Explain the reason for the fall in the number of rotifers after day 10 in flask Z.

Red squirrels and grey squirrels

Read the following information.

- In the twentieth century, red squirrels began to be replaced in Britain by grey squirrels introduced from North America.

- Red squirrels seem unable to survive in the presence of greys.

The numbers of red squirrels in Britain these days are much reduced.

- There is no evidence that grey squirrels chase out red squirrels, or that grey squirrels brought a disease with them from America that affects red squirrels.

- Red squirrels survive better than grey squirrels in pure conifer woods because they can get all their nourishment from conifer seeds.

- Grey squirrels need a variety of foods to survive, so they prefer mixed woodland.

3 a Suggest why grey squirrels have replaced red squirrels in many parts of the country.

b Suggest two ways in which the number of red squirrels could be increased.

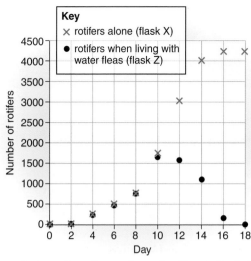

This graph shows how the numbers of rotifers in flasks X and Z changed over 18 days.

The brown areas in these maps show how the distribution of red squirrels in Britain changed between 1940 and 1991.

Summary

- Animals compete with each other for:

  a food

  b water

  c space to breed.

- Animals compete with both:

  a animals of the same species

  b animals of different species.

- When animals live in the same habitat they often avoid competition for food by feeding on different types of food.

3:6 Predators and prey

Animals that kill and eat other animals are called **predators**. The animals they eat are called **prey**. In the photograph, the killer whale is the predator. The leopard seal is its prey. Predators usually have more than one type of prey.

Look at the **food web** below. The arrows in the diagram show what feeds on what. For example, an arrow from 'leopard seals' to 'killer whales' means that the killer whale is a predator and the leopard seal is one of its prey.

a i Which other animals are prey for killer whales?

ii Which animals are predators of small fish?

iii Name an animal that is both predator and prey.

This photograph shows a killer whale catching a leopard seal.

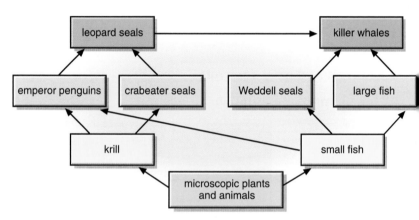

A food web shows what eats what.

Voles and owls

Owls are predators of voles. The chart below shows how the numbers of owls and voles in a forest varied over a ten-year period.

Owls are predators. Voles are among their prey species.

b i How many voles were there in year 3?

ii In which year was the number of owls 28?

c i Suggest why there was a large fall in the number of voles between years 5 and 6.

ii Suggest why there was a large fall in the number of owls between years 6 and 7.

iii Suggest why the number of voles rose between years 6 and 8.

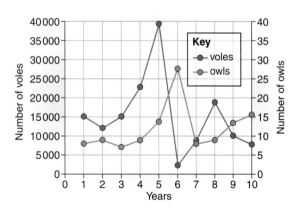

The numbers of predators and prey animals living in a habitat affect each other.

The populations of many predators and prey animals vary in this way – they change in a **cycle**.

Roach are fish that live in lakes.

```
┌─────────────────────┐        ┌─────────────────────┐
│ prey reproduce –    │──────▶ │ more food for       │
│ prey numbers        │        │ predators –         │
│ increase            │        │ predator numbers    │
│                     │        │ increase            │
└─────────────────────┘        └─────────────────────┘
        ▲                                │
        │                                ▼
┌─────────────────────┐        ┌─────────────────────┐
│ few predators       │◀────── │ prey numbers        │
│ remain              │        │ reduced –           │
│ – fewer prey eaten  │        │ many predators      │
│                     │        │ starve              │
└─────────────────────┘        └─────────────────────┘
```

The number of predators depends on how many prey animals there are to eat. The number of prey depends on how many predators are eating them.

Questions

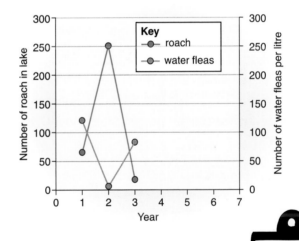

Water fleas are small aquatic animals about 3 mm in length.

Roach and water fleas

Year	Number of roach in lake	Number of water fleas per litre
1	70	120
2	250	5
3	20	80
4	100	40
5	30	260
6	190	20
7	75	40

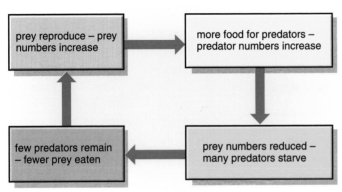

The table shows how the numbers of roach and water fleas in a lake varied over seven years.

1 Plot the data from the table on a graph. The axes and the data for the first three years have been drawn to show you how to do this.

2 Describe the pattern shown by the numbers of water fleas.

3 How does the pattern shown by the numbers of roach differ from the pattern shown by the numbers of water fleas?

4 Explain how the data show that roach are probably predators of water fleas.

5 The population of roach does not die out when the number of water fleas is very low. Suggest one reason why.

Summary

- Animals that eat other animals are called predators. The animals they eat are called prey.

- If the population of prey increases, more food is available for its predators so the predator population increases.

- If the population of predators increases, more food is needed so the population of prey decreases.

3:7 Populations

Deer and wolves

A farmer took 200 deer to a small, uninhabited island in 1915. There were no predators large enough to kill deer on the island.

The graph shows what happened to the population of deer.

a **i** Explain why the population of deer rose year after year until 1930.

    ii Suggest two reasons for the large fall in the population of deer between 1930 and 1935.

    iii The population of deer rose again until 1940 but peaked at a much lower level than before. Suggest an explanation for this.

In 1945, a pair of wolves (male and female) swam to the island. Wolves are predators of deer.

b Sketch a copy of the graph above.

    i On your copy, draw a line to show what might happen to the population of wolves between 1945 and 1960.

    ii Then, draw a line to show what might happen to the population of deer between 1945 and 1960.

    iii Explain the reasons for the shapes of the curves that you have drawn.

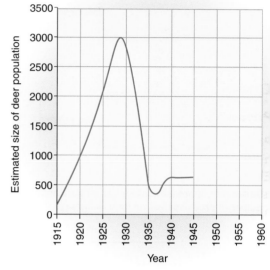

Sea shore populations

Look at the food web below. In a sea shore habitat, a disease killed a large number of the whelks.

c How might this affect the populations of:

    i mussels

    ii starfish?

Explain the reasons for your answers.

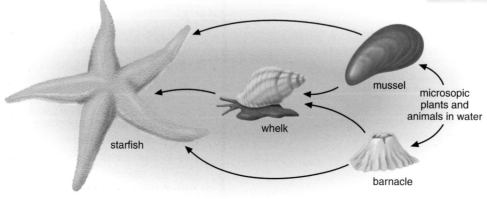

A food web for organisms on the sea shore.

Intercropping

In tropical regions, two crops are grown in the same field at the same time. This is called **intercropping**. The diagram shows how bean plants are grown between rows of maize plants.

d List three ways in which the maize plants will affect the bean plants.

Questions

Pheasants

Protection Island is an uninhabited nature reserve off the coast of the USA. Eight pheasants were released on the island in the spring of 1937. The number of pheasants was then counted every spring and autumn for the next five years. The graph shows the results.

When populations of different species live in the same space, they often affect each other.

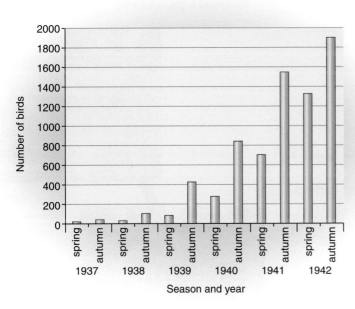

Graph to show how the pheasant population changed over five years.

Pheasants are quite large plant-eating birds.

1 By how much did the population of pheasants rise between the spring of 1937 and the spring of 1942?

2 Explain why the population of pheasants continued to rise for five years.

3 Explain why the population of pheasants increased between spring and autumn every year.

4 Suggest why the population of pheasants always decreased between the autumn of one year and spring of the next year.

5 After five years the pheasants were removed from the island. Suggest why this was done.

Summary

The size of a population may be affected by:

- available food
- competition for food
- competition for light
- predation or grazing
- disease.

3:8 Energy flow

The new oil wells

One hectare of the sugarcane crop shown in the photograph can produce enough fuel to drive a car round the world twice! And this fuel produces practically no pollution.

How can we get fuel from plants?

Farmers plant small pieces of sugarcane stem. Nine months later they can harvest up to 190 tonnes of sugarcane per hectare. From these crops, 75 million tonnes of sugar are produce each year. In countries like Brazil some of the sugarcane is fermented to produce ethanol. Many cars there have engines designed to run on pure ethanol.

The sugarcane crop produces a large mass of living material, and this living material contains a lot of energy.

The mass of the sugarcane crop is known as its **biomass**. Your mass is also biomass – as is the mass of all living organisms. It is called biomass because it has come from processes in living organisms. Plants are called **producers** because they produce all the biomass on Earth. They do this via a process called photosynthesis.

In Maintenance of Life you learned the equation for photosynthesis.

a Complete the equation for photosynthesis:

carbon dioxide + _____ (+ light energy) → sugar + _____

Plants use some of the energy from sunlight to convert carbon dioxide and water into sugars. This reaction has produced the countless millions of tonnes of living matter that exist on Earth. It has also produced the oxygen in the atmosphere that all living organisms use in respiration.

However, plants can only use a small proportion of the energy in sunlight.

b Scientists measured the amount of sunlight energy that was used by plants in an area of Britain. In one year, 7 000 000 kilojoules of sunlight energy reached each square metre of the area. Of this, only 90 000 kilojoules were used in photosynthesis. Calculate the proportion of sunlight energy that was used by the plants.

Food chains

When animals eat plants, they obtain biomass from the plant biomass. When one animal eats another animal, it obtains biomass from that animal. In the moorland **food chain** shown, the mouse obtains biomass when it eats the blackberries, and the kestrel obtains biomass when it eats the mouse.

Sugarcane is powerful stuff!

A moorland food chain.

The biomass contains carbohydrates that can be oxidised during respiration to release energy. So the mouse obtains energy from the blackberries and the kestrel obtains energy from the mouse.

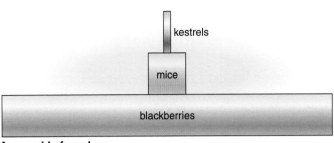

A pyramid of numbers.

Pyramid of biomass

In an area of moorland, there are many blackberry plants, a smaller number of mice, and very few kestrels. At Key Stage 3, you learned to represent this information as a **pyramid of numbers**.

We can measure the biomass of the organisms in a food chain, but this only makes sense if we measure the biomass per unit area of the habitat. So we usually express biomass in grams per square metre (g/m^2).

Some calculations of biomass from the moorland food chain are shown in the table. We can draw these to scale in a pyramid. This pyramid is called a pyramid of biomass.

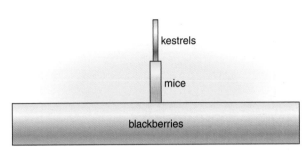

A pyramid of biomass.

c The diagram shows a rough drawing of a pyramid of biomass. Use the data in the table to draw the pyramid of biomass to scale. Use a horizontal scale of 2 mm = 5 g/m².

d Describe what happens to the biomass at each stage in the food chain.

e What proportion of the biomass of the blackberries is transferred to the kestrel?

Organism	Biomass (g/m² of moorland)
blackberries	500
mice	1
kestrels	0.1

Questions

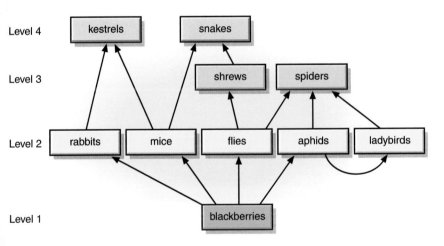

1 Name the producer in the moorland food web shown above.

2 Which level, 1 to 4, would have:

  a the greatest total biomass

  b the smallest total biomass?

3 Draw and label the pyramids of biomass you would expect for the food chains:

  a blackberries → flies → shrews → snakes

  b blackberries → aphids → ladybirds → spiders

Summary

- The energy that green plants trap from sunlight is the source of energy for all living organisms.

- The biomass at each stage in a food chain is less than it was in the previous stage.

- The biomass at each stage in a food chain can be drawn to scale as a pyramid of biomass.

People produce food in many different ways.

What do the photographs have in common? They all show ways of producing protein food for humans. But what people eat depends on where they live and what they can afford. To most people in the world, meat is a luxury they cannot afford.

Here you will learn why meat is so expensive compared with plant foods.

Cereals

Cereal crops usually contain both carbohydrates and protein – that is why your breakfast cereal is so good for you! The pie charts show the compositions of three crops.

a Which crop contains:

   i the highest proportion of carbohydrate

   ii the highest proportion of protein?

b Estimate the amount of fat in 199 g of soya.

When you eat plant foods, all the material and energy from the plant goes directly into your body. If that same plant food was fed to an animal, and then that animal was killed and eaten, not all of the original material and energy in the plant would be passed to your body.

This is because the animal, while it was alive, used up a lot of the energy and passed much of the plant material out of its body in faeces – so relatively little of the plant biomass got incorporated into the animal's biomass. This is why rearing animals is not a very efficient way of producing food.

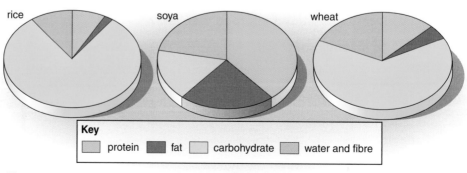

Key

protein   fat   carbohydrate   water and fibre

Rice, soya and wheat contain different proportions of protein, fat, carbohydrate, water and fibre.

Chickens

The diagram shows how much of the energy we supply in food to a free-range chicken is transferred to human food.

c i Calculate the proportion of energy in the cereal that is transferred to human food.

   ii Out of every 100 g of cereal we feed to chickens, how much is not transferred to human food?

Modern farming methods, such as rearing chickens in cages inside buildings, increase the efficiency of transferring energy from cereal to human food. It now takes only 3.6 kg of cereal food to produce 2.0 kg of body mass in chickens – but, even so, almost half of the cereal food still does not reach humans if we use it to feed chickens first.

165 kJ in chicken meat

1000 kJ in food

145 kJ in egg

Chickens are usually fed on cereals.

Fish

Fish are grown in ponds to provide food for humans. The bar chart shows the different yields obtained from growing herbivorous fish (which feed on water plants), and carnivorous fish (which eat insects and young herbivorous fish).

d i Explain why the yield from growing herbivorous fish is greater than that from growing carnivorous fish.

   ii By how much is the yield of herbivorous fish increased by adding fertiliser to the water?

   iii Explain why adding fertiliser increases the yield of herbivorous fish.

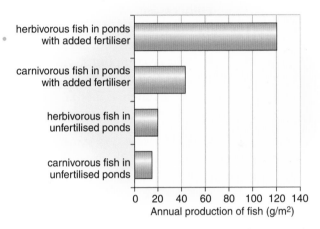

The yield of fish varies according to what the fish eat.

Questions

The diagram shows how many people an area of land the size of five football pitches will support with food.

1 Look back at the pie charts. Suggest why growing soya will support more people than growing wheat.

2 Explain why growing crops supports more people than rearing cattle.

3 Give some pros and cons of raising animals for food.

10 acres (5 football pitches) will support:

60 people growing soya

24 people growing wheat

10 people growing maize

2 people growing cattle

Crop farming can support many more people than livestock farming on the same area of land.

Summary

• At each stage in a food chain, less energy and material are contained in the biomass of the organisms.

• This means that it is more efficient to produce food by growing crops than by rearing animals.

3:10 Getting rid of faeces

Some of you may have been to scout or guide camp and used pit latrines. After using the latrine, you throw some soil over the faeces. This is not just to remove the smell, or to keep the flies off! Covering the faeces with soil helps them to decompose.

A pit latrine is a real outdoor loo – not much more than a hole in the ground!

Soil microbes

Faeces in the soil are broken down by **microbes**. These include bacteria, fungi and single-celled organisms. Bacteria and fungi digest faeces and other waste products, by producing digestive enzymes. The enzymes pass out of the microbe's body and onto the waste materials, which they break down into soluble compounds. These soluble compounds are then absorbed into the body of the microbe. Soil microbes obtain much of their food from waste materials such as faeces. The breakdown of waste materials by microbes is known as **decay**.

a All the material in faeces is broken down by microbes. Which enzyme must they produce that is not produced by most animals?

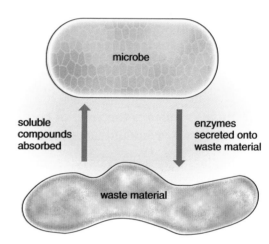
Soil microbes feed on other animals' waste.

Sewage works

The residents of a British city will produce thousands of tons of faeces in a year. The faeces are flushed down toilets and sent to a sewage works. Here, there is far too much faeces to bury, as happens in a pit latrine. So, another method is used to break down the faeces – but it uses similar microbes to those found in soil. The sewage is run into large tanks through which air is bubbled. The microbes in the tank digest 80% of the waste material within a few hours. The oxygen in the air speeds up the activity of the microbes.

In the activated sludge tank, microbes quickly break down waste material.

b Which process that occurs in the microbes uses oxygen?

Biological filters

There is still some waste material in the sewage after it leaves the sludge tank, so the next stage is to filter it. The sewage is allowed to trickle through filter beds. The stones in the filter bed are coated with a layer of microbes, which digest the remaining waste materials. Clean water then runs into rivers or the sea.

The filter bed leaves the water clean enough to flow back into rivers.

Muck-spreading

Faeces from cows on a farm are not dumped. They are spread on the fields as a 'natural' fertiliser. The faeces are broken down by soil microbes. Protein in the faeces is converted into nitrates by some of these microbes. Plants need nitrates to grow.

c What do plants make out of sugars and nitrates?

Farmers need to use fertilisers because they harvest crops. These crops have taken nitrates out of the soil. Farmers must replace the nitrates if they want a good crop next year. They can do this in two ways. They can buy chemical fertilisers or they can use animal faeces. Using animal faeces is known as **organic farming** because the fertiliser has come from living creatures, not chemical factories.

d Suggest the advantages and disadvantages of using natural and artificial fertilisers.

Compost heaps

Microbes break down dead organisms as well as waste materials. In autumn, in a garden, many plants lose their leaves. These leaves contain nutrients that can be recycled by soil microbes.

Many gardeners collect all the dead leaves and use them to make **compost**. Compost contains nutrients such as nitrates, so it acts as a natural fertiliser when it is spread on the garden.

The diagram shows one way of making compost. Layers of leaves are put in a large container. A layer of soil is placed between each layer of leaves. The sides of the container are perforated to allow air to circulate through the container. A lid keeps the rain off. The microbes in the soil digest the leaves to form compost.

Decay conditions

Decay occurs most quickly if conditions are moist, warm and there is a good supply of oxygen. Moisture is needed for the microbes to digest the waste outside their bodies. An increase in temperature increases the activity of the digestive enzymes. Oxygen is needed by the microbes for their respiration.

Question

A dead leaf was put onto soil in each of four beakers as shown.

In which beaker would the dead leaf decay quickest? Explain your answer as fully as possible.

As waste materials decay, valuable nutrients are released.

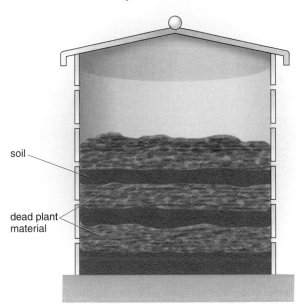
The formation of compost is another example of decay.

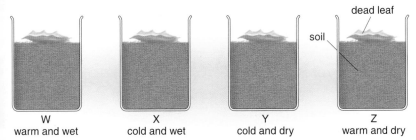

W warm and wet   X cold and wet   Y cold and dry   Z warm and dry

The beakers were kept under different conditions.

Summary

- Materials decay because they are broken down by microbes.
- Materials are digested by enzymes that pass out of the bodies of the microbes.
- Microbes digest materials fast in warm, moist conditions with a good supply of oxygen.
- Microbes are used to decay sewage.
- Microbes are used to decay dead plants to produce compost.
- The decay process releases nutrients that plants need for growth.

3:11 Cycles

This is the Amazon rainforest in South America.

Plants

The photograph shows a tropical rainforest. It exchanges thousands of tonnes of carbon dioxide with the atmosphere every year. There are two processes involved in this exchange – photosynthesis and respiration. You studied both of these processes in year 10. They are summarised for you in the diagram.

a Does a forest increase the amount of carbon dioxide in the atmosphere over a year, or decrease it? Explain the reason for your answer.

Animals

The giraffe in the photograph on the opposite page is eating tree leaves. It digests the leaves into sugars, amino acids, fatty acids and glycerol. All these compounds contain carbon. The carbon compounds are then made into the proteins and fats that form the cells of the animal's body. If a carnivore eats a herbivore, the carbon compounds in the herbivore are converted into carbon compounds in the carnivore.

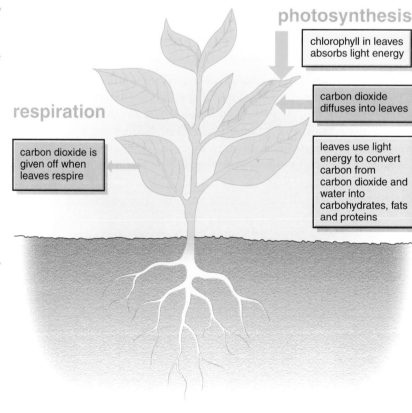

photosynthesis

chlorophyll in leaves absorbs light energy

carbon dioxide diffuses into leaves

leaves use light energy to convert carbon from carbon dioxide and water into carbohydrates, fats and proteins

respiration

carbon dioxide is given off when leaves respire

A summary of photosynthesis and respiration in green plants.

All animals respire. Some of their food is converted into sugars, which can be respired. The carbon in the sugars returns to the atmosphere as carbon dioxide.

b Explain why animals decrease in mass when they respire.

Decay organisms

When organisms die, small animals and microbes feed on their bodies. The carbon compounds in the dead organisms become carbon compounds in the bodies of these small organisms. When the small organisms respire, some of the carbon compounds from their food are converted into carbon dioxide.

Carbon compounds in the leaves are taken in by the giraffe.

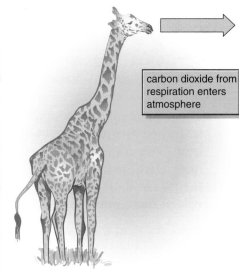

carbon dioxide from respiration enters atmosphere

Carbon that was originally in the giraffe's food eventually goes back into the atmosphere.

Putting it all together

Now we can group plants, animals and microbes into one cycle – the **carbon cycle**.

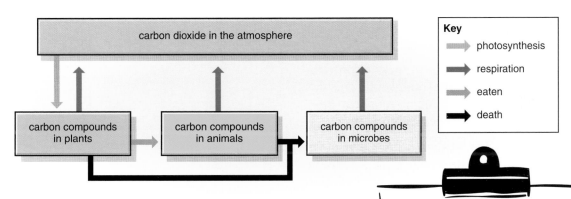

The carbon cycle.

Questions

1 The diagram shows the result of an experiment on soil organisms. Explain the results of the experiment.

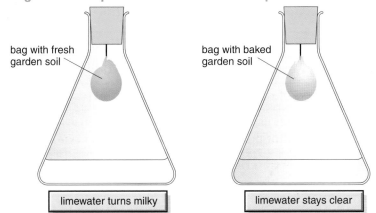

bag with fresh garden soil

bag with baked garden soil

limewater turns milky

limewater stays clear

The two flasks were left in the same conditions for several days.

2 You eat some potato crisps. The crisps contain carbon compounds.

 a How do plants make carbon compounds?

 b What happens in your body to the carbon compounds in the crisps?

Summary

- Plants produce carbon compounds from carbon dioxide in the atmosphere, by photosynthesis.

- Animals obtain carbon compounds by eating plants or other animals.

- Both animals and plants return carbon dioxide to the atmosphere during respiration.

- When animals and plants die, microbes obtain carbon compounds from their bodies.

- Microbes respire, releasing carbon dioxide into the atmosphere.

- The movement of carbon compounds from the atmosphere into organisms and back again is called the carbon cycle.

3:12 Human population growth

The photograph shows some spectators at the Olympic Games in Sydney, Australia, in 2000. About 100 000 people were there, from every country in the world. How many people do you think there are in the world? In the millennium year, 2000, there were about six billion. This is an enormous number, but what is more worrying is that the number is increasing rapidly.

a   **i**   Look at the graph showing estimates of world population. Describe the pattern shown in the graph.

       ii   Copy the graph. Use it to estimate the population in 3000 AD.

Six thousand years ago, the population of the world was about 0.2 billion. People lived in small groups, and most of the world was unaffected by human activities.

As the population increases, raw materials are rapidly being used up. Some of these resources, such as fossil fuels, are **non-renewable**. This means that once we have used them, no more can be made, so eventually supplies will run out.

As we use these raw materials, a great deal of waste is produced. Much of this waste causes pollution.

Using resources

The table shows how some of the world's resources are used by the industrialised world (European countries, USA and Japan, for example), and the developing world (poor countries in Africa and Asia, for example).

b   **i**   Suggest why industrialised countries consume so much of the world's energy resources.

       ii   Suggest why industrialised countries consume so much of the chemical production.

c   **i**   Look at the graph showing differences in population growth rates, on the page opposite. Describe the trends shown by the graph.

       ii   In 2000, what proportion of the population lived in developing countries?

       iii   Suggest reasons for the different population growth rates in industrialised regions and developing regions.

About 100 000 people came to watch the men's 100 m final at the 2000 Olympic Games, when Maurice Greene won the gold medal.

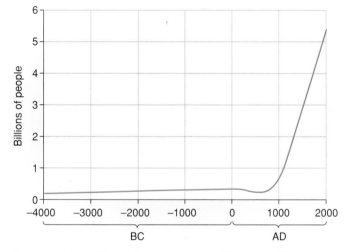

Estimates of world population from 4000 BC to 2000 AD.

Industrialised world	Developing world
25% of world population	75% of world population
uses 80% of total energy	uses 20% of total energy
each person uses 250–1000 litres of water per day	each person uses 20–40 litres of water per day
40% of this water is used in industry	93% of this water is used in agriculture
consumes 85% of chemical production	consumes 15% of chemical production
consumes 90% of cars	consumes 10% of cars
has 87% of world trade	has 13% of world trade
not affected by famine	100 million people affected by famine

Producing waste

The chart below shows the amount of municipal waste and industrial waste that needs to be got rid of each year, per person, in different parts of the world. Municipal waste includes sewage and what goes in your dustbin.

d **i** Describe the patterns shown in the chart.

ii Suggest why North American countries produce much more municipal waste than developing countries.

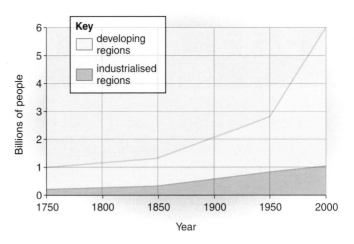

Differences in population growth rates in industrialised and developing regions.

Questions

The world is in danger of running out of resources. People in industrialised countries and developing countries might have very different ideas about how to solve the problem.

Look at the cartoon.

1 What is the solution proposed by the man from the industrialised country?

2 What is the solution proposed by the man from the developing country?

3 What do *you* think is the solution to the problem?

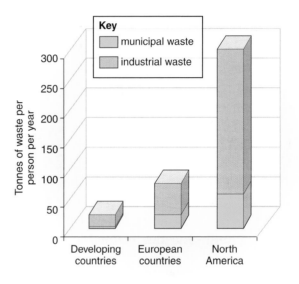

Getting rid of waste is a real problem – the more waste, the bigger the problem!

Graphic by Clive Offey in The New Internationalist

We all have to work together to conserve and share out the world's resources fairly.

Summary

- The human population is rising rapidly.

- Raw materials, including non-renewable energy resources, are rapidly being used up.

- More waste is being produced.

- Unless waste is properly handled, more pollution will be caused.

Homes

The photograph shows a familiar sight – land being swallowed up for new houses. Every year, we have to build more homes to house the increasing numbers of people in the world. Before building began, this land provided habitats for animals and plants. Every new home built for humans reduces the land available for animals and plants.

The next photograph shows a huge quarry, which provides the materials to build the houses. So, extracting raw materials from the Earth also reduces the amount of land available for animals and plants.

The new houses have to be supplied with electricity – so the demand for electricity goes up. Many parts of the world cannot afford to import fossil fuels to produce electricity – so they build dams for hydroelectric schemes. More habitats for animals and plants are lost.

The inhabitants of each new house will produce rubbish. The town council has to get rid of this rubbish. Most of the rubbish is dumped. Still more habitats are lost to animals and plants.

Cities are growing faster than the population as a whole. In 1950, only 29 people in every 100 in the world lived in cities. By 2000, the number of people living in cities had trebled. Now, 85% of the increase in population takes place in cities.

Cities import most of their food, fuel, building materials and water, whereas rural communities are often almost self-sufficient. Cities also produce much more waste per head of population than rural communities.

a i In England, the number of new houses being built is increasing much more rapidly than the number of people in the population. Suggest why this is happening.

   ii List the reasons why building new houses reduces the space available for plants and animals to live.

The more humans there are in the world, the less room there is for other animals and plants.

It is not just houses that use up land.

A huge area of land was flooded when this hydroelectric dam was built in Glen Canyon.

The more people there are, the more rubbish they make

Farms

The increase in population means that we need more food. To grow more food, more land is now used for agriculture. There are now very few parts of Britain where there is no agriculture at all.

Using farms for agriculture reduces the number of habitats for wild animals and plants.

Fertilisers and pesticides

Farms have other impacts on wildlife. Besides destroying the habitats of many kinds of animals and plants, many farms use chemicals that also affect them.

Farmers use **herbicides** to kill weeds in their crops. If these herbicides reach wild plants they will kill them too. Many of these wild plants provide food for animals such as butterflies. If we kill the wild plants the butterflies have nothing to feed on so they die too. The numbers of most kinds of butterflies in this country have drastically declined over the last 50 years as farmers have used more herbicides. If herbicides are washed by rain into streams and ponds they kill the plants growing there.

Farmers used **pesticides** mainly to kill animals that eat their crops. Most pesticides are used to kill insects. These pesticides also kill harmless insects that are food for birds. The populations of many kinds of birds have decreased over the last 50 years as farmers have increased the use of pesticides. If pesticides are washed by rain into streams and ponds they kill the animals living there.

Farmers use **fertilisers** to increase the yield of their crops. If fertilisers are washed into streams or ponds, they increase the growth of plants living there.

Questions

1 Trace the woodland from each map onto graph paper. Calculate the proportion of woodland that disappeared between 1892 and 1980.

2 Suggest why woodland disappeared between 1892 and 1959.

3 What was the biggest change to the village between 1959 and 1980? Describe how this might affect plants and animals living in the area.

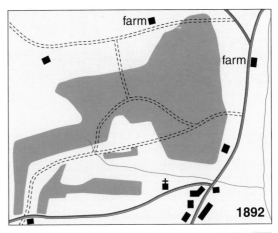

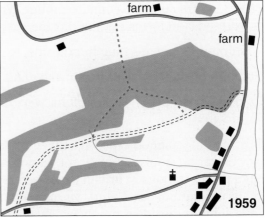

woodland
stream
road
track
bridleway
footpath
buildings
church (with tower)

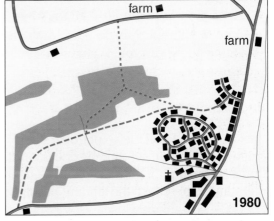

Land use around this village has changed a great deal between 1892 and 1980.

Summary

- Humans reduce the amount of land available for other animals and plants by building, quarrying, farming and dumping waste.

- Farms also affect living organisms by the use of pesticides, herbicides and fertilisers.

3:14 Acid rain

Power stations

Coal is burned to release energy. The main element in coal is carbon. During burning, this is oxidised to form carbon dioxide.

carbon + oxygen → carbon dioxide (+ energy)

Carbon dioxide dissolves in rainwater and makes it slightly acid.

Most kinds of coal also contain sulphur. When sulphur burns it is oxidised, and forms sulphur dioxide.

sulphur + oxygen → sulphur dioxide

Sulphur dioxide dissolves in rainwater and makes it more acid.

Acid rain has a pH of 4 or less. It has very damaging effects on the environment.

It is very difficult and expensive to remove sulphur dioxide from power station smoke, so in recent years a large number of coal-fired power stations in Britain have been replaced by stations that burn natural gas. Natural gas contains very little sulphur so little sulphur dioxide is produced when it burns.

a Some coal-fired power stations have 'scrubbers' to remove sulphur dioxide. The smoke is passed over a chemical. What type of chemical do you think this is? Give a reason for your answer.

A coal-burning power station. Large heaps of stored coal can be seen in the foreground.

Cars

Cars also burn fossil fuels – petrol or diesel. Some types of petrol contain sulphur, so sulphur dioxide is emitted in the exhaust fumes. Low-sulphur petrol and diesel are now available from fuel stations to reduce the amount of sulphur dioxide emitted.

Power stations and cars also produce nitrogen oxides. These oxides dissolve in rainwater too and make it more acid. Many cars are now fitted with catalytic converters that reduce the amounts of nitrogen oxides in the exhaust fumes.

Damage to trees

The photograph shows trees in the mountains of Norway that have been damaged by acid rain. One of the first signs of damage by acid rain is a condition called 'crown-loss'. The young leaves – those near the top of the tree – are killed by the acid rain.

b What material covers the outside of a leaf? Suggest why young leaves are killed by acid rain but older ones are not.

Crown-loss is not the only damage caused by acid rain. The acid affects the covering of the older leaves. This makes it easier for disease organisms to attack the tree.

Acid rain damages and kills trees.

The young root hairs of the trees are damaged when acid rainwater gets into the soil.

c What is the job of root hairs? How will the tree be affected if its root hairs are damaged?

Effect on freshwater organisms

When acid rain runs into streams and lakes, it makes the water more acid. As the water gets more acid, fewer animals and plants can survive. (Remember that pH 5 is ten times more acid than pH 6.) The bar chart shows how the pH of water affects which animals live in it. All the animals listed, except snails, are fish.

d i Which fish tolerates acid water the best?

ii What is the lowest pH in which snails live?

Questions

Look at the map.

1 Work out the average percentage of trees damaged in European countries.

2 If you looked at 1000 trees in Norway, how many would you expect to be damaged by acid rain?

3 Use an atlas to find the name of the country that has the smallest percentage of trees damaged by acid rain.

4 Ireland has a lower percentage of trees damaged by acid rain than Britain. Suggest an explanation for this.

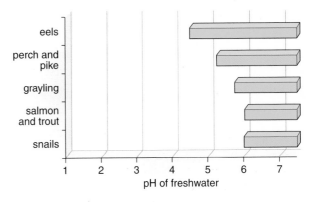

healthy tree | young leaves killed by acid rain | root hairs killed by acid rain – tree dies

Acid rain damages the roots of trees, as well as the leaves.

Different organisms are able to live in different ranges of pH.

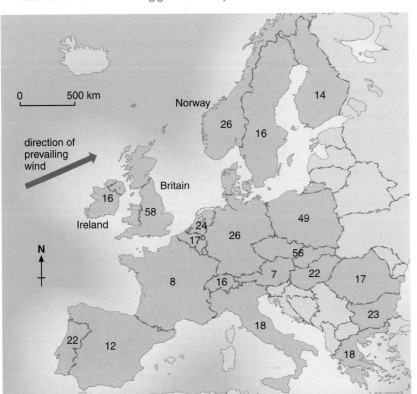

The percentage of trees damaged by acid rain in European countries.

Summary

- Burning fossil fuels, such as coal and oil, releases sulphur dioxide into the atmosphere.

- Nitrogen oxides are also released when fossil fuels are burned.

- Sulphur dioxide and nitrogen oxides dissolve in rainwater and make it more acid.

- Acid rain kills the young leaves of trees and may kill the root hairs. If the water in lakes and rivers becomes too acid, plants and animals cannot survive.

3:15 Global warming

The Earth's atmosphere is slowly warming up. The warming is caused by 'the greenhouse effect' – so called because the process is similar to the way in which a greenhouse warms up.

Earth's atmosphere is warming up because of an increase in the proportions of 'greenhouse gases' it contains. These gases are produced both by natural processes and by human activities.

Without the natural greenhouse gases, the temperature of the Earth would be 33 °C colder than it is at the moment. So most living things would not survive without the greenhouse effect!

But human activities are causing the concentrations of greenhouse gases in the atmosphere to rise above natural levels, and that is causing a great deal of concern.

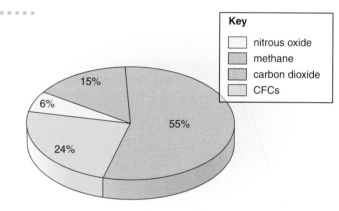
Global warming.

Greenhouse gases

The pie chart shows how much each gas contributes to the greenhouse effect. By far the biggest contributor is carbon dioxide.

Carbon dioxide

When you studied the carbon cycle (page 137), you learned that plants remove carbon dioxide from the atmosphere during photosynthesis, and most living organisms pass carbon dioxide back to the atmosphere when they respire. These two processes balanced each other for thousands of years. But in the last few centuries humans have interfered with this balance in two major ways.

1 There has been a massive increase in the combustion of fossil fuels both by industry and by use of motor vehicles. This is increasing the amount of carbon dioxide in the atmosphere.

2 Large areas of forest have been cleared both to produce timber and to clear land for agriculture. When trees are cut down, only the trunk is kept. The branches are burned. This combustion releases carbon dioxide into the atmosphere. The roots of the trees die, and are decomposed.

a Explain how decay of tree roots increases the carbon dioxide concentration of the atmosphere.

Cutting down trees also means that the amount of photosynthesis going on in the world is reduced. Trees take in millions of tonnes of carbon dioxide every year. Most of this is converted into the cells that form wood. We say that the carbon dioxide is 'locked up' in the wood. Many trees live for a hundred years or more, so the carbon dioxide remains 'locked up' for a long time.

The nations of the world are trying to reach agreement to reduce carbon dioxide emissions from burning fossil fuels.

Key

- [ ] nitrous oxide
- [ ] methane
- [ ] carbon dioxide
- [ ] CFCs

15%
6%
24%
55%

Four main gases cause the greenhouse effect.

The carbon locked away in the biomass of the forest is released suddenly into the atmosphere when trees are felled and burned.

Some nations, such as the USA, are arguing that they need not reduce carbon dioxide emissions because they have large areas of forest, which they will protect.

Carbon dioxide is responsible for just over half of the total greenhouse effect. You also need to learn about one of the other major greenhouse gases – methane.

Methane

Methane is a gas produced by certain types of microbes that can live where there is very little oxygen. They produce this gas when they break down organic materials. Many of these microbes are involved in the decay process.

Rice fields are under water for long periods, so there is very little oxygen in the soil. Bacteria in these soils produce a lot of methane.

Cows have a four-chambered stomach. Microbes live in these chambers and digest parts of the cow's food. Because there is very little oxygen in the cow's stomach, these microbes produce methane.

As the world's population has increased, so has the total area of rice fields and the number of cattle, to provide food for all the people. So, there has been an increase in the amount of methane in the atmosphere.

Methane is produced by bacteria living in flooded paddy fields.

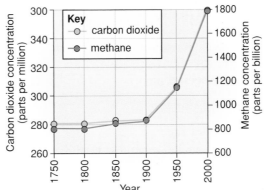

Concentrations of carbon dioxide and methane in the atmosphere since 1750.

b **i** Describe the patterns shown by the graph.

  ii Which of the two greenhouse gases has shown the greater increase in concentration over the last 250 years?

Effects of greenhouse gases

The increased concentrations of greenhouse gases are causing the temperature of the atmosphere to rise, slowly but surely. This rise will cause changes to climates around the world – some places will become wetter, others drier. The climate changes will change the areas where crops can be grown.

The warming of the atmosphere is causing melting of the polar icecaps. This will cause sea levels to rise. Some low-lying pieces of land will become flooded.

Question

Look at the cartoon. Explain why people in the two hemispheres of the Earth might have different views about how to reduce levels of greenhouse gases.

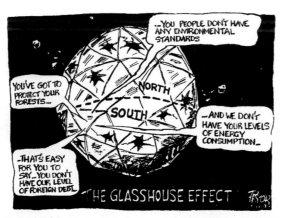

People who live in glass houses shouldn't throw stones.

Summary

- Increased combustion of fossil fuels has increased the amount of carbon dioxide in the atmosphere.

- Large scale deforestation has increased the release of carbon dioxide to the atmosphere by combustion and decay. It has also reduced the rate at which carbon dioxide is 'locked up' as wood.

- Increased numbers of cattle and rice fields have increased the amount of methane released into the atmosphere.

- Increasing levels of carbon dioxide and methane may be causing an increase in the 'greenhouse effect'.

- An increase in the Earth's temperature may cause climate changes and a rise in sea level.

3:16 Sustainable development

Every year a famine occurs somewhere in the world. Television news programmes often show us pictures of people squatting on the edges of cities in developing countries. All of us would like to see a better standard of living for the whole of the world's population. But we must not compromise the needs of future generations to improve our quality of life.

Improving quality of life without compromising future generations is known as **sustainable development**. This involves protecting the environment and using natural resources wisely.

Famine occurs when food is not in the right place at the right time.

What is going wrong?

In the last few pages, we have seen that:

◆ the world population is rising too fast

◆ forests are being destroyed

◆ natural resources are being used up

◆ pollution is affecting land, sea and water

◆ climates are changing.

Millions of people in the world live in very poor conditions.

What can we do about it?

Birth rate

Raising living standards and health care standards reduces the rate of population growth. The table shows data for some developing countries. The infant mortality rate in England is 9 per 1000 births.

Country	Birth rate per 1000 of population	Infant mortality rate per 1000 births	People with access to health care (%)	Females who can read (%)
Sierra Leone	48.1	146	36	11
Nigeria	46.6	99	67	40
Bangladesh	40.6	111	74	22
Thailand	20.0	28	59	91
Sri Lanka	20.7	25	90	84

People tend to have more children in poor regions.

Nearly half the children around here die before they are grown up; I am going to have several children so that even if some die, I will still be left with some.

a **What is the general relationship between:**

 i **the birth rate and the infant mortality rate**

 ii **the birth rate and access to health services**

 iii **the birth rate and the percentage of women who can read?**

b **Use the data to suggest how the birth rate in developing countries could be reduced.**

Energy use

c Look at the diagram showing energy use in different countries. Bangladesh is a developing country. Explain why the USA uses so much more energy than Bangladesh.

Most energy used in industrialised countries comes from non-renewable energy resources. So industrial countries are using up non-renewable energy resources far more quickly than developing countries.

d Suggest ways in which people in industrialised countries can reduce the amount of energy used.

At a recent conference, industrialised countries set themselves a target of using **renewable** energy sources to supply at least 10% of their energy needs.

e From your year 10 work on Energy, list the different types of renewable energy sources.

Renewable energy resources do not use up fossil fuels and they do not produce pollution. But they can have an impact on the environment.

f Describe the impact on the environment of:

　i using a tidal barrage to generate electricity

　ii using a wind farm to generate electricity.

280 gigajoules

110 gigajoules

1 gigajoule

United States　Japan　Bangladesh

The amount of energy used per head of population, per year, in different countries (1 gigajoule = 1 000 000 000 J).

Recycling

One way of conserving precious natural resources is to recycle them. We can all contribute to this by using recycling bins. Many local councils now provide households with two bins – one for rubbish that can be recycled and one for waste that cannot be recycled.

g How does recycling each of the following save natural resources?

　i newspaper

　ii bottles

　iii aluminium cans

Recycling materials helps to conserve natural resources.

Increasing food production

Over one billion people do not get enough food to eat. At least 400 million get less than 80% of the food they need to keep them active and healthy – so they do not grow correctly and they are more liable to catch diseases.

There is more than enough food in the world to feed everyone. Grain production has outstripped population growth in recent years. (In Europe we are now even paying farmers to *stop* growing food!) But much of this food is in the wrong place.

India is a production success story. Planting new strains of cereal crops helped it to double its production of wheat between 1965 and 1972. It even exported its surplus to neighbouring countries.

But half the hungry people in the world live in India. These people cannot afford to buy wheat.

h What is the best long-term solution to providing food for people who cannot afford to buy it?

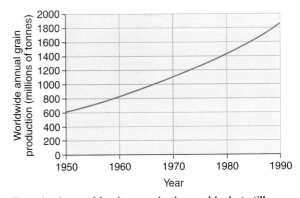

There is plenty of food grown in the world – but still people starve.

End of module questions

1 The photograph shows a seal pup.

Use information from the photograph to explain two ways in which the seal pup is adapted for survival in the Arctic.

2 The photograph shows an elephant. It is very hot and the elephant has covered itself with mud. It is flapping its ears.

2.1 Elephants have very large ears. They have no natural predators. Suggest how having large ears helps elephants to survive in a hot climate.

2.2 Suggest how the mud helps to keep the elephant cool.

3 The drawing shows a plant that lives in hot deserts.

Explain how each of the following helps the plant to survive:

3.1 the thick waxy coat on the leaves

3.2 the sharp prickles

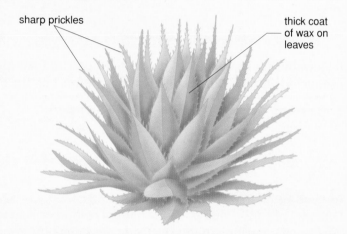

sharp prickles

thick coat of wax on leaves

4 Clover is a plant that grows in grassland. Clover plants were grown in plots of soil. The graph shows how the yield of clover was affected by the number of clover plants sown in each plot.

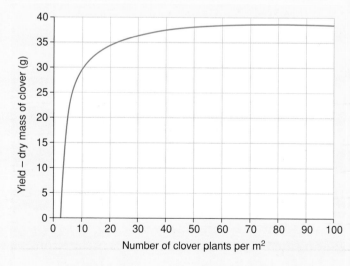

4.1 Describe the effect of the number of clover plants per m² on the yield of clover.

4.2 Give *two* factors for which clover plants compete.

4.3 Explain why each of these factors is needed for plant growth.

5 The diagram shows a food web for a lake.

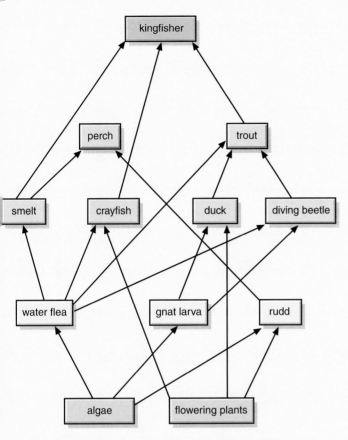

5.1 Name *one* animal that is eaten by crayfish.

5.2 Name *two* predators of gnat larvae.

Anglers begin fishing in the lake. They catch large numbers of trout.

5.3 How might this affect the populations of water fleas and smelt? Explain your answer in each case.

6 The table shows the results of a ten-year study of the populations of owls and voles in a forest.

Year	Number of voles (to the nearest thousand)	Number of owls
1	15 000	8
2	12 000	9
3	15 000	7
4	23 000	9
5	40 000	14
6	2 000	28
7	9 000	8
8	19 000	9
9	10 000	14
10	8 000	16

6.1 Copy and complete the graph for the numbers of voles and owls.

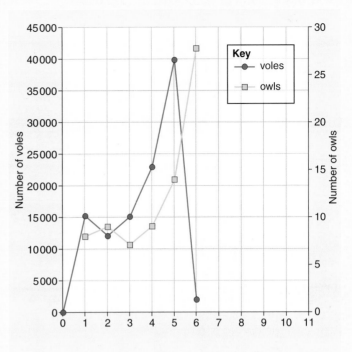

6.2 How is the number of owls related to the number of voles?

6.3 Suggest *three* reasons for the large fall in the number of voles between years 5 and 6.

7 The diagram shows a food web from a moor.

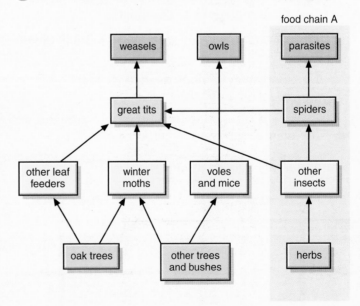

7.1 Name *two* producers in this food web.

7.2 Sketch a pyramid of biomass for food chain A.

8 The diagram shows what happens to the energy in the grass eaten by a bullock from 1 m² of grazing land.

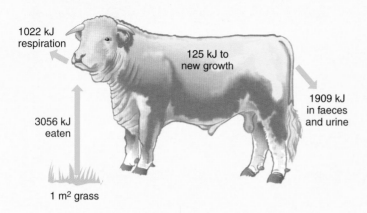

1022 kJ respiration

125 kJ to new growth

1909 kJ in faeces and urine

3056 kJ eaten

1 m² grass

8.1 Calculate the amount of energy lost via respiration.

8.2 Calculate the proportion of the energy in the grass that was transferred to new growth in the bullock.

8.3 Explain why it is more efficient to produce food by growing crops rather than by rearing animals.

9 A gardener decides to build a compost heap in the garden.

9.1 Why is compost useful to the gardener?

9.2 What type of organism breaks down dead plant material into compost?

9.3 Describe how these organisms break down dead plant material.

9.4 List the conditions needed for fast breakdown of compost.

10 The diagram shows the carbon cycle.

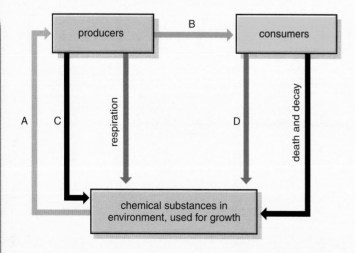

Describe the processes occurring at A, B, C and D.

11 The diagram shows changes to a farm between 1953 and 1983.

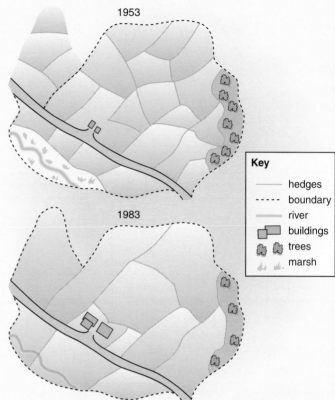

1953

1983

Key
- —— hedges
- ---- boundary
- ━━ river
- ▨ buildings
- 🌳 trees
- 〜 marsh

11.1 Describe the changes to the farm that took place between 1953 and 1983.

11.2 Explain how these changes might have affected the wildlife that lived in this area in 1953.

12 **12.1** Describe how acid rain is produced.

The graph shows how the pH of water in lakes affects the number of species of some of the animals that live there.

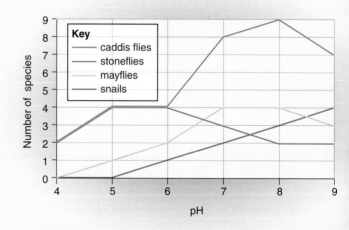

Key
- —— caddis flies
- —— stoneflies
- —— mayflies
- —— snails

12.2 Describe the effect of acid rain on the number of species of the four types of animal.

12.3 Describe the effects of acid rain on plants.

Module 7 – Patterns of chemical change

We rely on chemical reactions to turn raw materials into the many useful materials we use everyday. To make these reactions work on an industrial scale, we need to understand more about:

◆ reaction rates and how to alter them – why are some reactions too slow whilst other are dangerously fast?

◆ catalysts and enzymes – how can these be used to make reactions more efficient?

◆ reacting masses – how much of each reactant do we need and how much product will it make?

◆ energy changes – why do some reactions need vast amounts of energy put into them, whilst others give energy out?

◆ reversible reactions – why do some reactions go to completion, whilst others seem to 'stick'?

In this module you learn to understand these problems in terms of colliding particles and the breaking and making of chemical bonds.

Before you start, check what you remember about the patterns of chemical change.

1 Imagine you have mixed some acid and alkali in a test-tube. How could you tell a chemical reaction had occurred just by holding the test-tube?

2 Natural gas burns in air to give carbon dioxide and water. What else do you get from this reaction? (Think: why do we burn gas?)

3 Plants make food using two simple chemicals: carbon dioxide and water. This reaction takes energy in. What provides the energy for this reaction?

4 Your digestive system is full of enzymes. What do they help to do?

7:1 Rates of reaction

How fast?

You already have some idea about **reaction rates** from Module 5. For example, you saw that the reactivity series of metals could be found by looking at how quickly different metals react with acid.

a **Which metal reacts faster with sulphuric acid, iron or magnesium?**

- Some reactions are very fast indeed, some are very slow.

- In a car engine, the petrol/air mixture explodes. An explosion is a very fast reaction.

- The car body, made of steel, slowly reacts with air and water and turns to rust. This rusting can take many years.

Many things we use everyday are made using chemical reactions. These chemical reactions are carried out by the chemical industry.

Controlling reaction rates is very important in the chemical industry.

- If a reaction takes place too quickly, it might get out of control and cause an explosion.

- If a reaction takes place too slowly, the production costs will go up.

b **Imagine you are cooking a cake. What would happen to the cake if the reactions went too fast?**

Reaction rates need to be controlled. But, before you can control reaction rates, you need to be able to measure them.

Measuring reaction rates

To find how fast a reaction is going, you need to be able to time something. For example, you may want to know how long it takes for different metals to react in acid. You could time how long it takes for the metal to disappear completely.

You would need to:

- dissolve samples of different metals in acid;

- use a large amount of acid to make sure that all the metal reacts;

- use the same amount of each metal in order to make it a fair test;

- use the same amount of acid in each case to make it a fair test.

Metal (0.1 g)	Time taken to react completely (seconds)
calcium	13
magnesium	24
zinc	90
iron	120

Remember, the longer it takes for the reaction to occur, the slower the reaction is.

As the metal reacts, the mass of the metal left gets less. You can find out how much metal has already reacted by finding the mass of the metal left.

If you take away the mass of the metal left from the mass of the metal at the start of the reaction, you have worked out the mass of metal that has reacted.

mass of metal at start of reaction − mass of metal left = mass of metal reacted

To find the speed (or rate) of the reaction, you can divide the mass of metal reacted by the time taken:

$$\text{rate of reaction (g/s)} = \frac{\text{mass (g)}}{\text{time (s)}}$$

c Which of the metals shows the highest rate of reaction? What is the rate of reaction in grams per second?

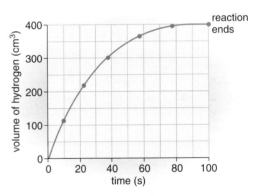

What can you measure?

To time a reaction, you need to measure either:

◆ the loss of the reacting chemicals (**reactants**); or

◆ the increase in the **products** of the reaction.

In a simple reaction between a metal and an acid:

reactants   **products**

magnesium + sulphuric acid → magnesium sulphate + hydrogen

you can measure how long it takes for one of the reactants (for example, the magnesium) to be used up. But this reaction also produces bubbles of hydrogen gas.

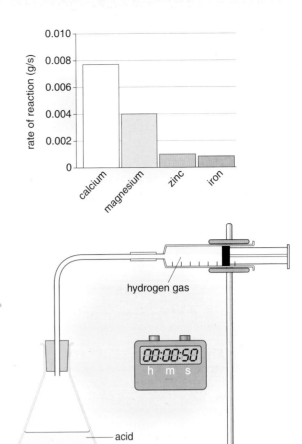

Measuring gas produced in a reaction.

Measuring the volume of a gas

You can measure how fast a gas is produced by using a **gas syringe**. As the gas is formed, it forces the barrel of the syringe back along a scale, showing the volume produced.

You can take readings every few seconds. You can then plot a graph of the volume of hydrogen formed against the time taken. This shows how the reaction slows down as the reactants are used up.

d How is the rate of reaction shown here changing with time?

Questions

1 Limestone reacts with acid, producing carbon dioxide gas. These results show the volume of gas produced over time.

Time (s)	0	20	40	60	80	100
Volume (cm³)	0	40	60	70	75	77

a Plot a volume/time graph.

b What is the rate of gas production over the first 20 seconds?

c Has the reaction nearly finished after 100 s? How can you tell?

Summary

• Different reactions can run at very different rates.

• In industry it is very important to control the rate of reaction.

• You can follow the rate of a reaction either by measuring how fast a reactant is used up, or by measuring how fast a product is formed.

7:2 Speeding things up

Many of the things that we use every day are made using chemical reactions. If you can speed up a reaction, you can usually make things cheaper. So how can you speed up a reaction?

All chemicals are made up of particles. A reaction takes place when particles bump into each other. Anything you can do to make the particles bump into each other more often will speed up the reaction.

This can be done by:

- increasing the **surface area** of a solid;
- increasing the **concentration** of a solution.

Investigating surface area

Marble chips are made of calcium carbonate. They react with hydrochloric acid, giving off carbon dioxide gas.

If you drop one large lump of marble into a beaker of hydrochloric acid you can see steady fizzing. But if you use the same amount of marble and grind it to a powder, you see that the reaction foams up out of the beaker.

a   What is happening to cause this foaming?

The powder reacts much more quickly than the lump of marble. This is because the acid particles can only bump into the marble particles that are exposed at the surface of the marble. The powder has more of its surface area exposed. So the powdered marble reacts faster.

b   Chewing food breaks it into smaller pieces. Digesting food is a chemical reaction. Why does chewing your food well help you to digest it?

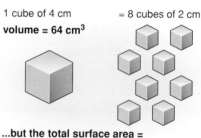

1 cube of 4 cm   = 8 cubes of 2 cm

volume = 64 cm³

...but the total surface area =

$1 \times 6 \times 16 = $ **96 cm²** $8 \times 6 \times 4 = $ **192 cm²**

Dividing the 4 cm cube into eight 2 cm cubes doubles the surface area.

Following the reaction

When marble reacts with acid a gas is produced. It is this gas that causes the bubbles. The gas is carbon dioxide. The carbon dioxide escapes into the air.

If this reaction takes place in an open beaker on top of a balance then you will notice that the mass of what is left in the beaker goes down.

If you measure how much mass is lost in a given time, you can work out the rate of the reaction.

The graph shows how the reaction rate speeds up when you use smaller marble chips.

c   What is the mass loss per second for the 1 mm chips?

d   How long would it take for the mass to drop by 1 g for the 1 mm chips?

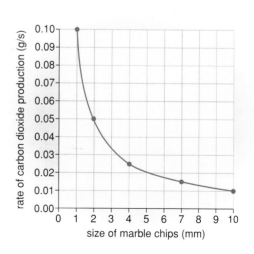

Investigating concentration

The reaction between marble chips and acid can be used to show how the reaction rate changes as you change the concentration of the acid.

You can do this very simply by dropping marble chips into beakers of acid. You need to use acid of different concentrations. You should not be surprised to find that a stronger acid gives a faster reaction. What is the explanation?

Remember, before two particles can react, they must meet!

At low concentrations, the acid particles will be widely spread in the water and so will bump into the marble chips less often.

At higher concentrations there will be more acid particles in the water so there will be more collisions with the marble chips.

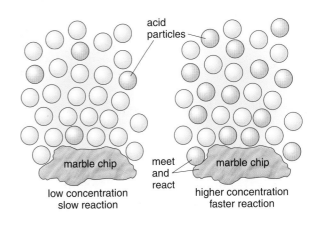

e How could you reduce the concentration of an acid?

f Explain in your own words why this would slow the reaction down.

Pressure, too

In reactions involving gases, gas **pressure** acts like concentration. The greater the pressure the closer the particles are together. This will mean they have more chance of bumping into one another.

Graphs drawn for rate against concentration and rate against pressure look very similar.

g What do you think would happen to the rate of a reaction between the gases if you doubled the pressure?

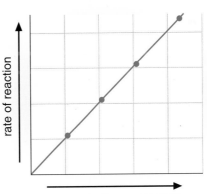

Questions

1 Copy and complete the following sentences. Choose from:

    increases   **particles**   **reaction**   **speed**

Before a chemical _____ can take place, the reacting _____ must meet. Anything that _____ the chances of the particles meeting will _____ up the reaction.

2 Copy the sentence below. Choose words from each group of three to make three correct sentences.

For reactions with solids/solutions/gases, the rate of reaction may be increased by increasing the pressure/concentration/surface area of the reactant.

3 In an experiment with marble and acid, 2 g of carbon dioxide were formed in 100 s. What was the rate of reaction?
50 g/s, 2 g/s, 0.5 g/s, 0.2 g/s or 0.02 g/s?

Summary

- It is often important to speed up reactions in industry.

- Particles must meet before they can react.

- Reactions can be speeded up by breaking up any solids and so increasing the surface area.

- Reactions can be speeded up by increasing the concentration of solutions or the pressure in gases.

7:3 Heat up to speed up

If you think a reaction is going too slowly in the school laboratory, you might ask for permission to heat the chemicals up.

It is a common experience in chemistry that heating makes things happen faster. Meat cooks faster in a hotter oven, but you keep milk cool in the fridge to stop it 'going off'.

a These bottles of milk are the same age. Which do you think was left in a warm room, and which was left in the fridge.

What might surprise you is just how much an increase in temperature affects the rate of reaction. The 'rule of thumb' for most reactions is that the rate will double for every 10 °C or so rise in temperature.

Which bottle of milk would you like to drink?

Following a reaction

Sodium thiosulphate is a chemical used in photography. If you mix a clear solution of sodium thiosulphate with hydrochloric acid, a reaction occurs. A creamy-yellow **precipitate** of sulphur is produced. (A precipitate is a solid that is formed from a solution.)

The precipitate does not start to form immediately. It begins to appear after a short time. The precipitate slowly turns the mixture cloudy.

You can follow the reaction. Stand the beaker on a pencil cross. Look down and time how long the cross takes to disappear.

b Which would take longer to disappear, the cross under a hot mixture or under a cold mixture?

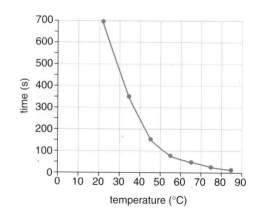
Going, going, gone! The thiosulphate/acid reaction turns the solution cloudy.

Seeing the pattern

You can do this experiment at different temperatures. You can then plot the time taken for the cross to disappear against the temperature. The higher the temperature, the shorter the time taken. This is because the rate of reaction goes up.

c You have to use the same amount of acid and thiosulphate each time. Explain why.

d From this graph, approximately what rise in temperature doubles the reaction rate? (Over what temperature range does the reaction time halve?)

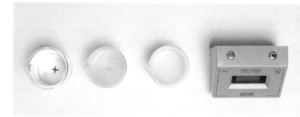

A rate/temperature graph

From looking at a rate/temperature graph you might expect all industrial reactions to be run at as high a temperature as possible.

But cost is also important. You need a lot of energy to reach very high temperatures, and energy costs money. Industrial chemists are always on the lookout for the most cost-effective ways to run their chemical reactions. (This is discussed in the next couple of pages.)

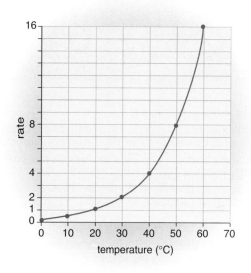

What causes this temperature effect?

To understand why temperature has this effect, you need to think about what is going on at the particle level.

For a reaction to occur, particles must bump into one another. But if they only bump gently together, nothing will happen.

The particles must bump into each other with enough energy to break apart. Then a reaction can occur.

Raising the temperature gives the particles more energy. This makes them move faster, so they have more chance of breaking up when they crash together.

The energy needed to make a reaction start like this is called the **activation energy**.

e Why doesn't a Bunsen burner light as soon as you turn on the gas?

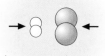
low energy – head on

no reaction

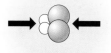
high energy – head on

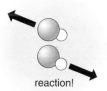
reaction!

You need the right kind of collision before you get a reaction.

Questions

1 Copy the sentence below. Choose words from each pair to make two correct sentences.

   Chemical reactions speed up/slow down when the temperature is raised/lowered.

2 Copy and complete the following sentences. Choose from:

   activation   energy   particles   reaction

   For a _____ to start, the _____ must crash into each other with enough _____ to break apart. This is called the _____ energy.

3 Superglue sets because of a chemical reaction. Where will superglue set fastest, in a fridge, a room or an oven? Why?

4 Photographs are developed using chemical solutions. The chemicals have to react for just the right amount of time. Why is the water temperature important for this?

Summary
- The rate of a chemical reaction increases if the temperature increases.
- Particles must collide with enough energy to break their bonds if they are to react.
- This amount of energy is called the activation energy.
- Raising the temperature means that more particles reach their activation energy levels.

7:4 Catalysts and enzymes

Everlasting activity!

Hydrogen peroxide is an unstable compound that is made of hydrogen and oxygen. Left on its own, it will slowly break down into water and oxygen gas.

hydrogen peroxide → water + oxygen

Manganese dioxide is a black solid. If you drop some manganese dioxide into hydrogen peroxide a reaction happens. The hydrogen peroxide starts to fizz rapidly as oxygen is given off. Nothing particularly surprising in that, you might think – but:

◆ the manganese dioxide is not changed in the reaction;

◆ if you filter the reaction mixture after the reaction you will get the same amount of manganese dioxide back;

◆ you can then use the manganese dioxide again and again!

a Look at these diagrams. Explain how they show that manganese dioxide is not taking part directly in this reaction.

What is happening?

Hydrogen peroxide would have reacted slowly on its own. The manganese dioxide has simply speeded up the reaction. The manganese dioxide has acted as a **catalyst**.

$$\text{hydrogen peroxide} \xrightarrow{\text{catalyst}} \text{water} + \text{oxygen}$$

Catalysts make reactions go faster by making the activation energy smaller. This makes it easier for the reaction to occur.

b Why do you think industrial chemists might be very interested in catalysts?

Catalysts at work

Catalysts are very important in industry, because they allow reactions to take place faster and at lower temperatures. This, of course, saves money!

Transition metals or their oxides are often used as catalysts.

◆ Iron is used to make ammonia in the Haber process (see page 176).

◆ Nickel is used to turn oils into fats to make margarine.

You need to find the right catalyst for the job!

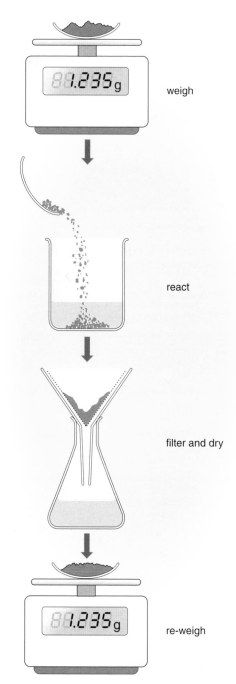

weigh

react

filter and dry

re-weigh

Manganese dioxide speeds up the breakdown of hydrogen peroxide, but remains unchanged itself.

Enzymes

If you add a drop of blood or some chopped liver to hydrogen peroxide the effect is even more dramatic than adding manganese dioxide. This is because of the presence of a biological, protein-based catalyst called catalase.

These biological catalysts are called **enzymes**. Their action can be very powerful. Most life processes, for example digestion and respiration, depend on enzyme action.

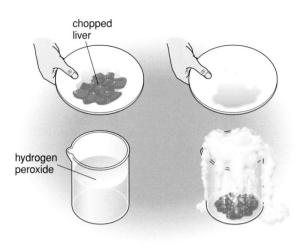

So what's different?

With a catalyst, the rate of reaction also increases as the temperature increases. The rate of reaction doubles for every 10 °C or so.

From 0 °C up to about 40 °C, enzymes behave in a similar way. But their action tails off rapidly at about 45 °C. By about 60 °C enzymes stop working altogether.

Chopped liver catalysis in action!

c In what ways are enzymes similar to other catalysts? In what ways are they different?

Enzymes are different because they are proteins. Like the proteins in food, enzymes break down (become cooked!) at higher temperatures. It should not surprise you that the best temperature for enzyme action is body temperature.

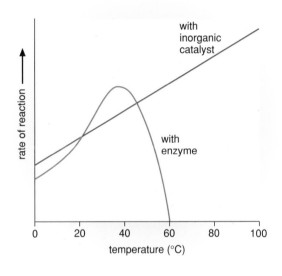

d Why is it that enzyme action drops away so rapidly above 45 °C?

Enzymes are also affected by pH.

The enzymes that help to digest the food in your stomach work best at very low pH. That's why your stomach is full of hydrochloric acid. Other enzymes work best at other different pH levels.

Enzyme action peaks at 37 °C – that's body temperature.

Questions

1 Copy and complete the following sentences. Choose from:

   catalysts   enzymes   transition   working

   In industry, _____ metals are often used as _____ to speed up reactions. _____ are also used to speed up reactions, but these stop _____ above 45 °C.

2 Suggest a reason why your body temperature is maintained at 37 °C.

3 Fresh milk will last 8 days in the fridge (5 °C).

   a Approximately how long would you expect fresh milk to last at room temperature (25 °C)?

   b How long would fresh milk last on a very hot summer's day (35 °C)?

Summary

• Catalysts speed up chemical reactions without being used up themselves.

• Transition metals are often used as catalysts. They are very important in industry.

• Enzymes are biological catalysts that work best at warm rather than hot conditions.

7:5 Traditional uses of enzymes

All living things use enzymes to control their chemical reactions. Some of these processes have been turned to human advantage for centuries.

Brewing

Sugars are foods full of energy. They are a fuel your body can use. The sugar you have in your body is called glucose. You react glucose with the oxygen you breathe to make carbon dioxide, water and the energy you need for life.

Some organisms, such as **yeast**, are able to use their special enzymes to get energy from sugar without needing oxygen. This process is called **fermentation**.

If living yeast cells are put into a sugary solution at about 37 °C, they start to grow. As they grow, they turn the sugar into alcohol. They also produce lots of carbon dioxide gas, which is allowed to escape.

$$\text{sugar} \xrightarrow[\text{yeast enzymes}]{\text{fermentation}} \text{alcohol} + \text{carbon dioxide}$$

Fermentation has been used for centuries to make alcoholic drinks such as beer and wine.

a Beer is made from barley mash. What is used to provide the sugary solution needed to make wine?

Many traditional festivals celebrate the importance of enzyme-based chemistry.

Baking

Fermentation is also used when we make bread. Some yeast and a small amount of sugar are mixed with water and flour to make the bread dough.

Fermentation begins in this dough. However, the carbon dioxide is trapped in the dough and cannot escape. The carbon dioxide forms tiny bubbles within the dough. If the dough is left in a warm place, the bubbles get larger and larger, making the dough 'rise'. This makes the bread light and fluffy when it is baked.

b What is the best temperature to use for the bread to rise successfully?

c What effect will baking have on the enzymes as the temperature rises?

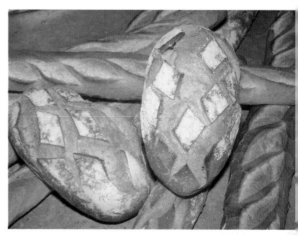

Sometimes it is the carbon dioxide that is important.

Testing for carbon dioxide

Carbon dioxide is a colourless gas that has no smell. It will also put out a burning splint. If you want to be sure that a gas is carbon dioxide, you should use the limewater test.

◆ Bubble the gas through clear limewater.

◆ If the solution turns milky, the gas is carbon dioxide.

You can easily try the carbon dioxide test by breathing out through limewater.

How it works

Limewater is a clear solution of calcium hydroxide. When you react calcium hydroxide with carbon dioxide, you get insoluble calcium carbonate. It is the calcium carbonate that forms a white solid and which turns the solution 'milky'.

$$\text{calcium hydroxide} + \text{carbon dioxide} \rightarrow \text{calcium carbonate} + \text{water}$$

(clear solution)   (white solid)

d Describe a simple way in which you could test the gas given off by fermenting fruit juice to see if it was carbon dioxide.

Cheese and yoghurt

Some bacteria get their energy from the sugar in milk. The sugar in milk is called **lactose**. These bacteria make **lactic acid** rather than alcohol. The lactic acid makes the milk curdle to form cheese or yoghurt. You can buy some types of yoghurt with the live bacteria still in them.

e You can 'grow your own' yoghurt by adding 'live' yoghurt to milk. The live bacteria grow and their enzymes curdle the milk. What would be the best temperature for this?

> **DIGGING DEEPER**
> Some people eat 'live' yoghurt to encourage the special bacteria to grow in their stomachs. These 'good' bacteria help to stop other bacteria getting established and causing food poisoning.

Questions

1 Alcohol can be used to kill microbes. If you are making wine, fermentation stops when you reach about 12% alcohol, even if there is sugar left. Suggest why the fermentation stops.

2 Sarah put her bread in a very hot oven to rise – but it didn't rise at all! Why not?

3 Unwanted bacteria cause our food to decay. This is because the bacteria use enzymes to break the food down. Enzyme reactions work at their fastest at about 37 °C. Explain why food keeps longer in the fridge than left out in the kitchen.

4 Why is it not a good idea to keep food warm for long periods of time?

> **Summary**
> • Living cells use chemical reactions to produce new materials.
> • Yeast cells convert sugar into carbon dioxide and alcohol.
> • This process is called fermentation and is used to brew beer and make bread rise.
> • A simple laboratory test for carbon dioxide is that it turns limewater milky.
> • Bacteria produce yoghurt from milk.

7:6 Enzymes at work

The use of enzyme technology has increased over recent years. This is because new uses for enzymes have been discovered.

Baby foods

The production of baby foods is now very big business. At first, baby foods were simply meals that had been mashed up for small people without teeth. But very young babies can have difficulty digesting 'adult' foods, even if they are mashed up.

To overcome this problem, many baby foods are now 'pre-digested' using the enzyme **protease**. Protease starts the breakdown of the proteins in the food before the food is put in the jar. This means that young babies can digest the food more easily.

a **Prot**ease breaks down **prot**eins. What food group do you think is broken down by the enzyme **carbohydr**ase?

'Biological' washing powders

Many stubborn stains on clothing are caused by proteins, fats and oils. These stubborn stains do not wash out easily in water. 'Biological' washing powders use special enzymes. These enzymes help to break up these chemicals.

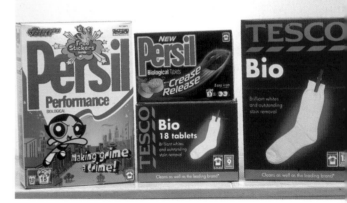

- Protease is used to break up proteins.
- **Lipase** is used to break up fats and oils.

b Some people do not like to use enzyme-rich washing powders in case they get the enzymes on their hands. What might these enzymes do to your skin?

Glucose

The sugar you have in your sugar bowl is called **sucrose**. This sugar is very sweet. But, it can only be extracted from sugar beet or sugar cane. This makes it quite expensive.

The carbohydrate **starch** is much more common in nature. For example, starch is produced in vast quantities in corn. Starch can be converted easily to the sugar **glucose** using the enzyme **carbohydrase**.

c Many sports drinks contain glucose. Why might athletes need extra glucose?

A cheap source of starch.

Fructose syrup

Glucose syrup is not usually used in food. Glucose is not as sweet as sucrose, so you would need to use lots of glucose to make foods sweet enough. This would increase the energy content of foods. As a result, glucose cannot be used in slimming foods.

d Why do people on diets want to reduce the amount of sugar they eat?

Fortunately another enzyme can help. This enzyme is called **isomerase**. Isomerase can be used to convert glucose into another sugar, called **fructose**. Fructose is even sweeter than sucrose, and so needs to be added to foods in small amounts.

Enzymes are very useful

Enzymes work best at relatively low temperatures and ordinary pressures. This means that enzymes are very useful for many industrial processes.

Without enzymes, the chemical reactions might need to run at very high temperatures or pressures. This would mean high energy costs and expensive equipment.

But enzymes can also present problems. This is because enzymes can be broken down quite easily and so lose their useful properties.

Enzymes are often water-soluble. They can get washed out or mixed up with the products of the reaction.

Enzyme reactions have to take place in big vats. All the enzymes must be replaced every time a new reaction is started.

e Draw up a table to show the advantages and disadvantages of using enzymes in industry.

These foods have a low sugar content – so fructose will be used instead of glucose.

Questions

1 Copy and complete the following sentences. Choose from:

  enzymes   equipment   lower   money   temperatures

  _____ are widely used in industry as they make reactions work at low _____ and pressures. This can save a lot of _____ as there are _____ energy costs and less expensive _____ is needed.

2 Suggest one reason why an enzyme might stop working.

3 Carbohydrase, lipase and protease are three types of enzyme. Which could be used to:

  • remove an oil stain from a carpet?

  • make glucose from carbohydrate in bread?

  • remove bloodstains from a shirt?

Summary

• In industry, enzymes are used to make reactions work at normal temperatures and pressures, which saves money.

• Enzymes are used in biological washing powders to digest stains, to pre-digest baby food and to make glucose and fructose syrups from corn starch.

7:7 Chemistry by numbers

Relative atomic mass

Atoms are very, very, very small. This makes it difficult to talk about their tiny masses. Instead, the masses of atoms are usually just compared to each other.

◆ Hydrogen, the smallest atom, is 1 on this scale.

◆ A helium atom is four times heavier than a hydrogen atom, so it is 4.

◆ A carbon atom is twelve times heavier than a hydrogen atom, so it is 12, and so on.

4 is the **relative atomic mass** for helium. We use the abbreviation A_r for relative atomic mass. Relative atomic masses have been calculated for all elements. You can look them up in tables. You can also find them on the periodic table in the data sheets at the back of this book.

a **Find the relative atomic masses for fluorine (F), silicon (Si) and iron (Fe).**

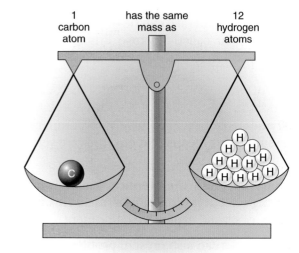

1 carbon atom   has the same mass as   12 hydrogen atoms

Formula mass

Molecules are also very, very, very small. It makes sense to compare their masses on the same scale we use for atoms.

If you know the formula of a compound, you can find its **formula mass** by adding up the relative atomic masses of all the atoms in the molecule. We use M_r to stand for formula mass.

Some examples should help.

Water
 formula: H_2O (A_r H = 1, O = 16)
 formula mass (M_r) = $(2 \times 1) + 16 = 18$

Methane
 formula: CH_4 (A_r H = 1, C = 12)
 formula mass (M_r) = $12 + (4 \times 1) = 16$

Carbon dioxide
 formula: CO_2 (A_r C = 12, O = 16)
 formula mass (M_r) = $12 + (2 \times 16) = 44$

Calcium carbonate
 formula: $CaCO_3$ (A_r Ca = 40, C = 12, O = 16)
 formula mass (M_r) = $40 + 12 + (3 \times 16) = 100$

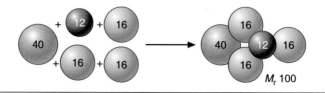

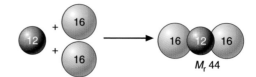

Calculate the formula mass (M_r) for:

◆ calcium oxide, CaO (Ca = 40, O = 16)

◆ iron(II) sulphide, FeS (Fe = 56, S = 32)

◆ sodium nitrate, $NaNO_3$ (Na = 23, N = 14, O = 16)

◆ aluminium oxide, Al_2O_3 (Al = 27, O = 16)

Some history

You know about atoms and elements and how they combine to form compounds. You can read all about it in a book! But how was all this worked out?

Most of what we know came from careful and detailed experimental work by scientists such as John Dalton, who lived 200 years ago.

John Dalton studied the way elements combined to form compounds. For example, he measured very carefully the masses of sodium and chlorine that had combined to form sodium chloride. You will know sodium chloride better as common salt.

What he found was that the elements always combined in the same proportions.

Not everyone agreed with his ideas at first. He kept on taking more and more measurements to support his ideas. Today his work forms the basis of our understanding of chemical compounds. When you write the formula NaCl for sodium chloride, you can thank John Dalton!

Source	Sodium (%)	Chlorine (%)
from the sea	39.34	60.66
from Siberia	39.34	60.66
from Cheshire	39.34	60.66
made in the laboratory	39.34	60.66

c Design a poster to celebrate the work of the famous English scientist, John Dalton. Include the key features that make him so important in the history of science.

Questions

1 Copy and complete the following sentence. Choose from:

atoms   formula   masses

The _____ mass (M_r) of a compound is found by adding up the relative atomic _____ (A_r) of all the _____ in that compound.

2 Magnesium oxide has the formula mass 40. Is the formula of magnesium oxide Mg_2O, MgO or MgO_2? (Mg = 24, O = 16)

3 Red copper oxide has the formula mass 144. Is the formula for red copper oxide Cu_2O, CuO or CuO_2? (Cu = 64, O = 16)

4 Carbon has two oxides, which have the formula masses 28 and 44. What are their formulae? (C = 12, O = 16)

Summary

• The atoms of different elements have different masses.

• The masses of the atoms may be compared by their relative atomic mass (A_r).

• The relative formula mass (M_r) of a compound can be found by adding up the relative atomic masses of the atoms.

Calculations using relative atomic and formula masses can be very useful. For example, you can work out the percentage of metal in different metal ores. This is important for mining and metal refining companies. It helps people to answer questions about the ores they are using.

Case study 1: How much lead is there in galena?

Galena is the silver-grey ore of lead. It is the natural form of lead sulphide (PbS). But if you are buying lead ore to make lead, you will want to know how much lead you will get from every tonne of lead ore. To do this you need to calculate the percentage of lead in lead sulphide.

formula: PbS

$$\text{formula mass } (M_r) = \underset{207}{\overset{\text{mass of lead}}{207}} + 32 = \underset{\underset{\text{lead sulphide}}{\text{mass of}}}{239}$$

A sample of galena.

So the percentage of lead in galena is:

$$\frac{\text{mass of lead}}{\text{mass of lead sulphide}} \times 100 = \frac{207}{239} \times 100 = 86.6\%$$

a 1 tonne is 1000 kg. How many kilograms of lead could you get from 1 tonne of galena?

Case study 2: Which ore to use?

Haematite (Fe_2O_3) and **pyrite** (FeS_2) are both ores of iron. Which one gives the most iron per tonne of ore?

The percentage of iron in each compound can be easily calculated from the A_r and M_r values. (Fe = 56, O = 16)

Haematite is Fe_2O_3

$M_r = (2 \times 56) + (3 \times 16) = 160$

amount of iron $= (2 \times 56) = 112$

percentage of iron $= 112/160 \times 100 = 70\%$

A sample of haematite.

Pyrite is FeS_2

$M_r = 56 + (2 \times 32) = 120$

amount of iron $= 56$

percentage of iron $= 56/120 \times 100 = 47\%$

b Pyrite is called Fools' Gold. It is of very little value compared to gold. How does it compare to haematite as an iron ore?

c How many kilograms of iron could you get from 1 tonne (1000 kg) of haematite?

A sample of pyrite.

Case study 3: Quicklime from limestone

Quicklime (calcium oxide) is used as a fertiliser. It neutralises acid soils and improves the texture of the soil.

Quicklime is made by heating limestone in a kiln. Limestone is made of calcium carbonate. The limestone breaks down and gives off carbon dioxide when it is heated.

But how much quicklime do you get from the limestone? You can find out by some simple calculations.

Step 1: Look at the equations

$$\text{calcium carbonate} \xrightarrow{\text{heat}} \text{calcium oxide} + \text{carbon dioxide}$$
$$CaCO_3 \longrightarrow CaO + CO_2$$

From this you can see that you get one particle of calcium oxide from each particle of calcium carbonate.

Step 2: Now calculate the formula masses
(Ca = 40, C = 12, O = 16)

M_r of $CaCO_3 = 40 + 12 + (3 \times 16) = 100$

M_r of $CaO = 40 + 16 = 56$

Step 3: Compare the formula masses

For example, if you heated 100 g of calcium carbonate you would get just 56 g of calcium oxide. From this you can calculate the percentage.

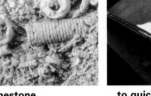

From limestone...   ...to quicklime.

d What is the percentage of CaO in $CaCO_3$?

e How may kilograms of quicklime could you get from 1 tonne of limestone?

f How many kilograms of carbon dioxide would you get from 1 tonne of limestone? (Hint: You don't need to work out the formula mass for this. Just look at the equation and your answer to question e.)

Questions

1 a Find the formula mass of magnesium oxide (MgO). (Mg = 24, O = 16)

   b Calculate the percentage of magnesium in magnesium oxide.

2 a Find the formula mass of sodium chloride (NaCl). (Na = 23, Cl = 35.5)

   b Calculate the percentage of chlorine in sodium chloride.

3 Copper carbonate breaks down to give black copper(II) oxide when heated. (Cu = 64, C = 12, O = 16)

   $$CuCO_3 \rightarrow CuO + CO_2$$

   a Calculate the formula masses of copper carbonate and copper(II) oxide.

   b Calculate the percentage of CuO in $CuCO_3$.

Summary
- If you know the formula of a compound you can calculate the percentage of each element in it by mass.

- If you know the balanced chemical equation for a reaction, you can work out how much of the products to expect.

7:9 How much? (2)

Finding reacting masses

If you know the balanced chemical equation for a reaction, you can work out the proportion of the reactants you need for industrial (or laboratory) reactions. This is important as it:

♦ uses the reactants efficiently;

♦ makes sure the reaction runs smoothly.

Case study 1: Making iron sulphide

If you heat iron and sulphur they react to make iron sulphide. You may have performed this experiment yourself, to show the formation of a new compound from two elements.

If the mixture is made up in the right amounts, a very clear reaction starts. An orange-red glow spreads through the mixture.

But how can you be sure that you have the 'right' mixture to start with?

Iron and sulphur.

Getting the mixture right

iron + sulphur → iron sulphide

Step 1: Write down the balanced equation

$Fe + S \rightarrow FeS$

Step 2: Add the A_r and M_r values

$56 + 32 \rightarrow 88$

Step 3: From the A_r and M_r values, work out the ratio of iron to sulphur

The iron to sulphur mass ratio for the perfect reaction is:

56:32

The chemical reaction.

a Reduce 56:32 to its simplest ratio. If you had 7 g of iron, how much sulphur would you need?

b Try Steps 1 to 3 for the copper and sulphur reaction.

copper + sulphur → copper sulphide

Step 1: $Cu + S \rightarrow CuS$ (Cu = 64, S = 32)

Step 2: _____ + _____ → 96

Step 3: The ratio is _____ : _____ . This can be simplified down to _____ .

How many grams of sulphur would you need to react with 10 g of copper?

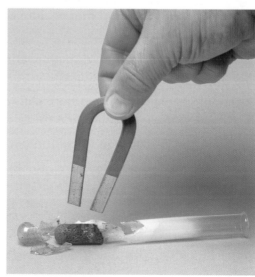

The new compound.

Case study 2: The perfect thermit

Aluminium and iron(III) oxide react in a spectacular thermit reaction. The aluminium pushes the iron out of its compound, giving out so much heat energy that the iron melts. This reaction is still used to weld iron railway lines together in position on the tracks.

Thermit reactions can be spectacular in the laboratory, too. But they are very difficult reactions to 'get right' and often just fizzle out. To be sure of success, you need the correct proportions of iron(III) oxide and aluminium. Fortunately you can calculate this ratio. (A_r Fe = 56, O = 16, Al = 27)

The word equation is:

iron(III) oxide   + aluminium → aluminium oxide + iron

Step 1: Write out the balanced equation

$$Fe_2O_3 \quad + \quad 2Al \quad → \quad Al_2O_3 \quad + \quad 2Fe$$

Step 2: Calculate the M_r values

$$(2 \times 56) + (3 \times 16) + \quad (2 \times 27) \quad →$$

Step 3: Work out the ratio of iron(III) oxide to aluminium

160:54 (which is approximately 3:1 by mass)

A thermit reaction in use.

c How many grams of aluminium powder would you need to mix with 80 g of iron(III) oxide to give a perfect thermit?

Questions

1 Copy and complete the following sentences. Choose from:

> chemical   formula   proportions   reaction

You can work out the _____ of the different chemicals needed in a _____ by looking at the balanced _____ equation. You then need to compare the _____ masses.

2 Magnesium displaces iron from a solution of green iron(II) sulphate solution. (Fe = 56, Mg = 24)

$$Mg + FeSO_4 → Fe + MgSO_4$$

  a Copy this equation and add the atomic masses of Mg and Fe.

  b How many grams of iron would be displaced by 24 g of magnesium?

  c How many grams of iron would be displaced by 3 g of magnesium?

3 Magnesium will displace copper from black copper oxide in a thermit reaction.

$$Mg + CuO → MgO + Cu$$

How many grammes of magnesium would you need to mix with 8 g of oxide for the perfect reaction?

(Mg = 24, Cu = 64, O = 16)

Summary
- If you know the balanced chemical equation for a reaction, you can work out the proportions of each reactant that are needed by mass.

7:10 Energy changes

Give it out

It is not always easy to tell when a chemical reaction has occurred. For example, if you mix cold, dilute hydrochloric acid with some cold sodium hydroxide solution, you will not see any obvious change. Two colourless liquids just mix to form another colourless liquid. If you hold the test-tube you will *feel* that something has happened. The test-tube will have got warmer!

a How else could you tell that this reaction had occurred?

Chemical changes are often accompanied by changes in temperature. This is because energy is transferred to or from the surroundings. In this case, heat energy has been given out during a neutralisation reaction. Chemical reactions that give out heat energy like this are called **exothermic** reactions.

The neutralisation reaction is:

acid + alkali → salt + water + **energy**

For example, the reaction we are talking about is:

hydrochloric acid + sodium hydroxide → sodium chloride + water + **energy**

$$HCl + NaOH \rightarrow NaCl + H_2O + \textbf{energy}$$

Many chemical reactions are exothermic like this. Reactions that start as soon as the chemicals are mixed are usually exothermic.

Metals dissolving in acids

metal + acid → salt + hydrogen + **energy**

For example:

$$Mg + H_2SO_4 \rightarrow MgSO_4 + H_2 + \textbf{energy}$$

b Name two other metals that would react in this way.

Metals displacing other metals from their salts

For example:

zinc metal + copper sulphate → zinc sulphate + copper metal + **energy**

$$Zn + CuSO_4 \rightarrow ZnSO_4 + Cu + \textbf{energy}$$

c Name another metal that could push copper from copper sulphate.

Metals corroding

For example:

calcium + oxygen → calcium oxide + **energy**

$$2Ca + O_2 \rightarrow 2CaO + \textbf{energy}$$

d Why do you think calcium is often stored under oil?

You could follow the rise in temperature during neutralisation with a temperature sensor connected to a computer.

Calcium and magnesium both fizz in acid. The test-tubes will get hot.

calcium   magnesium

Fresh pieces of calcium soon corrode when left in the air.

Combustion reactions

When you burn a fuel in air, the reaction is called a **combustion reaction**.

The combustion reaction of a fuel such as methane is very exothermic. In fact, when you burn a fuel, you are not usually bothered about the chemical products of the reaction. It is the heat energy output that you're after!

> fuel + oxygen → waste gases + **energy**

For example:

> $CH_4 + 2O_2 → CO_2 + 2H_2O + $ **energy**

There is a difference between a neutralisation reaction and a combustion reaction. The difference is that fuels need a kick-start of energy before the reaction begins (the activation energy, see page 157). This is true for most chemical reactions.

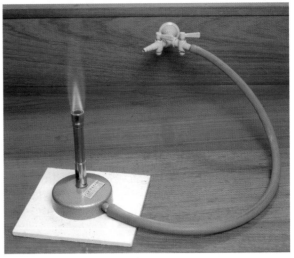

Fuels need a kick-start to burn. Then their combustion reactions are strongly exothermic.

e What problems might you have if fuels did not need a kick-start of energy to react?

Data analysis

Harry was studying the exothermic reaction between magnesium ribbon and sulphuric acid. He used the data-logging equipment shown in the photo on the previous page. He measured the temperature rise when different amounts of magnesium were added to beakers containing identical amounts of acid. The printouts are shown here.

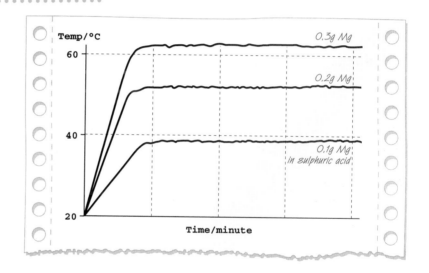

f From the printouts, find the maximum temperature rise when 0.1 g, 0.2 g and 0.3 g of magnesium were used.

g Plot a graph of mass (on the x-axis) against temperature rise (on the y-axis).

h Describe the graph you got in question g. Try to explain why you got this graph.

Questions

1 Copy and complete the following sentences. Choose from:

> energy   exothermic   kick-start   reactions

Many chemical reactions give out _____ to the surroundings. These are called _____ reactions. But even exothermic _____ may need a _____ of energy to get them going.

2 Which of the following reactions are exothermic?

- sodium metal reacting and dissolving in water
- iron filings burning in a sparkler
- dynamite exploding

Summary

- Exothermic reactions give out energy to the surroundings.

- Even exothermic reactions often need an initial kick-start of energy to get the reaction started.

- This 'kick-start' of energy is called the activation energy.

7:11 More energy changes

Going down

You can make a pleasant summer drink by adding a spoonful of baking soda to a glass of lemon juice. When you do this a chemical reaction occurs:

$$\text{sodium hydrogencarbonate} + \text{citric acid} \rightarrow \text{sodium citrate} + \text{carbon dioxide} + \text{water}$$

(baking soda)   (lemon juice)

a What would you see happening in this reaction? Does this suggest that a chemical reaction is occurring?

If you were holding the glass as you stirred in the baking soda, you would also feel a change in temperature. A temperature change is another indication that a chemical reaction is happening. But in this case, the temperature goes down!

No ice is needed for this summer drink!

Take it in

Reactions that take energy in from their surroundings are called **endothermic** reactions. It is fairly rare for endothermic reactions to 'go on their own' like this one does. You usually need to pump energy into them to make them work.

For example, the production of aluminium by electrolysis is an endothermic reaction.

aluminium oxide + **electrical energy** $\rightarrow$ aluminium + oxygen

b The aluminium ions and oxygen ions in aluminium oxide are held together by strong ionic bonds. What is the electrical energy doing in this reaction?

One of the most important endothermic reactions in the world is photosynthesis. Plants use the energy from sunlight to make complex chemicals. For example, plants make glucose from carbon dioxide and water.

carbon dioxide + water + **sunlight energy** $\rightarrow$ glucose + oxygen

c When you respire, the glucose from your food reacts with the oxygen you breathe to give carbon dioxide and water. Respiration is the photosynthesis reaction backwards! Is respiration exothermic or endothermic?

The Sun drives this essential endothermic reaction.

Data analysis: Energy from food

You need energy for life. You get this energy from the exothermic chemical reactions of respiration.

How much energy is there stored in the different types of food? How much energy do you actually need to live?

You can find out how much energy there is in a crisp, for example. You can do this by burning a crisp under a tube of water and seeing how hot the water gets. You can work out how much energy was released if you know how much the temperature rose for a set amount of water. This is the same amount of energy as you would get from the food when you respire.

This type of simple experiment will only give you a rough idea of the energy content of food. It is not very accurate.

d Give the main reason why this simple experiment is not very accurate.

Research scientists with special equipment have used the same idea. They have been able to calculate the energy content of all common foods. You will see the results of their work on food labels.

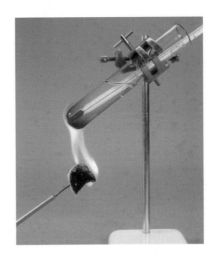

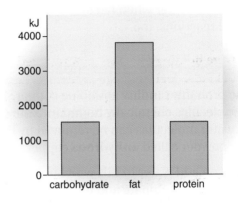
The amount of energy in 100 g of different foods.

	Per 100 g	Per serving
total energy	312 kJ	655 kJ
protein	4.7 g	9.9 g
carbohydrate	13.6 g	28.6 g
fat	0.2 g	0.4 g

Information from a typical food label.

e Use the graph (above right) to work out how much energy you would get from the fat in one serving of this food.

The energy requirements for the chemistry of life have also been established. You can now match the energy content of the food you eat to your daily energy needs.

Your main energy foods are carbohydrates and fats (or oils). Proteins may be used for energy, but are mainly used for growth and repair.

f Which food type contains the most concentrated energy store?

g Why does a ballet dancer need more energy than an office worker?

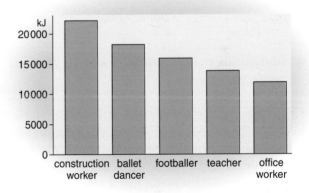
The amount of energy you need each day depends on your job.

Questions

1 Hydrogen is the fuel of the future. It burns to give water and energy. Burning hydrogen is pollution free. Hydrogen can be made by the electrolysis of water. The electricity needed could come from a solar cell.

Two reactions are mentioned here. Which is endothermic and which is exothermic?

Summary
- Endothermic reactions take in more energy than they give out.

Foundation 173

7:12 Reversible reactions

So far you have looked at chemical reactions as one-way processes.

    reactants → products

For example, if you burn wood you get carbon dioxide and water. You cannot easily get the wood and oxygen back again.

But you also know many processes that can go both backwards and forwards. For example, water turns to ice if cooled, but melts back to water when heated. This happens in some chemical reactions, too.

Most chemical reactions are 'one way'...

A reversible chemical reaction

You are probably familiar with blue copper sulphate. It has water molecules chemically bound into the crystal structure. These water molecules can be removed by heating. This leaves a *white* powder called **anhydrous** copper sulphate.

But you can add water to this white powder. The water joins with the copper sulphate and the blue colour reappears.

This **reversible reaction** is a chemical test for water!

... but some are reversible

$$\text{hydrated copper sulphate (blue)} \underset{\text{water added}}{\overset{\substack{\text{water driven} \\ \text{off by heat}}}{\rightleftharpoons}} \text{anhydrous copper sulphate (white)} + \text{water}$$

a Anhydrous means 'without water'. What do you think 'hydrated' means?

Heat it/cool it!

If you heat ammonium chloride, it turns directly from a solid to a gas. It **sublimes**. It then reappears as a white solid at the cool end of the tube. This is not just a physical change. Instead, it is another reversible chemical change.

$$\text{ammonium chloride (white solid)} \underset{\text{cool}}{\overset{\text{heat}}{\rightleftharpoons}} \text{hydrogen chloride} + \text{ammonia (colourless gases)}$$

$$NH_4Cl(s) \rightleftharpoons HCl(g) + NH_3(g)$$

The link between this reaction and the 'water test' is temperature. Heating drives the reaction to the right, but the reaction reverses as it cools down.

b You have to put heat energy into this reaction to make the ammonium chloride sublime. Is this reaction exothermic or endothermic?

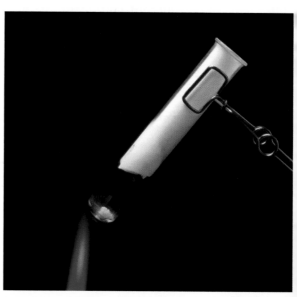

Ammonium chloride breaks up when heated, only to re-form at the cool end of the tube.

Energy changes in reversible reactions

Calcium carbonate breaks down to calcium oxide and carbon dioxide when heated. However, these chemicals recombine slowly when cold.

$$\text{calcium carbonate} \underset{\text{cool}}{\overset{\text{heat}}{\rightleftharpoons}} \text{calcium oxide + carbon dioxide}$$

$$CaCO_3 \rightleftharpoons CaO + CO_2$$

The reaction from left to right is endothermic. Energy has to be put in to make it work. The reaction from right to left is exothermic. In fact the amount of energy transferred in this reaction is the same in either direction. It is just taken in in one direction and given back out in the other.

c Explain why the mixture gets hot when you perform the 'water test' with anhydrous copper sulphate.

Forward and back reactions

You can think of reversible reactions in terms of the 'forward reaction' and the 'back reaction'.

$$A + B \underset{\text{back reaction}}{\overset{\text{forward reaction}}{\rightleftharpoons}} C + D$$

If you pass steam over heated iron, the iron is oxidised to iron oxide. This is the forward reaction.

But if hydrogen is now pushed back over the hot iron oxide, the reaction is reversed. The iron oxide is reduced back to iron. This is the back reaction.

$$\text{iron + steam} \underset{\text{back reaction}}{\overset{\text{forward reaction}}{\rightleftharpoons}} \text{iron oxide + hydrogen}$$

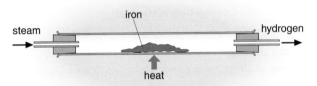

Steam can be passed over hot iron. Iron oxide forms.

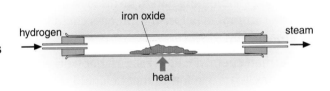

Hydrogen can be passed over iron oxide. Iron is re-formed.

d Describe the 'sublimation' of ammonium chloride in terms of the forward and back reactions.

Questions

1 Copy and complete the following sentences. Choose from:

anhydrous   copper   recombines   reversible   water

Some chemical reactions are _____ . If you heat blue _____ sulphate crystals, water is driven off. If you add water to white _____ copper sulphate, the water _____ , giving the blue colour again. This is used as a test for _____ .

2 If it took 10 kJ of energy to make some ammonium chloride sublime, how much energy would you get back when it re-formed?

Summary

- Some chemical reactions are reversible.

- If a reversible reaction is exothermic in one direction it is endothermic in the opposite direction. The same amount of energy is transferred in each case.

- The reversible reaction of anhydrous copper sulphate can be used as a test for water.

7:13 The Haber process

Ammonia for fertilisers

Plants need nitrogen to grow well. Unfortunately, plants cannot use the nitrogen in the atmosphere.

However, nitrogen can be made to react with hydrogen to form ammonia. Ammonia can then be used to make nitrogen-providing **fertilisers** for plants.

$$\text{nitrogen + hydrogen} \underset{\text{back reaction}}{\overset{\text{forward reaction}}{\rightleftharpoons}} \text{ammonia}$$

Unfortunately, this reaction is reversible. Some of the ammonia that forms breaks down to form nitrogen and hydrogen again. This means that the **yield** of ammonia (the amount of ammonia you get from the reaction) is low. It is also a very slow reaction.

a Why doesn't all the nitrogen and hydrogen turn to ammonia eventually?

Fritz Haber and the Haber process

The first attempts to make ammonia in this way gave very little ammonia. Something had to be done to increase the percentage yield of ammonia before this process could be used commercially.

A German chemist called Fritz Haber worked on the problem for many years. He found that he could make the reaction run reasonably well.

He used a moderately high temperature. He used an iron catalyst to make the reaction run fast enough. He also used a high pressure – this improves the yield.

Even so, the yield of ammonia was still much less than 50%.

b Why is this low yield a problem? (What could be done with the unreacted gases?)

Finally Fritz Haber found the solution. Ammonia boils at only –33 °C. If you cool ammonia you can turn it into a liquid. Hydrogen and nitrogen remain as gases at –33 °C.

Haber found he could remove the ammonia that formed by turning it into a liquid. He then recycled the remaining nitrogen and hydrogen. This makes the process continuous and eventually turns all the reactants to ammonia.

c Explain how Haber's solution solved the problem.

Fritz Haber's work solved the problem and earned him the Nobel Prize in 1918.

Fritz Haber – the father of fertilisers.

d This reaction needs nitrogen and hydrogen. Where do you get the nitrogen from? Where do you get the hydrogen from?

Data analysis

This chart shows how the yield of ammonia varies with temperature and pressure.

e A typical Haber plant may run at 450 °C and 200 atmospheres pressure. What is the percentage yield?

f What would the yield be if the pressure was increased to 250 atmospheres at
  i 350 °C and
  ii 450 °C?

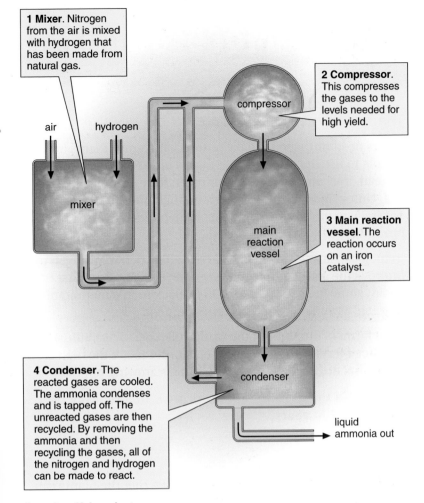

1 Mixer. Nitrogen from the air is mixed with hydrogen that has been made from natural gas.

2 Compressor. This compresses the gases to the levels needed for high yield.

3 Main reaction vessel. The reaction occurs on an iron catalyst.

4 Condenser. The reacted gases are cooled. The ammonia condenses and is tapped off. The unreacted gases are then recycled. By removing the ammonia and then recycling the gases, all of the nitrogen and hydrogen can be made to react.

A modern Haber plant.

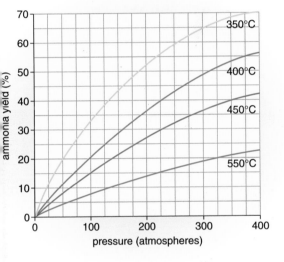

How the yield varies with temperature and pressure.

DIGGING DEEPER
100 years ago people became concerned that the population in Europe was growing very fast. How could enough food be grown to feed them?

Questions

1 Copy and complete the following sentences. Choose from:

ammonia   catalyst   condenses   hydrogen   nitrogen

The Haber process uses _____ from the air and _____ from natural gas. These are passed over a _____ of iron at a high temperature (about 450 °C) and a high pressure (about 200 atmospheres). Some of the nitrogen and hydrogen react to form _____ . On cooling, the ammonia _____ to a liquid and is removed.

2 a From the chart, does raising the temperature give a higher or lower yield of ammonia?

  b Why are high temperatures still used, despite this?

Summary

• Ammonia is made from nitrogen and hydrogen by the Haber process.

• A catalyst is used to speed up the reaction, but the yield is low.

• The ammonia is removed by cooling the mixture and the gases are recycled.

The importance of fertilisers

Plants need nitrogen to make proteins and grow. Plants are unable to use the nitrogen that makes up 80% of the air. Instead, they are forced to get nitrogen from chemicals in the soil. Unfortunately, there is rarely enough nitrogen available naturally to grow crops on the scale demanded by modern farming.

In the past, farmers used natural materials rich in nitrogen to improve the soil – animal manure and vegetable compost. Today, some farmers are trying to go back to this method of farming, as 'organic' food becomes popular.

Most farmers throughout the world still have to use industrially produced fertilisers. They need to, in order to get the high crop yields that are needed to feed the world's growing population.

a Why did the need for fertilisers grow dramatically over the last 100 years?

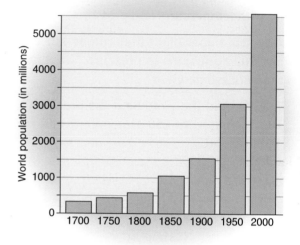

The world's population has increased hugely since 1700.

Nitric acid

Fertilisers must contain nitrogen in a form that the plants can take in and use. Compounds of ammonia (NH_3) and compounds of nitric acid (HNO_3) are suitable.

Nitric acid can be made by oxidising ammonia. The ammonia will have been made by the Haber process.

The oxidation of ammonia is a two-stage process.

In the first stage the ammonia and oxygen are passed over a hot platinum catalyst. The ammonia is oxidised to nitrogen monoxide.

b The nitrogen in ammonia is oxidised to nitrogen monoxide. What is the hydrogen in ammonia oxidised to?

c Write the word equation for this reaction.

The nitrogen monoxide is then cooled and mixed with more oxygen. The nitrogen monoxide/oxygen mixture is then passed up a tower against a steady trickle of water. Nitric acid forms and runs out at the base. This is the second stage.

d Write this second reaction out as a word equation.

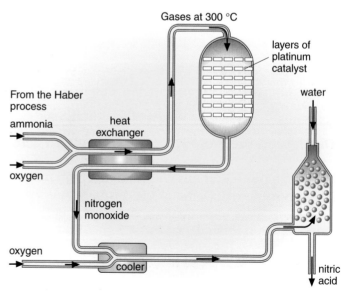

The production of nitric acid.

Ammonium nitrate fertiliser

One of the most commonly used 'nitrogen' fertilisers is ammonium nitrate (NH_4NO_3). Ammonium nitrate is made by reacting ammonium hydroxide with nitric acid. This is a neutralisation reaction.

$$\text{ammonium hydroxide} + \text{nitric acid} \rightarrow \text{ammonium nitrate} + \text{water}$$

$$NH_4OH + HNO_3 \rightarrow NH_4NO_3 + H_2O$$

The solution is then evaporated to give ammonium nitrate crystals.

e   Ammonium nitrate carries a 'double dose' of nitrogen when compared to other fertilisers such as ammonium sulphate. What do you think the expression 'double dose' means?

Nitrate problems

Manufactured fertilisers have worked wonders on crop production. Yields have gone up and food is cheap. But there are problems.

If fertilisers wash into rivers, they can upset the natural balance and make algae grow out of control. These 'algal blooms' end up by poisoning the fish in the river.

Another serious problem can be caused by nitrate fertilisers getting into drinking water. This occurred recently in East Anglia. In East Anglia, huge fields of wheat are sprayed with lots of fertiliser to keep the crop yields high.

The problem is that the nitrates can react with the iron in your blood. This reduces the blood's ability to carry oxygen. In its extreme form it causes 'blue baby syndrome', in which a baby turns blue due to lack of oxygen.

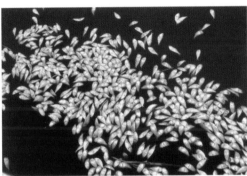

These fish are dead or dying because of the lack of oxygen in the water caused by an algal bloom.

f   East Anglia also has a problem with its lakes and rivers. Many parts of the Norfolk Broads are now covered by thick algal growths that have killed the fish. What might have caused this?

Questions

1   Copy and complete the following sentences. Choose from:

   crop   fertiliser   nitrate   nitric   water

   Ammonium nitrate _____ is made from ammonia and _____ acid. Farmers use this to get high _____ yields. But if _____ fertilisers get into lakes, rivers or drinking _____ they can cause problems.

2   a   Fertiliser is expensive. You need to know what return you will get for your money. The table shows crop yields of wheat and the amount of fertiliser that has been used. Plot a scatter graph of these figures.

Kilograms of fertiliser per hectare of land	0	50	100	150	200	250
Tonnes of grain grown per hectare	5	6	7	8	8	7

   b   What is the maximum amount of fertiliser to add to avoid waste?

Summary
- Many farmers use nitrogen fertilisers to increase their crop yields.
- These fertilisers are made from ammonia and nitric acid.
- Nitric acid is made by the catalytic oxidation of ammonia.
- Fertilisers can cause problems if they get into lakes or into drinking water.

End of module questions

1 This label is from a can of adhesive spray.

   a Choose a word from the list to complete the sentence:

     corrosive

     highly flammable

     irritant

     oxidising

   The hazard symbol warns us that the spray is _____.

   b The propellant gas used is butane, C_4H_{10}. Which two elements combine to make butane?

Do not spray on or near a naked flame or incandescent material.

No smoking when in use.

2 Jessica is investigating the way hydrogen peroxide breaks down when manganese dioxide powder is added.

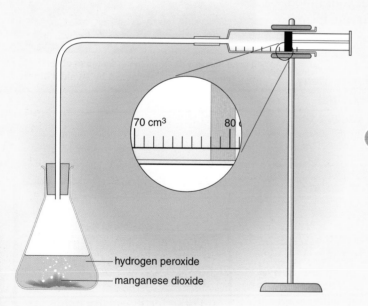

70 cm³   80 c

— hydrogen peroxide
— manganese dioxide

   a What is the volume of gas that has been collected?

   b In this reaction the hydrogen peroxide breaks down to form water and the gas that is being collected. What is the gas?

     hydrogen peroxide $\rightarrow$ water + _____
        (H_2O_2) (H_2O)

   c What would happen if you plunged a glowing splint into a tube of this gas?

   d The manganese dioxide is acting as a catalyst in this reaction. Explain what a catalyst does.

   e What does this hazard symbol tell you about hydrogen peroxide?

   f Jessica decided to find out if nickel oxide and copper oxide would work as well as manganese dioxide. Suggests three things she would need to do to make this a fair test.

   g Rupinder tried this experiment with some liver from the butchers: the reaction went so fast that it bubbled out of the beaker! Jessica thought she'd try this too, so she saved some cooked liver from her school dinner. But when she tried it, nothing happened at all. Explain why Rupinder's sample of liver worked but Jessica's sample of liver did not.

3 The diagram shows a candle burning.

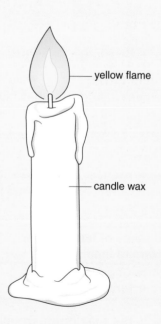

— yellow flame

— candle wax

a Copy and complete the following sentences. Choose from:

electrical

heat

light

kinetic

an endothermic

an exothermic

a neutralisation

a reduction

When a candle burns it transfers _____ and _____ energy to the surroundings. When candle wax burns it is _____ reaction.

b Candle wax is made of large molecules containing carbon and hydrogen. Complete the word equation for burning candle wax:

$$\text{candle wax} + \text{oxygen} \rightarrow \text{carbon dioxide} + \underline{\hspace{2cm}}$$

4 The chart shows the main processes involved in the manufacture of ammonia:

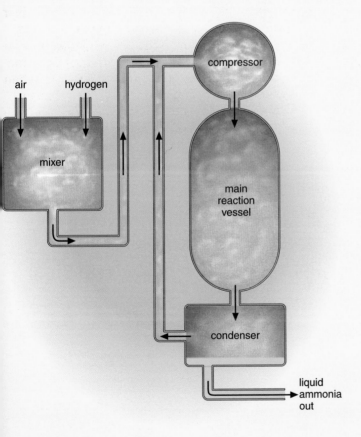

nitrogen + hydrogen $\rightleftharpoons$ ammonia

a Why doesn't all the nitrogen and hydrogen turn to ammonia in the main reaction vessel?

b How is the ammonia removed from the system so that the unused nitrogen and hydrogen may be recycled?

c What is the source of the nitrogen for this reaction?

d Calculate the percentage by mass of nitrogen in ammonia NH_3 (relative atomic masses are N = 14, H = 1).

5 Magnesium ribbon reacts with hydrochloric acid.

a Balance the symbolic equation for this reaction.

$$Mg + HCl \rightarrow MgCl_2 + H_2$$

b The graph shows the volume of gas given off against time when 0.1 g of magnesium ribbon is dissolved in an excess of 1 M hydrochloric acid.

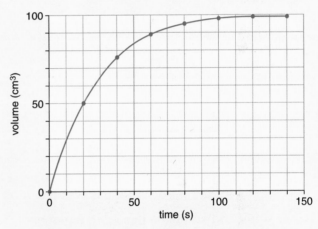

What is the maximum volume of gas you would expect to get if you dissolved 0.1 g of magnesium ribbon in an excess of 2 M hydrochloric acid (i.e. an acid that is twice as strong)?

c Copy the graph above onto graph paper. Draw a graph on the same axes to show what you would expect to happen if you dissolved 0.1 g of magnesium ribbon in an excess of 2 M hydrochloric acid, as in part **b**.

d Give one other way in which this reaction could be made to go faster.

6 Alan put a beaker containing 200 cm^3 of 1 M hydrochloric acid and a watch glass with 1 g of limestone chips onto an electric balance. He then zeroed the display on the balance. After this he tipped the limestone into the acid, placed the watch glass back on the balance next to the beaker, and noted the readings on the scale every 20 seconds.

Here are his results:

Time (seconds)	20	40	60	80	100	120	140	160	180
Balance reading (g)	−0.12	−0.23	−0.33	−0.40	−0.43	−0.44	−0.44	−0.44	−0.44

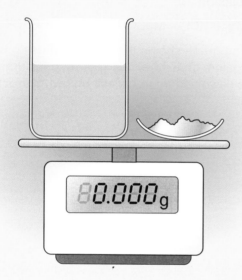

a Alan held some limewater over the beaker and it turned milky. What gas was given off?

b Copy and complete this word equation:

$$\text{calcium carbonate} + \text{hydrochloric acid} \rightarrow \text{calcium chloride} + \underline{}$$

c Explain why the reading on the balance scale dropped below zero.

d Plot a graph of Alan's results. Put the time along the x-axis and the mass loss in grams along the y-axis.

e What would Alan have *seen* happening during the first minute or so?

f Suggest *two* ways in which Alan would have known that the reaction was finished after 2 minutes.

g Alan repeated the experiment exactly, except he used 1 g of powdered limestone instead of limestone chips. Explain how this experiment would have looked different from the first one.

h On your graph from part **d**, sketch what you think the graph line for part **g** would have looked like.

i Explain your answer to part **h**.

7 Titanium metal is obtained from an ore called rutile, TiO$_2$. The atomic mass of titanium is 48, while that of oxygen is 16.

a What is the formula mass of rutile?

b How much of that total mass is the titanium?

c What percentage of titanium is there in rutile? (You need to show your working.)

d If you had 1 tonne (1000 kg) of rutile, how much titanium metal could you get from this?

Module 11 – Forces

For thousands of years, people have looked up at the night sky and watched the movement of the stars and planets across the sky. Physicists and astronomers such as Galileo, Newton and Einstein discovered how, by understanding forces, we could make sense of what we see in space, as well as how things move here on Earth. They showed that the same ideas about forces and motion work for giant stars and for the movement of everyday objects such as falling stones and moving cars.

In this module, you will find out about how forces can affect the way things move. Gravity is a very important force, and you will find out about how gravity governs how things move here on Earth and in space, as well as the life and death of stars, and even of the Universe itself.

In this photo, taken by the New Technology Telescope in Chile, clouds of gas are seen deep in space. They are pulled together by gravity. Where the clouds become hot and dense, new stars can be seen forming.

Before you start this module, check that you can recall the answers to the following questions about movement, forces and space:

1 What two quantities do you need to know if you are going to measure the speed of an object as it moves between two points?

2 How would you calculate the object's speed from these two quantities?

3 What is the name of the force which always acts opposite to the direction in which an object is moving?

4 How does the spinning of the Earth give rise to night and day?

5 For what purposes are satellites sent into orbit around the Earth?

Forces affect the way things move. You cannot see forces, but you can see how they change an object's speed.

This race doesn't seem very fair. Everyone has to travel the same distance, but the racing driver will get to the finishing line first.

The table shows how long each competitor took to travel 1000 m.

Competitor	Time taken (s)
runner	200
cyclist	100
racing driver	25

a Work out the cyclist's average speed. (Remember: speed = distance travelled/time taken.)

Plotting graphs

We can use the information in the table to draw a graph which shows how the competitors moved during the race. This is a **distance–time graph**.

b Look at the graph. What quantity is shown on the horizontal axis? What quantity is shown on the vertical axis?

A graph like this allows us to compare the speeds of moving objects.

◆ The graph for the racing driver is steepest, because his speed is greatest.

◆ The runner is slowest, so the slope of his graph is the least.

◆ The cyclist's speed is in between, so the slope of her graph is in between the other two.

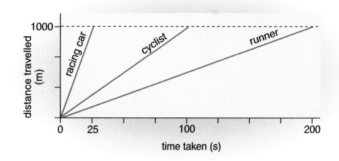

A picture paints a thousand words

A graph is a good way of summarising information about how something has moved.

'The bus left my stop and took 30 s to travel 250 m to the next stop. It waited there for 10 s while the passengers got off. Then it took 50 s to travel 500 m to the bus station.'

Look for these features of the graph:

The middle section of the graph is horizontal; the bus was stationary.

The last section of the graph is steepest; the bus was travelling fastest.

c How would the slope of the graph change if the bus was travelling very slowly in heavy traffic?

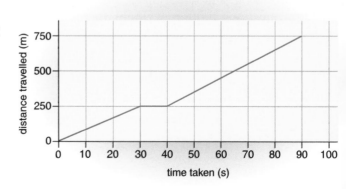

Often you simply say how fast something is moving – its **speed**. Sometimes it is important to know the direction in which an object is moving. If you give speed and direction, we call this its **velocity** – for example, 'The ball rolled towards the goal at 5 m/s.'

Questions

1 The graphs represent the motion of four different objects. Which graph is for:

a a stationary object;

b the fastest of the four?

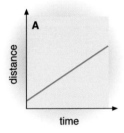

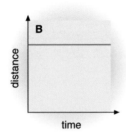

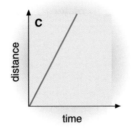

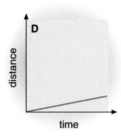

2 Sketch a graph like the ones in question 1 to represent this motion:

'I cycled along the road as fast as I could for 20 s. Then I stopped for 20 s.'

3 The table shows how far a train has travelled along its route during part of its journey.

Distance travelled (m)	0	80	160	240	320
Time taken (s)	0	2	4	6	8

a Draw a distance–time graph to show this data.

b Was the train running at a steady speed? How can you tell?

c Use the figures in the last column of the table to work out the train's speed.

4 What *two* things must you know in order to tell the velocity of something?

Summary

- A distance–time graph can show us how an object is moving.

- The steeper the graph, the greater the object's speed.

- Velocity means speed in a given direction.

11.2 Speeding up

Some cars are advertised like this: '0 to 60 miles per hour in 8.0 seconds!' This tells you how good it is at speeding up. If the train was advertised like this, it might say: '0 to 180 miles per hour in 10 minutes!'

The train can go much faster than the car, but it takes much longer to get up speed. *Speeding up* is known as *accelerating*. If the train accelerated like the car, all of the passengers would be in danger of falling over as it set off.

People accelerate, too. At the beginning of a race, you accelerate away from the starting line. If someone is catching up behind you, you might accelerate in order to keep your lead.

a   When might a bus accelerate?

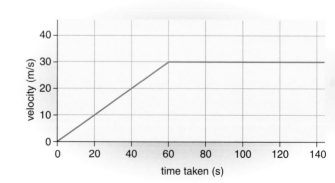

An accelerating car

The car in the picture is setting off. The picture shows its position every second. The gaps between the images of the car get longer as it speeds up.

The graph shows how the car's velocity along the road changes. It starts at zero, because the car isn't moving at first. Then the graph goes up at a steady rate, showing that the car's speed is increasing steadily. We say that its **acceleration** is constant.

b   How would the picture of the car look if the car was moving at a steady speed? What can you say about the gaps between the images?

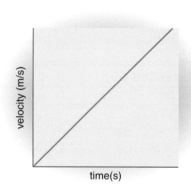

Velocity–time graphs

Here is another **velocity–time graph**. It shows how the velocity of a train changes as it leaves a station. Take care! This is not the same as a distance–time graph. Always check the labels on the axes. A velocity–time graph has:

◆ time taken on the horizontal axis;

◆ velocity on the vertical axis.

c   Which axis is the same as for a distance–time graph? Which is different?

The graph for the train is in two parts.

At first, the train is speeding up at a steady rate. It has constant acceleration. The graph is a straight line, sloping upwards. The steeper the slope, the greater the acceleration.

When it has reached top speed, the train no longer accelerates. It has constant velocity. The graph is a horizontal straight line.

1 From the graph, find the train's velocity after 20 s. What is its greatest velocity?

Spy in the cab

A lorry driver does a lot of driving in a day. The lorry speeds up and slows down. Its speed is recorded by an instrument called a tachograph.

The tachograph makes a graph to show the lorry's speed. The line on the graph goes up and down as the lorry's speed changes.

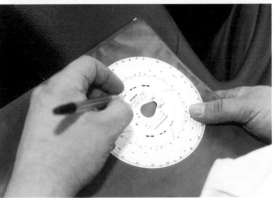

Questions

1 Give a single word that means the same as 'speeding up'.

2 Look at the four velocity–time graphs.

  a Which graph is for a car travelling at constant velocity?

  b Which graph is for the car with the greatest acceleration?

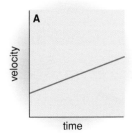

A

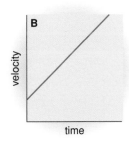

B

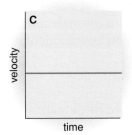

C

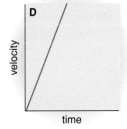

D

3 The graph shows how the velocities of two cars changed.

  a Which car was not moving at the start?

  b How fast was the other car moving at the start?

  c Which car had the greater acceleration? How can you tell?

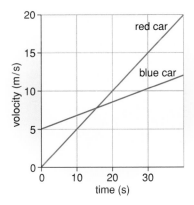

4 A tachograph chart shows how a lorry's speed has changed during its journey.

  a What does the graph look like when the lorry has been travelling at a steady speed?

  b Police can check the chart. How can they tell if the driver stopped for a rest?

  c Why do you think that drivers sometimes call it 'the spy in the cab'?

Summary

- A velocity–time graph can show us if an object's velocity is changing.

- The steeper the graph, the more rapidly the object's velocity is changing – the more it is accelerating.

11:3 Acceleration

The trolley in the photo is running down a ramp. As it moves, it picks up speed. It is accelerating.

The students are using two light gates to measure the trolley's acceleration.

◆ Light gate 1 measures its velocity near the top of the slope, where it is going slowly.

◆ Light gate 2 measures its velocity near the foot of the slope, where it is moving faster.

The computer uses this information to work out the trolley's acceleration.

a If the students tilted the ramp so that it was steeper, would the trolley's acceleration increase or decrease?

Calculating acceleration

The computer needs three pieces of information to work out the trolley's acceleration: two measurements of velocity, and the time interval between them. It gets this information from the light gates. The worked example shows how it calculates the acceleration.

Worked example 1

Step 1 Calculate the change in velocity by finding the difference between the two velocity measurements.

Change in velocity = 6.0 m/s – 1.0 m/s = 5.0 m/s

Step 2 Divide by the time taken for this change.

$$\text{Acceleration} = \frac{5.0 \text{ m/s}}{2.0 \text{ m/s}} = 2.5 \text{ m/s}^2$$

How quickly is the trolley's velocity changing?

The meaning of acceleration

Imagine you are at the start of a 100 m sprint race. If you are to win, you want to get up to speed as quickly as possible. You want your acceleration to be high. 'Acceleration' means 'how quickly your velocity changes'. A better way to say this is:

The acceleration of an object is the rate at which its velocity changes.

From the worked example above, you can see how to write this as an equation:

$$\text{Acceleration} = \frac{\text{change in velocity}}{\text{time taken for change}}$$

Acceleration is measured in m/s^2 (metres per second squared). An acceleration of 1 m/s^2 means that your velocity is changing by 1 m/s every second.

Sprinters have to accelerate as much as they can at the start of a race.

b If your acceleration is 10 m/s², by how much does your velocity change in 1 s? And in 2 s?

Worked example 2

A train sets off from a station. After 50 s, its speed is 20 m/s. What is its acceleration? (The graph shows the same information.)

Step 1 Calculate the change in the train's velocity.

Change in velocity = 20 m/s – 0 m/s = 20 m/s

(Its velocity has increased by 20 m/s.)

Step 2 Divide by the time taken.

$$\text{Acceleration} = \frac{\text{change in velocity}}{\text{time taken}} = \frac{20 \text{ m/s}}{50 \text{ s}} = 0.4 \text{ m/s}^2$$

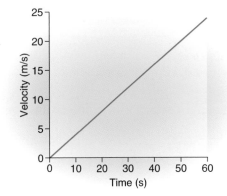

c A stone is dropped over a high cliff. After 2 s, its velocity is 20 m/s. What is its acceleration?

Questions

1 What are the units of each quantity in the list?

time   distance moved   speed   velocity   acceleration

2 Look at the quantities in this list:

distance travelled   time taken
change in velocity   maximum velocity

a Which *two* of these quantities do you need to know in order to calculate acceleration?

b Write down the equation which shows how to calculate acceleration from these quantities.

3 An old car can accelerate from 0 m/s to 20 m/s in 10 s. What is its acceleration?

4 The table shows how the velocity of a car changes at the start of a short trip. Study the table and answer the questions.

a What is the car's top speed during the journey?

Velocity (m/s)	0	5	10	15	15	15
Time (s)	0	2	4	6	8	10

b By how much does the car's velocity change during the first 4 s of its journey?

c What is the car's acceleration during this time?

DIGGING DEEPER

We think of 100 m sprinters as being the fastest runners. However, because they are stationary at the start of the race, and have to accelerate to reach top speed, their time for 100 m is reduced. Athletes running 200 m often complete the second 100 m in a shorter time than the record for 100 m.

Summary

- An object's acceleration is the rate at which its velocity is changing.

- $$\text{Acceleration} = \frac{\text{change in velocity}}{\text{time taken}}.$$

- Acceleration is measured in m/s².

11:4 Gravity

If you take a ride on the Oblivion rollercoaster at Alton Towers, the forces which push and pull on you keep changing. At the end of the ride, your car waits for 4 s above a vertical drop. Then it suddenly falls into a smoke-filled pit.

The force of gravity pulls the Oblivion car downwards. The car goes faster and faster as it falls.

Mass and weight

The Earth's gravity pulls on every object on its surface, and on every object below and above the surface. It pulls straight downwards, towards the centre of the Earth.

The force of the Earth's gravity on you is called your **weight**. Because weight is a force, it is measured in **newtons** (N). What people usually call the *weight* of something is really its *mass*.

a Gravity is a force which pulls things downwards. Name a force which slows things down when they are moving. What units is this force measured in?

Far out in space, a long way from the Earth or any other object, you would be completely weightless. There's nothing there to pull on you. But that doesn't mean you have completely disappeared! Your weight is zero, but your mass is just the same as on Earth. You're made of just as many kilograms of atoms and molecules, whether you're on Earth or in space. It's just that there is no gravity pulling on you.

If your *mass* is 60 kg, it stays the same wherever you are. Your *weight* changes because gravity is stronger in some places than others.

The strength of gravity

You can measure the weight of something using a newtonmeter.

The Earth's gravity pulls on each kilogram on the Earth's surface with a force of about 10 N. If you know the mass of something (in kg), you can work out its weight:

Weight on Earth (N) = mass (kg) × 10 N/kg

In other words, multiply the mass by 10 and change the units to newtons.

b What will be the weight of a child on the surface of the Earth if his mass is 50 kg?

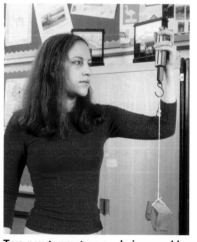

Two newtonmeters are being used here to measure the weight of a brick and of a person.

Falling

Look at the photograph. Gravity makes the ball fall. The multiflash photograph shows that it goes faster and faster as it falls. Gravity makes things accelerate as they fall.

It's easier to see this if you roll a ball down a slope, because the pull of gravity down the slope is weaker. The ball speeds up as it rolls down towards the bottom.

c How can you tell from the photograph that the ball is accelerating as it falls?

A ball accelerates as it falls. Its position is shown at intervals of one-tenth of a second.

Questions

1 Copy the table, putting the correct unit for each quantity in the second column.

Force	
Mass	
Weight	

2 Work out the weight (in newtons, N) of each of the following things, on the Earth's surface:

   a a 1 kg book

   b a 50 kg person

   c a 500 kg car.

3 Because it is much smaller than the Earth, the Moon's gravity is weaker than the Earth's. The Moon pulls with a force of 1.6 N on each kg of an object's mass. Calculate the weight on the Moon of each object in Question 2.

4 Copy out the sentences below. Use the correct scientific words to replace the words underlined:

   If you throw a ball up in the air, it comes back down because of the Earth's <u>pull</u>. As it falls, it <u>speeds up</u>.

5 A boy weighs himself in the lab, using a newtonmeter. He finds that his weight is 520 N. What is his mass?

DIGGING DEEPER

If you go on a rollercoaster ride, you may experience some sudden accelerations. The greatest acceleration is not when you are falling under gravity, but when you suddenly change direction.

Summary

- Weight is the force of the Earth's gravity pulling on an object.

- Close to the Earth's surface,

  weight (N) =
      mass (kg) × 10 N/kg

- Gravity makes things accelerate (go faster) as they fall.

11:5 Balanced forces

When you are sitting comfortably in your chair, there are two forces acting on you:

◆ the force of gravity (your weight) is pulling downwards on you;

◆ the chair is pushing upwards on you.

These two forces are balanced, and you stay on the chair. Without the upward push of the chair, you would descend through the floor.

Now, if your chair turns out to be an ejector seat, it may give you an extra large upward push. There is an unbalanced force on you – more force upwards than downwards. The unbalanced force makes you fly upwards.

a Look at the drawing showing two balanced forces. What can you say about the sizes of these two forces?

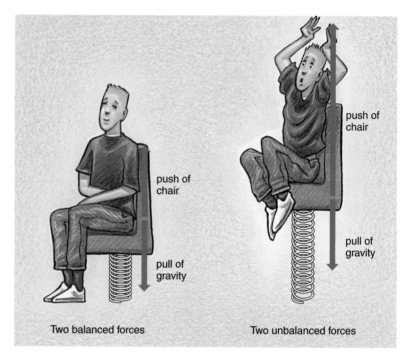

Two balanced forces   Two unbalanced forces

Balanced and unbalanced

We can represent forces by arrows. The arrow shows the direction of the force. The size of the force is given in newtons (N).

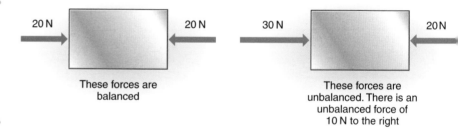

20 N → ← 20 N   These forces are balanced

30 N → ← 20 N   These forces are unbalanced. There is an unbalanced force of 10 N to the right

The effects of balanced forces

You can see that an object will not start to move if the forces on it are balanced. It is more surprising to find that a moving object will continue to move at a steady speed when the forces on it are balanced.

◆ The force of the engine is trying to make the car speed up.

◆ The force of air resistance is trying to slow the car down.

These two effects cancel out, so the car doesn't speed up or slow down.

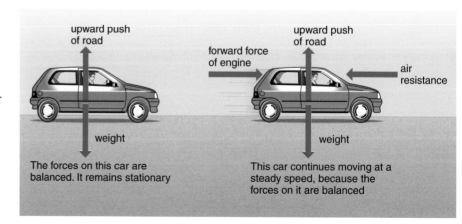

upward push of road
weight
The forces on this car are balanced. It remains stationary

upward push of road
forward force of engine
air resistance
weight
This car continues moving at a steady speed, because the forces on it are balanced

b The parachutist in the picture is falling at a steady speed. Are the forces acting on her balanced or unbalanced?

Push meets shove

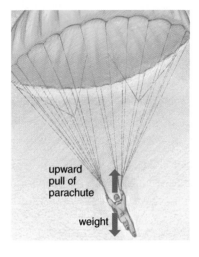

upward
pull of
parachute

weight

The car in the photo has crashed into a lamppost. The car exerted a force on the lamppost, and the lamppost exerted a force on the car. The two forces were equal in size but opposite in direction. Unfortunately, the lamppost was stronger than the car, and so the car was more badly damaged than the lamppost.

You can feel the forces two objects exert on each other by holding two magnets close together, so that they repel each other. You can feel one magnet being pushed to the right while the other is pushed to the left. The two magnetic forces are equal in size but opposite in direction.

Whenever two objects interact, the forces they exert on each other are equal and opposite.

c If you held the magnets so that they attracted each other, what would you feel? What could you say about the forces they exert on each other?

Questions

1 Imagine you are riding on the Oblivion rollercoaster shown in the photo on page 190.

   a When you are waiting to drop, are the forces on you balanced or unbalanced?

   b Are they balanced or unbalanced as you start to drop?

2 The student in the picture is standing on the floor. Two forces act on her: her weight, and the push of the floor.

   a Draw a diagram to show these two forces.

   b What can you say about the sizes of these forces?

   c Are these forces balanced or unbalanced?

3 When you sit on a chair, you push downwards on the chair, and it pushes up on you.

   a What can you say about the sizes of these forces?

   b What can you say about their directions?

DIGGING DEEPER
You cannot pull yourself up by your shoelaces because of the equal and opposite forces betwen two interacting objects. The harder you pull upwards on your shoelace, the harder it pulls downwards on your hand.

Summary
- Balanced forces do not affect an object's motion. It will remain stationary, or continue to move at a steady speed in a straight line.

- When two bodies interact, they exert equal and opposite forces on each other.

11:6 Unbalanced forces

The world's biggest ships are oil tankers, up to 500 m long. They are very difficult to control.

The engines can provide a force to drive the ship forwards, backwards or sideways. The force of drag (friction with the water) tends to slow the tanker down.

The crew must control these forces carefully. A giant supertanker takes a very long time to slow down, and a small mistake in the timing can result in a disastrous collision.

a **When should a tanker's engines be put into reverse, to provide a backwards push?**

This oil tanker has hit the rocks.

Steady as she goes

The ferry captain can control the ship's speed by changing the force of the engine. To change the ferry's speed, the forces on it must be unbalanced.

For most of its journey, the ferry maintains a steady speed. The engines give a forward push to balance the drag of the water.

If the captain wants to go faster, the force of the engines must be increased so that it is greater than the drag of the water.

To go slower, the force of the engines must be reduced. It's the drag of the water that slows the ferry down.

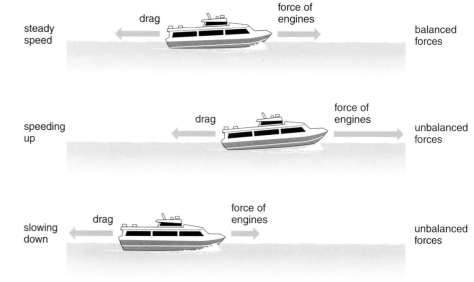

steady speed — drag / force of engines — balanced forces

speeding up — drag / force of engines — unbalanced forces

slowing down — drag / force of engines — unbalanced forces

b **You are rowing a boat across a lake. You stop rowing and quickly come to a halt. What force causes you to stop?**

A SeaCat ferry rises out of the water. This reduces the drag force on it.

Changing direction

The forces must be unbalanced to change an object's *speed*. Unbalanced forces may also change the *direction* in which an object is moving.

When a ferry comes into dock, it must change its direction in order to reach its berth. An unbalanced sideways force is needed to make it change direction.

sideways force of engines

Masses large and small

A large ferry has a large mass – millions of kilograms – so it needs a big unbalanced force to make it accelerate. A speedboat has a much smaller mass. It needs a much smaller unbalanced force to give it the same acceleration. That is why the motor of a speedboat is so much smaller than a ferry's large engines.

The larger an object's mass, the greater the force needed to give it a particular acceleration.

c   Alex has filled the back of his car with sacks of cement. When he drives off, he finds that it takes a long time to get up to speed on the main road. Explain why this is.

Questions

1   Copy the table. In the second column, write whether the forces must be balanced or unbalanced.

speeding up (accelerating)	forces
steady speed	forces
slowing down	forces
changing direction	forces

2   This car is travelling fast along the road. The diagram shows the forces on the car. Will the car speed up, slow down or carry on at the same speed? Why?

air resistance
500 N

force of engine
700 N

3   These two cars are waiting at the traffic lights. When the lights change, they will accelerate away. The driver of the bigger car (B) thinks he will have the greater acceleration. Is he correct? Explain your answer.

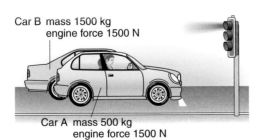

Car B mass 1500 kg
engine force 1500 N

Car A mass 500 kg
engine force 1500 N

Summary

- An unbalanced force affects an object's motion.

- It may start the object moving, speed it up, or slow it down.

- The greater the unbalanced force, the greater the acceleration it produces.

This driver was unlucky – and cras... into the finishing post!

Racing drivers need to be sure that their cars are in good condition before they go out on the track. A single misjudgement can lead to a nasty accident. Fortunately, racing cars are now designed to withstand strong impacts, so serious casualties are rare.

Avoiding skidding

Stewart is driving along the road. Just in time, he notices the STOP sign ahead. He applies the brakes and comes to a halt at the junction.

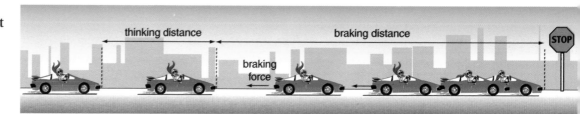

It takes a short time – about two-thirds of a second – for Stewart to react when he sees the sign. During that time, the car travels a short distance along the road. This is the **thinking distance**.

The brakes provide a backward force to slow the car. The brakes increase the friction between the tyres and the road. The distance travelled by the car while the brakes are on is called the **braking distance**.

So the **stopping distance** is made up of these two distances:

Stopping distance = thinking distance + braking distance

If Stewart had noticed the STOP sign a little later, he would have had to press harder on the brakes. Then the frictional force might not have been great enough to stop the car in time; the car would have gone into a skid. You may have done this yourself, while riding a bike.

a   Copy the following sentence, choosing the correct word from the pair underlined:

The faster a car travels, the <u>greater/less</u> the braking force needed to stop it in a given time.

Dangerous driving

Drivers need to think ahead, to make sure they are ready to stop safely if necessary. Several factors affect how quickly they can stop:

◆ How fast the car is moving

The faster the car is moving, the further it will travel before the force of the brakes can bring it to a halt.

◆ How quickly the driver can react

The driver may be tired, or under the influence of alcohol or drugs. A tired or drugged driver is slow to react, so the thinking distance is greater.

◆ The state of the road

◆ The condition of the car

If the road is wet or icy, the driver has to apply the brakes gently, to avoid skidding. A smaller braking force takes longer to stop the car. If the car's brakes are worn, the braking force will again be reduced. The MOT test helps to ensure that most cars are roadworthy.

This man's driving has attracted the attention of the police.

b Why do smooth tyres give a smaller braking force?

If visibility is poor (because of rain or snow, or because you are on a winding road) it is important to drive more slowly. You get less warning of the need to stop.

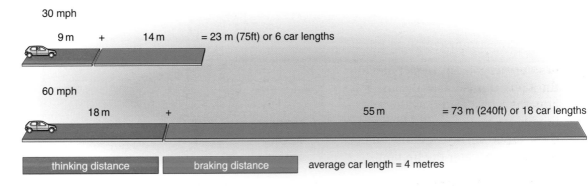

30 mph

9 m + 14 m = 23 m (75ft) or 6 car lengths

60 mph

18 m + 55 m = 73 m (240ft) or 18 car lengths

thinking distance   braking distance   average car length = 4 metres

This diagram, from the Highway Code, shows the stopping distances for cars travelling in good conditions at two different speeds.

Questions

1 What *two* distances add together to make the stopping distance of a car?

2 The *thinking time* is the time it takes between when a driver sees the need to stop and the time they step on the brakes. How might this be affected if the driver has been drinking alcohol, or is very tired from driving for a long time?

3 Look at the diagram from the Highway Code. It shows stopping distances when road conditions are good.

   a What road conditions might increase the stopping distance of a car?

   b What is the stopping distance for a car travelling at 30 mph?

   c Explain why the thinking distance is twice as much at 60 mph as at 30 mph.

   d A child steps out into the road, 80 m ahead of a car. The car is travelling at 60 mph. Can the driver be sure of stopping in time? (Think carefully about your answer.)

Summary

• A faster-moving vehicle needs a bigger force to stop it quickly.

• The stopping distance of a car depends on its speed, the speed of the driver's reactions, the road conditions and the condition of the car

11:8 Moving through the air

When the space shuttle comes in to land, it is travelling very fast. Because it is moving so fast, there is a lot of friction with the air, which helps to slow it down. The outside of the shuttle gets very hot. It is covered with special heat-resistant tiles to prevent the astronauts inside from being cooked.

Friction in fluids

The picture shows how you can see the effect of the air's friction. Drop a ball and a crumpled piece of paper. The ball reaches the ground first. The paper is slowed down by the force of **air resistance** (friction with the air).

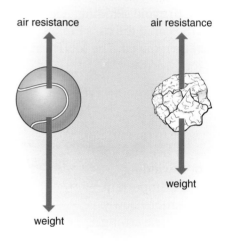

◆ Gravity pulls the ball and the paper downwards.

◆ Air resistance opposes gravity.

Friction acts on any object moving through a gas (such as the air) or a liquid (such as water). Gases and liquids are known as **fluids**, because they can flow. The faster the object moves, the greater the friction.

a Look at the diagram which shows the forces on the ball and the paper. Explain why the paper falls at a steady speed. Why does the ball accelerate?

Falling step-by-step

How do the forces change as the paper falls?

◆ At first, only gravity acts. This makes the paper accelerate.

◆ Friction increases as the paper moves faster.

◆ Soon friction balances gravity.

The paper falls the rest of the way to the floor at a steady speed, known as **terminal velocity**.

b How can you tell from the picture when the paper reaches its terminal velocity?

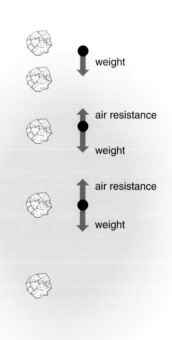

Top speed

Cars have to push their way through the air, too. When the driver presses hard on the accelerator pedal, the engine provides a big force to push the car forward. At top speed, air resistance pushes back with an equal force. The car can't go any faster than this.

Racing cars have big engines and a streamlined shape, so that they can go faster than an ordinary car.

c Explain why a car can go faster if it has a streamlined shape.

This skydiver is moving at terminal velocity. She can feel the air rushing past, making the force of air resistance.

Questions

1 Copy the sentences below. Use words from the list to fill the gaps.

> accelerate   balance   air resistance   gravity

- If you drop a shuttlecock, the force of _____ makes it _____ downwards.

- As it moves downwards, the force of _____ increases.

- When the forces _____ , the shuttlecock has reached its terminal velocity.

2 **a** Draw a diagram of a car moving at top speed. Show the forces acting on it: the driving force of the engine, and the force of air resistance.

b What can you say about the sizes of these forces?

c Suggest **two** things that could be changed so that the car could go even faster.

3 Look at these graphs. Which graph might show how the force of air resistance changes when a shuttlecock is dropped towards the ground?

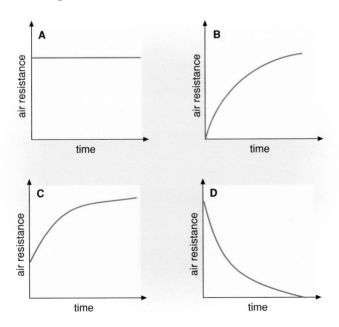

Summary

- Friction increases as an object moves faster through a fluid.

- A falling object reaches top speed when friction balances the pull of gravity

Any object which is moving has **kinetic energy**. The car and the lorry in the picture both have kinetic energy. The faster they go, the more kinetic energy they have.

When the photo was taken, the car and the lorry were travelling at the same speed. The lorry has much more kinetic energy than the car, because it has much more mass.

Kinetic energy depends on two quantities: mass and speed.

◆ Greater mass means more kinetic energy.

◆ Greater speed means more kinetic energy.

a A car is accelerating along the road. Is its kinetic energy increasing, decreasing or staying the same?

Increasing kinetic energy

This aircraft is getting up speed as it races down the runway, ready for take-off. Its kinetic energy increases as it goes faster.

To increase its kinetic energy, the aircraft burns fuel. You can see the dirty exhaust fumes coming from its engines. The energy stored in the fuel is being transferred to the aircraft as kinetic energy.

In a similar way, energy is transferred when you start running. You have to push hard on the ground to increase your speed. Energy stored in your muscles is transferred to your body, giving you more kinetic energy.

b Use these ideas to explain why a lot more fuel is used in getting a lorry up to top speed, compared with a car.

Calculating kinetic energy

Here is how to calculate the kinetic energy of a moving object:

Kinetic energy $= \frac{1}{2} \times \text{mass} \times (\text{speed})^2$

Like all forms of energy, kinetic energy is measured in joules (J).

Worked example

Calculate the kinetic energy of a runner of mass 60 kg, running at 10 m/s.

First, write down the equation for kinetic energy:

Kinetic energy $= \frac{1}{2} \times \text{mass} \times (\text{speed})^2$

Now substitute in the values from the question.

Kinetic energy $= \frac{1}{2} \times 60 \text{ kg} \times (10 \text{ m/s})^2$

Take care with the calculation! It is only the speed which is squared – the brackets are there to remind you of this.

Kinetic energy $= \frac{1}{2} \times 60 \times (10)^2 \text{ J} = \frac{1}{2} \times 60 \times 100 \text{ J} = 3000 \text{ J}$

(With practice, you will be able to do this calculation in one step.)

c Calculate the kinetic energy of a stone of mass 4 kg falling at 20 m/s. (If your answer is 1600 J, try again!)

The table shows some calculated values of kinetic energy for different objects, moving at their top speeds.

Object	Mass (kg)	Top speed (m/s)	Kinetic energy (J)
hummingbird	0.003	8	0.096
peregrine falcon	0.8	12.7	64.5
sprinter	60	10	3 000
family car	800	30	360 000
jumbo jet	400 000	250	12 500 000 000

Questions

1 Copy and complete the table, to show the units for each quantity involved in calculating an object's kinetic energy.

Quantity	Unit
mass	
speed	
kinetic energy	

2 Look at the table which shows values of kinetic energy for various objects. The peregrine falcon moves faster than a sprinter, but its kinetic energy is much less than the sprinter's. Explain why this is so.

3 Calculate the kinetic energy of a car of mass 600 kg moving at 20 m/s.

4 Which has more kinetic energy, a runner of mass 60 kg moving at 10 m/s or a runner of mass 100 kg moving at 6 m/s?

DIGGING DEEPER
Although Isaac Newton discovered a lot of what we now know about forces, he knew nothing about energy. The scientific idea of energy was not invented until long after he died.

Summary
- The greater its mass and the greater its speed, the greater an object's kinetic energy.
- Kinetic energy $= \frac{1}{2} \times \text{mass} \times (\text{speed})^2$

11.10 Forces doing work

Here are some things that you might think of as 'hard work': chopping wood, washing the dishes, writing an essay for your English homework, watching a video of a Shakespeare play. But this isn't what scientists mean by **work**.

In science, you do work if you use a **force** to do something: pushing or pulling something along, or lifting something up, or changing the shape of something.

a In the picture, who is doing work (in the scientific sense), the boy or the girl? Explain your answer.

Forces moving

Here are some examples of forces doing work:

A The log will not slide easily along the ground, because of friction. You need to pull it with a force to make it move along.

B The car is stationary. You need to push it with a force to start it moving.

C The shopping bag is heavy. You need to use a force to lift it onto the table.

D The spring is stiff. You need to use a force to stretch it.

Forces transferring energy

You need energy to do work – pulling, pushing, lifting, stretching. If you carry on doing work, you will eventually run out of energy. The force you use is transferring energy from you to the object you are moving.

Here is where your energy goes in the examples above:

A The log and the ground get warm, because of the rubbing of friction. Your energy has been transferred as **heat**.

B The car starts to move. Your energy has been transferred to it as **kinetic energy**.

C The shopping bag is higher than before. Its **gravitational potential energy (GPE)** has increased.

D The spring is ready to snap back when you release it. It is a store of **elastic potential energy**.

b What form of energy appears when a force does work against friction?

c What form of energy is stored when an elastic (springy) object is stretched?

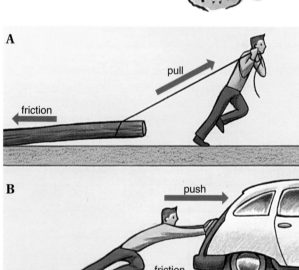

How much work?

The amount of energy transferred by a force tells you the amount of work the force has done. The amount of work is measured in joules (J), just like the amount of energy.

Work done = energy transferred

A bigger force transfers more energy, and the further it moves, the more energy it transfers. So the amount of work done is the force multiplied by the distance moved:

Work done = force × distance moved in the direction of the force

The picture shows why we have to say *in the direction of the force*. The lifting force does work when it is raising the bag, because the bag is getting higher and its GPE is increasing. The lifting force does no work when the bag is moving sideways, because the bag isn't getting any higher.

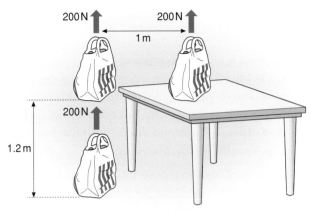

Worked example

The shopping bag is lifted by a 200 N force onto a table, 1.2 m high. How much work is done by the lifting force?

Work done = force × distance moved in the direction of the force

Substitute in the values from the question:

Work done = 200 N × 1.2 m = 240 J

Remember that the answer will come out in joules (J).

d How much work would be done in lifting the same bag onto a higher table, 1.5 m high?

Questions

1 What are the correct units for the quantities shown in the table? Copy the table and fill in the second column. Choose from

    metre (m)   joule (J)   newton (N)

Quantity	Units
energy transferred	
work done	
force	
distance moved	

2 Are these people doing work (in the scientific sense)? Explain your answers.

  a A man pushing a shopping trolley.

  b A child stretching a rubber band.

  c A boy sitting watching a science programme on TV.

3 How much work is done when someone pushes a car for 50 m with a force of 400 N?

4 A crane lifts a car 20 m into the air, using a force of 5000 N. How much work is done by the crane?

Summary

- Doing work is a way of transferring energy using a force:

- Work done = energy transferred

- To calculate work done: Work done = force × distance moved in the direction of the force

No-one has ever seen the Solar System looking like this. You would have to travel far out into space to be able to look down and see the planets in their orbits. It is hard to tell, but the orbits of the planets are not quite circular. Their shape is called an **ellipse**, a squashed circle, with the Sun close to the centre. Pluto's orbit is the most elliptical.

Planets closest to the Sun travel fastest, and take the least time to complete one orbit. Pluto takes the longest time for one orbit – almost 250 Earth years!

a Which planet is closest to the Sun?

b Is Pluto always furthest from the Sun?

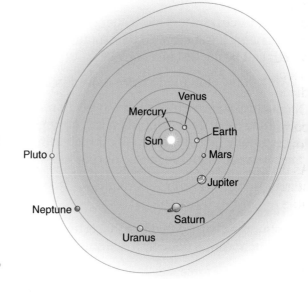

Held by gravity

The Earth's orbit around the Sun is almost circular. The Earth moves around the Sun at a distance of about 150 000 000 km (150 million kilometres). It travels at almost 30 km/s – that's about 1000 times the motorway speed limit.

Moving objects tend to keep moving in straight lines. It takes an unbalanced force to make them follow a curved path. What force keeps the Earth in its orbit around the Sun?

The Sun's mass is about 2 million million million million million kilograms. This gives it a strong gravitational pull. It is the force of the Sun's gravity, pulling on the mass of the Earth, which holds it in its orbit.

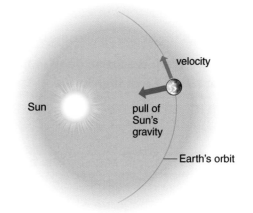

The speed of the Earth and the pull of the Sun's gravity combine to keep the Earth in its orbit. The Earth must move fast, otherwise it would fall in towards the Sun.

Each planet feels the pull of the Sun's gravity. The furthest planets feel only a weak pull, because the force of gravity decreases quickly as you move away from the Sun.

The Earth has a gravitational pull, too. The Earth's gravity pulls on the Moon and holds it in its orbit around the Earth.

The Moon is held in its orbit by the Earth's gravity.

Comets also orbit the Sun. A comet is a frozen ball of ice and dust, much smaller than a planet. They spend most of their time far out in space, beyond the most distant planets. Occasionally, a comet will move in towards the Sun.

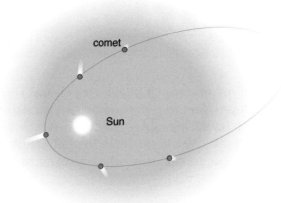

As the comet warms up, dust and gas evaporate from it. This starts to glow, forming the comet's tail. That's when we may be able to see the comet.

c Is the orbit of a comet circular or elliptical?

Questions

1 Copy the sentences below. Use words from the list to fill the gaps.

> comets   gravity   **Sun**   planets

The Solar System consists of the _____ and everything which orbits around it, including _____ and the _____ . The force of _____ holds them in their orbits.

2 Draw a diagram to show a comet in its orbit around the Sun. Where in its orbit is a comet when we can see it?

3 Astronomers have found planets orbiting around distant stars. The drawing shows three such planets.

a Which of the planets shown moves most quickly?

b Which takes longest to orbit its star?

c Which planet is pulled on most strongly by the star's gravity? How can you tell?

4 Imagine that the Earth suddenly stopped dead in its orbit.

a What unbalanced force would be pulling on the Earth?

b In which direction would the Earth start to move?

DIGGING DEEPER
If you draw an accurate diagram of the Earth's elliptical orbit, you will not be able to tell that it is not perfectly circular. Our distance from the Sun varies by about 1% during the year, and our eyes cannot see such a small variation in the size of a circle.

Summary

- Planets and comets travel along elliptical orbits around the Sun.

- They are held in their orbits by the force of gravity.

- They must travel at just the right speed if they are to stay in their orbit.

Do you ever watch satellite television? The signals relayed from a satellite out in space are picked up by a dish on the outside of the house. Weather forecasters also make use of satellites, to photograph cloud patterns and to make other measurements.

Over the poles

Some **satellites** are used to monitor the Earth. They travel along orbits quite close to the Earth's surface – perhaps 500 km up. They take about 90 minutes to make one complete orbit.

As they orbit, the Earth is turning beneath them. This means that they get a different view during each orbit.

The pull of the Earth's gravity keeps these satellites in their orbits, just as the planets are kept in orbit round the Sun by the pull of its gravity. Without the Earth's gravity, satellites would fly off into space.

a How can satellites help weather forecasters?

Far out in space

The satellites that relay television programmes are known as **communications satellites**. They are much farther out in space than monitoring satellites – about 40 000 km away. The Earth's gravity is much weaker out there, so the satellites need only travel quite slowly to stay in their orbits. They take much longer to orbit the Earth – 24 hours in fact.

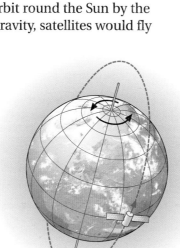

A monitoring satellite in a polar orbit.

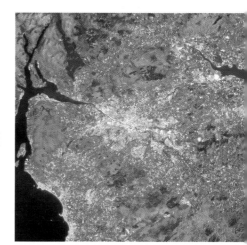

Monitoring satellites can make detailed images of the Earth's surface, such as this view of Glasgow and central Scotland.

Their orbit has been chosen specially. They are directly above the equator, and they travel around at the same rate that the Earth is spinning. This means that they appear to stay at the same point in the sky all the time. A television satellite dish points directly at the satellite which is sending it signals.

This special orbit is described as **geostationary**, which means 'Earth-stationary'. If you could look down on the Earth from the satellite, you would see that you were directly above a fixed point on the equator all the time. If the satellite was in an orbit closer to the Earth, or farther away, it would move gradually across the sky, and your dish would have to move round to keep track of it.

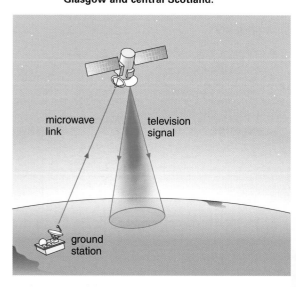

microwave link

television signal

ground station

There is only room for about 400 satellites spaced out around the orbit. If there were more, they would be too close together and your dish would pick up signals from two or more at the same time, and this would cause interference.

b If you look at the satellite dishes on houses in your neighbourhood, they all appear to be pointing in the same direction. Why is this?

International calls

If you have relatives or friends living in a distant part of the world, it is likely that your phonecalls to them are transmitted via communications satellites. The signal is beamed up to the satellite, and then sent down to a distant receiving station.

c Draw a diagram to show how a phonecall could be transmitted from the UK to India via a communications satellite.

This mobile telephone can be used in remote parts of the world. Its aerial sends signals up to a communications satellite.

DIGGING DEEPER
If you have a telephone conversation with someone on the other side of the world, you may notice a short delay before you hear their reply to your questions. This is partly because the signal has to travel out into space and back again; it is also partly due to delays introduced by the electronic switching systems used.

Questions

1 Copy the table; choose words from the list to fill the spaces in the first column.

geostationary   orbit   gravity   satellite   communications

	A spacecraft travelling around the Earth
	The path of a spacecraft travelling around the Earth
	Describes a spacecraft used for transmitting television programmes
	Describes the path of a spacecraft used for transmitting television programmes
	The force which keeps a spacecraft moving along a circular path

2 How might these people benefit from satellites?

a A meteorologist (weather forecaster).

b A sports fan.

c Someone from Australia working in the UK.

3 Many satellites orbit the Earth:

• monitoring satellites orbit close to the Earth;

• communications satellites orbit about 40 000 km away;

• the Moon is the Earth's natural satellite, about 400 000 km away.

a Which of these travels fastest? Which travels most slowly?

b Why does a communications satellite feel a weaker pull of the Earth's gravity than a monitoring satellite?

Summary

• Satellites orbit the Earth; they are held in their orbits by the Earth's gravity.

• Monitoring satellites provide useful information about the Earth's surface, e.g. for weather forecasting.

• Communications satellites are further out, in geostationary orbits, taking 24 hours to complete one orbit. They transmit television and telephone signals.

The Sun is a star – a fairly average star. Beyond the Solar System, there are billions more.

It can be difficult to see the stars in the night sky. It may be cloudy, and streetlights may fill the sky with light. But if you can find a dark place on a clear night, you'll see that the sky is filled with hundreds of stars.

The Sun belongs to a vast group of stars called the **Milky Way**. You may be able to see the Milky Way as a broad, cloudy band of stars, stretching across the night sky. (It's quite difficult to see this from the UK, but you may have seen it more clearly on a foreign holiday.) This cluster of billions of stars is our **galaxy**.

The Milky Way is a broad band of stars across the night sky.

Star city

If you could look at our galaxy from far off, you would see that it is like a flat disc with a spiral shape. There is a huge cluster of stars at the centre, and two spiral arms trailing out into space. Our Sun is halfway out along one of the arms.

We don't see our galaxy as a spiral or as a disc. That's because we're inside it. When we look across the disc, we see the thick band of stars we call the Milky Way. In other directions we see fewer stars and more black space.

It is impossible to count all the stars in the Milky Way. There are probably about 100 000 million of them. A galaxy is like a giant city of stars. Our home is in the Solar System, far from the city centre, out in the suburbs.

The stars in a galaxy are far apart. It takes a spacecraft several years to reach the furthest planets, but it would take many centuries to reach the next star. The distances between stars are millions of times greater than the distances between planets in the Solar System.

Our solar system

The Milky Way is a spiral galaxy.

a Put these in order, from smallest to biggest:

   planet   Solar System   galaxy   star

More stars, more galaxies

With binoculars or a telescope, you can see many more stars in the night sky. These are all part of our own galaxy. But far beyond our galaxy there are other galaxies, and you may be able to see some of them if you know where to look.

Astronomers have seen and photographed many more galaxies. Some are spirals, like the Milky Way; others have more irregular shapes. They believe there may be as many as 100 000 million galaxies in the **Universe**.

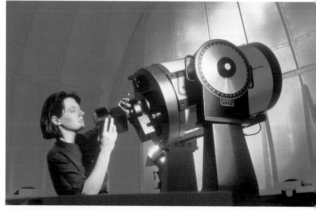

The bigger the telescope, the more light it can collect from distant stars.

The Universe is the whole of space that we can possibly see. It contains all the matter and energy we can know about.

- stars in one galaxy: 100 000 000 000
- galaxies in Universe: 100 000 000 000

    so stars in Universe: 10 000 000 000 000 000 000 000

That's a lot of stars!

b Check that calculation: add up all the zeroes in the first two numbers. Are there the same number of zeroes in the final number?

Sticking together

Stars group together to form a galaxy. They are attracted to each other by gravity. Gravity stops a galaxy from falling apart.

Astronomers have found that galaxies are grouped together as well. A galaxy is a very big object with lots of mass, so its gravity is strong and spreads far out into empty space. Galaxies attract each other, and so they cluster together. The same force that holds us onto the Earth's surface holds giant galaxy clusters together.

Because galaxies cluster together, there is lots of empty space in between them.

Powerful telescopes can show up other galaxies like these, far beyond the Milky Way.

Questions

1 Copy and complete these definitions. Choose words from the list to fill the gaps:

   the Universe   a galaxy   gravity   the Milky Way

   a A group of millions of stars is called _____.

   b Our galaxy is called _____.

   c The force that holds a galaxy together is _____.

   d All the matter and energy we can know about make up _____.

2 **a** Make a sketch to show the shape of our galaxy.

   b Mark the position of the Sun.

3 Imagine that you had an ultra-fast spaceship. Describe what you would see if you set off into space, travelling right across the Universe.

4 Which contains most stars: a galaxy, the Solar System, the Universe?

DIGGING DEEPER
It may be hard to believe, but there are more stars in the Universe than there are grains of sand on all the beaches in the world.

Summary
- The Sun is just one of billions of stars which make up our galaxy, the Milky Way.

- The stars in a galaxy are held together by the force of gravity.

- The stars in a galaxy are far apart, compared with the distances between planets. Galaxies are far apart, compared with the distances between stars.

Astronomers believe that our Sun is a fairly ordinary star, roughly halfway through its life. But how did it begin? And why will it end?

Birth of a star

When astronomers use powerful telescopes to look at distant galaxies, they can see giant dust clouds where new stars are forming. This gives them an idea about how the solar system formed.

Most scientists think that the solar system formed from a giant, swirling cloud of dust and gas. The gravity of each particle in the cloud pulled on all the others, so that they got closer and closer together.

◆ Gravity pulled together a lot of gas (mostly hydrogen) to form the Sun. As it got more and more squashed together, it got hotter and hotter as the molecules bounced off each other.

◆ Dust collected together to form the inner rocky planets – Mercury, Venus, Earth and Mars.

◆ Further out, where it was cooler, gases collected together to form the outer planets.

a **Name two rocky planets and two gassy planets.**

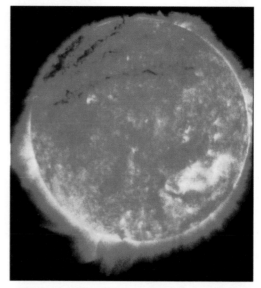

Space telescopes show that the surface of the Sun is patterned with hotter and cooler regions.

A scientific idea of how the solar system formed.

Billions of years

The Sun has lasted for about 5 billion years, and will probably last for another 7.5 billion years. It is very stable, because the inward pull of gravity is balanced by the outward force of the hot particles pushing against each other.

Towards the end of its life, the Sun will expand and become cooler – a **red giant**. It is likely to swallow up the inner planets, including the Earth. Later, its gravity will pull it back in so that it becomes a small, bright star – a **white dwarf**. The matter in such a star is highly compressed, with a density millions of times more than any matter on Earth.

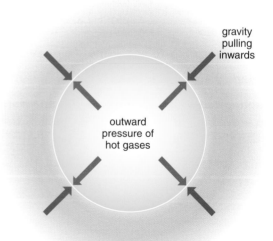

gravity pulling inwards

outward pressure of hot gases

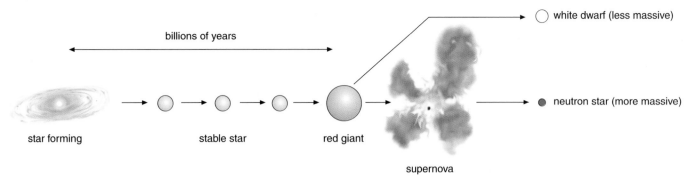

billions of years

star forming   stable star   red giant

white dwarf (less massive)

supernova

neutron star (more massive)

The life of stars; how they end up depends on their mass.

Heavier stars

A star which is heavier than the Sun has a different history. After becoming a red giant, it collapses inwards and then explodes outwards – a **supernova**. Gas and dust fly out into space. The small remnant becomes a very dense **neutron star**.

b What is the likely lifespan of the Sun, in billions of years?

c Which is hotter, a red giant or a white dwarf?

Questions

1 Copy the table. Choose words from the list to fill the first column.

neutron star   red giant   gravity
dust and gas   white dwarf

	The force which pulls matter together to form a star.
	The matter from which a star forms.
	The Sun will become this when it swells up and cools.
	The Sun will become this towards the end of its life.
	What remains of a star after it has exploded as a supernova.

2 **a** What gas did the Sun mostly form from?

  b Why does the Sun have a strong gravitational pull?

3 Which is denser, a red giant or a white dwarf?

4 Draw a diagram to show the different stages in the life of the Sun.

DIGGING DEEPER
The Sun is a ball of gas. Because of this, it rotates in a different way from the Earth. By watching sunspots as they travelled around, astronomers noticed that the Sun spins faster at its equator than at its poles. (Time for one rotation = 25 days at equator, 35 days at poles.)

Summary

- The force of gravity causes stars, and the planets which orbit them, to form from clouds of dust and gas in space.

- Eventually, the Sun will expand to become a red giant, and then contract to become a white dwarf.

- A heavier star may explode as a supernova, leaving a neutron star behind.

Astronomers have discovered dozens of planets in orbit around other stars. But is there any evidence that any of them are inhabited by living creatures? And is there life elsewhere in the solar system?

A century ago, an American called Percival Lowell made a detailed study of Mars. He expected to see evidence of life there. His telescope gave him a rather blurred view, and he thought he could see signs of a network of canals, constructed by martian engineers. Now we know that there are no seas or canals on Mars.

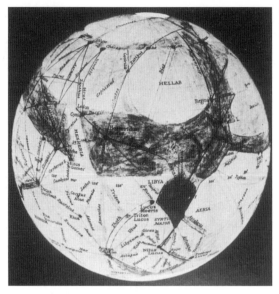
One of Percival Lowell's drawings of 'seas' and 'canals' on Mars.

Looking for life

One way to look for life in the solar system is to send a spacecraft. We can receive pictures back on Earth, or a robot machine might collect samples and return them to Earth. Spacecraft have visited some likely places, including Mars and one of Jupiter's moons called Europa. Images and samples can be examined to see if they contain anything living, or any fossils. So far, nothing has been found.

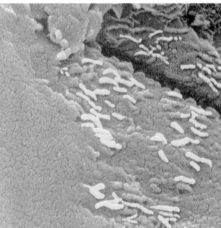

This lump of rock is a meteorite which came from Mars. Some scientists claim to have found fossilised bacteria in it, but many others disagree with their findings.

Checking the atmosphere

When a spacecraft was sent to Jupiter, it looked back towards Earth. It could detect the oxygen in our atmosphere. Oxygen is a good indicator of life; on a dead planet, the oxygen has all been used up and is trapped in rocks. On Earth, plants produce oxygen so that animals can live.

Scientists look for such signs of life in the atmospheres of other planets. They might also place a sample of material from another planet in a sealed container to see if the air around it changes because of the presence of living organisms.

a Why are plants necessary if animals are to live?

This spacecraft has landed on Mars. A small rover vehicle has moved over to the rock on the right. By checking soil and atmospheric gases, such a craft could look for signs of life.

Listening for life

Because we broadcast radio and television signals around the world, we are sending messages out into space all the time. Observers on a different planet might detect these and wonder whether there was intelligent life on Earth.

Radio telescopes provide lots of useful information about stars and other galaxies, but so far they have not detected signals from intelligent creatures elsewhere in space.

Scientists have been listening out for radio signals coming from space for over 40 years. (This is known as the Search for Extra-Terrestrial Intelligence, SETI.) They hope to find meaningful, regular signals which would indicate that another civilisation was trying to get in touch; so far, they have detected nothing but random 'noise'.

- Some scientists argue that there are billions of planets in the Universe. Many are similar to Earth, and so are likely to support life.

- Other scientists argue that, if there is intelligent life elsewhere, it would have made contact with us by now.

b What do you think?

Questions

1 What do the letters 'SETI' stand for?

2 When the Earth formed, its atmosphere was mostly nitrogen, carbon dioxide and sulphur dioxide. Now the atmosphere contains 20% oxygen. Why has its composition changed?

3 Saturn has a rocky moon called Titan. List some ways in which we could look for evidence of life on Titan.

4 We could try to make contact with an alien civilisation by sending signals out into space. Do you think we should try this? What signals should we send?

DIGGING DEEPER

In the nineteenth century, scientists took very seriously the idea that there were people similar to us on Mars. They debated the ways in which they might differ from us, and how we should behave when we eventually met them.

Summary

- Scientists have used various methods to look for life elsewhere in the solar system and beyond. So far, they have been unsuccessful.

Astronomers have discovered planets orbiting around distant stars.
Could one of these planets be home to intelligent life?

Here is a discussion from an imaginary chat-room for astronomy students.

Starmaster: *We've notched up over 70 extra-solar planets now. What do you think the chances are of finding life out there?*

OllieG: *Pretty low, I reckon. They're mostly giant planets and close to their stars. Would you want to live on a hot Jupiter? I don't think there could be much more than a bunch of bacteria out there, at most.*

Smith@Oxford: *Perhaps you're thinking too much about life on Earth. It could be completely different out there – evolution has turned up some pretty strange creatures. Think of those worms living in red-hot water in the ocean depths. And there are bacteria living in cracks in the rocks hundreds of metres below the Earth's surface.*

OllieG: *Did you ever meet an intelligent worm or bacteria?*

Starmaster: *What should we be looking for if we want to find life on a distant planet?*

Smith@Oxford: *There's a chance we might be able to see the planet's atmosphere. At least, we might pick up light from the planet and be able to analyse it, find out what it's made of. Look for methane and oxygen.*

Astropat: *Can I join in? What's methane got to do with it?*

Smith@Oxford: *Animals produce methane. Plants produce oxygen. Methane gets oxidised quickly, so if there's any there, there must be animals or rotting plants producing it.*

OllieG: *Sounds a smelly old planet. I'm not going if there's no oxygen.*

Starmaster: *Who said anything about going there?*

OllieG: *It's one of the options.*

Astropat: *It would take several lifetimes. These planets are light-years away. Better to send a signal. We might get a reply before we die.*

Starmaster: *Isn't that dangerous? Drawing attention to ourselves, inviting attention from aliens?*

OllieG: *You won't get a Nobel prize if you don't take chances. And what's the alternative?*

Starmaster: *Just sit quiet and listen. Perhaps there's someone out there trying to make contact.*

Astropat: *But that still leaves you with the same problem. Are you going to reply if you pick up their signals?*

Smith@Oxford: *We've got a radio telescope here. We could put in a bid to use it when it's not in service, either to send signals or to search for them.*

You can't have intelligent life with just one head

OllieG:	*Any chance of using it on the quiet? We don't want too many people asking awkward questions.*
Astropat:	*Don't you think a lot of people would want to have a say in this?*
OllieG:	*There's always people ready to get in the way of scientific progress.*
Smith@Oxford:	*Yes, it's the next logical step really, making contact with other intelligent civilisations.*

Questions

Science is a mixture of facts, theories and debates. Here are some questions about factual information in the chat-room discussion.

1 The newly discovered planets are described as *extra-solar planets*. What does *extra-solar* mean?

2 The new planets are described as *hot Jupiters*. They are as big as Jupiter, or bigger. Why are they hot? Why might they be difficult for life to exist on?

3 The gas we use for cooking is methane, CH_4. When it burns, it combines with oxygen from the air. What two substances are produced? Why is methane in a planet's atmosphere a sign of life?

Here are some questions about scientific theories.

4 Do the people in the discussion appear to believe in the theory of evolution?

5 Many people do not accept the theory of evolution. What alternative ideas do they have?

6 If living creatures were found on another planet, would it change their ideas?

Here are some questions about debates in science.

7 In the chat-room discussion, who seems to be most prepared to take risks and ignore other people's ideas? Give an example to support your answer.

8 Who seems to think that science moves ahead with its own momentum, rather than being under human control? Give an example to support your answer.

9 The students are suggesting a project to contact alien civilisations. What are the dangers of this?

10 How could the students' project be debated more widely? Who should be involved in the debate? Who should decide whether the project should go ahead?

11 Give an example of a scientific idea or problem which has been in the public eye recently. Who has been involved in the debate? Where could you find out about the debate? Is there any way you could contribute to the debate?

End of module questions

1 A truck is moving along a straight road. The table shows how its position changes with time.

Distance travelled (m)	0	250	500	750	1000
Time taken (s)	0	10	20	30	40

a Draw a distance–time graph to represent the truck's motion.

b Explain how you can tell from the graph that the truck is moving at a steady speed.

c How far did the truck travel in the first 10 s? Use this information to calculate the truck's speed.

d What other piece of information would you need in order to know the truck's *velocity*?

2

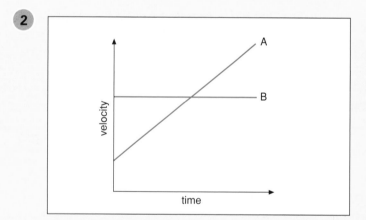

The graph represents the motion of two cars, A and B.

a Which car is moving at a steady speed, A or B?

b Explain how you can tell this from the graph.

c Is the other car speeding up or slowing down?

3 A cyclist is travelling along a straight road. She reaches the top of a steep slope, and speeds up as she runs downhill.

At the top of the hill, her speed is 5 m/s. 4 s later, she is moving at 13 m/s.

a By how much has her speed increased during the 4 s?

b Calculate her acceleration, giving the correct units.

4 The car in the picture is moving along a straight road at a steady speed. The arrows show the forces acting on the car.

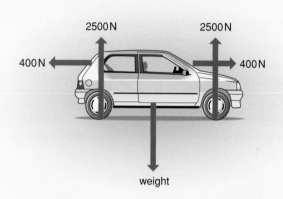

a Are the forces acting on the car balanced or unbalanced? Give a reason to support your answer.

b How big is the force of air resistance on the car?

c How big is the weight of the car?

5 The drawings show a parachutist at different points in his free fall. The arrows indicate the forces acting on him.

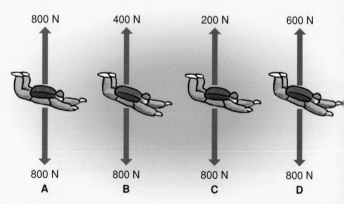

a At point A, he is moving at a steady speed. Explain how you can tell this from the diagram.

b At the other three points, the parachutist is accelerating (speeding up). At which point does he have the greatest acceleration? Explain your answer.

6 The stopping distance of a car as it travels along a road is made up of the thinking distance and the braking distance:

$$\text{Stopping distance} = \text{thinking distance} + \text{braking distance}.$$

a Explain as fully as you can why the braking distance may be greater if the road is wet or icy.

b Explain as fully as you can why the stopping distance may be greater if the driver has been drinking alcohol.

7 A sprinter of mass 80 kg is running at 10 m/s. Calculate her kinetic energy in joules (J).

8 The boy in the picture pushes a heavy box for a distance of 10 m along the ground. If the boy's pushing force is 150 N, calculate the work he does in pushing the box.

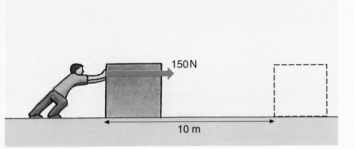

9 Jupiter is a planet with several moons in orbit around it. The diagram shows the orbits of four of these moons.

a What force holds the moons in their orbits?

b Which moon takes longest to make a complete orbit around Jupiter? Give a reason for your answer.

10 The diagram shows two satellites in orbit around the Earth.

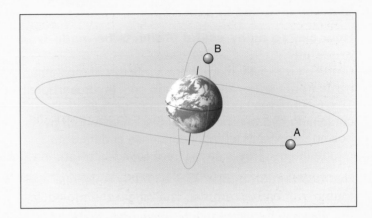

a Satellite A is in a geostationary orbit. How long does it take to orbit the Earth?

b Suggest a use for satellite A.

c Satellite B is a monitoring satellite. Explain how its orbit allows it to monitor the whole of the Earth's surface.

11 The Sun is a star in the Milky Way galaxy.

a What is a galaxy?

b The Sun formed from a cloud of dust and gas in space. Explain how this happened.

c Eventually, the Sun will swell up so that it engulfs the Earth. What type of star will it have become?

12 The atmosphere of the Earth contains a lot of oxygen. So far, no other planets or moons in the solar system have been found with as much oxygen in their atmospheres.

Explain what this suggests about the existence of life on these other planets and moons.

Recap material – paper 2

Module 06: Earth materials

Material included in paper 2

How can so many useful products be made from crude oil?

Crude oil is mostly made from a mixture of molecules made from carbon and hydrogen only (hydrocarbons). This mixture may be separated into fractions containing hydrocarbons of similar chain length by boiling the oil and letting it condense at different temperatures. This is called fractional distillation.

Hydrocarbon properties vary with the molecular size (number of carbon atoms). The bigger the molecule, the higher the boiling point, which makes the hydrocarbon less volatile. Large hydrocarbons can be heated and 'cracked' (broken down) to make smaller and more useful molecules, some of which are used as fuels. A hot catalyst is used to speed up this thermal decomposition. Other products of cracking are used to make plastics (polymers) such as poly(ethene) and poly(propene).

Fuels containing carbon and hydrogen release carbon dioxide and water into the atmosphere when burnt. They may also contain some sulphur, which forms sulphur dioxide.

Why have all mountains on Earth not worn away by now?

At the surface of the Earth younger sedimentary rocks are found on top of older ones. They can show evidence about how they formed, such as ripple marks caused by current or wave action, or horizontal bedding caused by discontinuous deposition.

Older sedimentary rock layers can sometimes be found tilted, folded, fractured (faulted) and even overturned. This shows evidence of enormous forces and that the Earth's crust is unstable in places.

Recap questions

1. A chemical engineer was analysing a new oil to see if it contained a fraction suitable for use as petrol. From a book of data she obtained the following boiling points for hydrocarbons.

Number of carbon atoms	Boiling point (°C)
6	69
7	99
8	
9	151
10	174

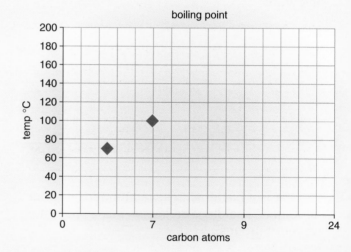

a Copy and complete the graph, drawing a line of best fit

b At what temperature do you think a hydrocarbon with 8 carbon atoms would boil?

c The engineer read that petrol contains chains with 8 carbon atoms. When she distilled her oil she got three fractions.

Fraction	Temperature collected (°C)	Amount collected (cm³)
1	99	40
2	126	30
3	151	30

Which fraction would be best to use for petrol? Explain your answer.

d If this oil was processed commercially, what volume of 'petrol' would you get from every 100 litres of oil? Show your working

2 Fuels are chemicals we burn to get energy.

a Copy and complete the generalised word equation for this:

fuel + _____ → waste gases + energy

b Is this reaction endothermic or exothermic?

c Most fuels contain carbon and hydrogen atoms. Which two new compounds are formed when these fuels burn?

d Write this as a word equation:

fuel + _____ → _____ + _____

e Fossil fuels often contain sulphur. What gas is formed from these atoms when the fuel burns?

f Why is this a problem?

3 Copy and complete the following sentences. Use the words below to fill the gaps.

erosion overturned mountains forces youngest

Sedimentary rocks form in horizontal layers with the _____ at the top. But in places you can find them folded, faulted, tilted to high angles or even _____. This shows that the surface of the Earth is very unstable and that powerful _____ are at work. These forces can slowly build up new _____ to replace those worn down by _____.

4 Some igneous rocks found in the mountains of Scotland formed during a period of mountain building 400 million years ago, some 40 km down in the Earth's crust.

a How is it that these rocks can be seen at the surface today?

b Copy and use the table below to work out just how fast (or slow!) this process has been.

time taken	amount of erosion
400 million years	40 km that's...
400 000 000 years	40 000 metres or...
	40 000 000 millimetres
divide both by 4 ...	
100 000 000 years	_____millimetres
now divide by 1000 000	
100 years	_____millimetres
divide by 10...	
10 years	___ millimetre
1 year	_____ millimetre

5 The Atlantic Ocean is getting wider! In places it is 400 km wide. Using lasers we can measure this distance very accurately – and we can see that it is getting wider by 2 cm every year!

If we go back in time, that means that the Ocean will have been smaller and smaller. Go back far enough and it will not exist at all!

Copy and complete this table and use it to work out how old the Atlantic Ocean is. (Note: this is just a rough approximation.)

distance	time taken
2 cm	1 year
2 m	_____ years
20 m	1000 years
20 km	1_____ years
2000 km	_____ years
4000 km	_____years

Module 09: Energy

Material included in paper 2

Heat energy is transferred out of buildings by conduction, convection and radiation. By understanding these mechanisms, we can show how to reduce the rate of heat loss from buildings.

Electrical devices can perform many useful energy transfers. However, some of the energy transferred is wasted; the devices are not 100% efficient. All of the energy transferred eventually ends up in the environment, making it warmer.

Electricity is generated in a variety of ways; each has an impact on the environment.

- Burning fossil fuels produces waste gases, including carbon dioxide (which increases the greenhouse effect) and sulphur dioxide (which produces acid rain).
- Nuclear power stations produce radioactive waste.
- Wind farms can be ugly and noisy.
- Hydroelectric and tidal schemes flood land which might have other uses.

Each method of generating electricity has other advantages and disadvantages. For example:

- Nuclear power stations are slow to start up.
- Solar cells are expensive, but useful in remote locations.
- Wind and solar power are dependent on the climate; tidal power depends on the state of the tide.

You should be able to compare their merits, including the various costs involved, and the need to match supply and demand.

Recap questions

1. In the UK, most of our electricity comes from power stations where fossil fuels are burned. In order to use less fossil fuels, an increasing amount of electricity is generated in power stations which use alternatives to fossil fuels.

    a Give one reason why it is desirable to find alternatives to fossil fuels.

    b The table shows three ways of generating electricity. Unfortunately, none of these can be relied on to provide a steady supply of electricity. Copy the table, and in the second column, explain why the supply from each varies considerably.

Method of supply	Reason why supply varies
Tidal power station	
Wind generators	
Solar cells	

    c New nuclear power stations may be built in the UK. Explain why this may lead to concern among people who live nearby.

    d Solar cells are expensive to make, so the electricity they produce is costly. State one situation in which they would be a good choice for producing electricity, and give a reason to support your choice.

2. Ayan wants to save some money on her heating bills. She also wants to help to protect the environment.

    The local council recently sent her a leaflet about saving energy around the home. Here is a table from the leaflet that shows you how insulating your house can save you money:

Type of insulation	Cost to install	Saving each year on your fuel bill
Loft insulation	£200	£100
Double glazing	£1500	£50
Hot water cylinder jacket	£10	£60
Aluminium foil behind radiators	£2	£10
Cavity wall insulation	£500	£100
Draught excluders	£60	£15

Ayan can't afford to make all the changes this year.

    a Which two types of insulation will save more money from her bill in one year than they cost to install?

    b How many years will it take for Ayan to save back the installation cost of:

        i   Loft insulation?

        ii Draught excluders?

        iii Double glazing?

    c Ayan decides that she can afford to spend up to £500 on insulation this year. What forms of insulation would you advise her to spend her money on? Explain your answer.

d Ayan's house is heated using oil. Is oil a renewable or non-renewable energy resource?

e Oil is burnt to heat the water in Ayan's boiler. Which greenhouse gas does burning oil produce?

f Explain why installing insulation will help to protect the environment.

3 In the Kyoto agreement many countries of the world agreed to reduce the amount of carbon dioxide they produce. The government need to build a new power station. Three plans have been submitted from three different companies.

Company	Energy for power station	Cost per Unit of electricity
PowerJen	Nuclear	2.4p
Fidlerfan	Wind	2.6p
Thornelectric	Coal	1.3p

a Which power station uses a renewable energy source?

b Which power station will cause most carbon dioxide to be released into the atmosphere?

c Which power station are local residents most likely to object to?

d The UK is a very wealthy country. Which power station are they most likely to build if they want to minimise carbon dioxide emissions?

e Poor countries need power stations to help them develop. Why might poor countries feel that the Kyoto agreement is unfair?

4 Recently there have been many fires on lorries travelling through tunnels. Fires in tunnels get very hot.

In order to put the fires out, firemen need to get close to the base of the fire. Kent fire department want to buy a new suit to protect firemen when they are putting out fires in tunnels.

Kent fire department has found three different fireproof materials that the suits can be made from. Each material is a different colour:

- Black
- Red
- Silver

a Which colour material will protect the fire officers best?

b Name three ways in which heat may be transferred from the fire to the fire officer.

5 Louise gets into an elevator and goes up three floors. The lift motor uses 27 Mj of electrical energy to gain 11Mj of gravitational energy. The rest of the energy is lost as heat.

a Draw an energy transfer diagram for Louise's trip in the elevator.

b How much heat energy is lost?

c Show that the elevator's efficiency is about 40%

d The elevator motor is painted black. Why might this be?

Efficiency = useful energy transferred by device/total energy supplied to the device

6 Martin is a rally driver. When he slams the brakes on in his car the brakes glow red-hot. Draw an energy transfer diagram to show the energy transfers that take place when Martin slams on the brakes.

Material included in paper 2

Potential difference, current and resistance are related by:

p.d. (V) = current (A) × resistance (Ω)

The graphs show how p.d. and current are related for three devices.

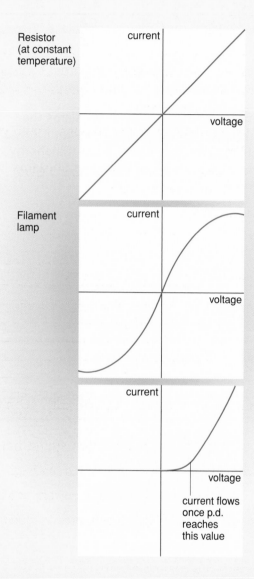

Resistor (at constant temperature)

Filament lamp

current flows once p.d. reaches this value

A light dependent resistor has less resistance when light falls on it; a thermistor has less resistance when it is hotter.

When a wire carrying a current is placed in a magnetic field, a force acts on it. The greater the current and the stronger the field, the greater the force. This is made use of in electric motors and circuit breakers.

A voltage can be induced by moving a magnet into and out of a coil of wire, or by rotating a coil in a magnetic field. To increase the induced voltage:

- use a stronger magnetic field;
- increase the speed of movement;
- use a coil with more turns, or a greater area.

An a.c. generator has slip rings and brushes to lead the current away. You should be able to explain how such a generator works.

Recap questions

1 The diagram shows an experiment to investigate a thermistor. The thermistor is connected in series with a lamp, an ammeter and a battery. As the water is heated, the thermistor gets hotter.

The graph shows how the current flowing through the thermistor depends on its temperature.

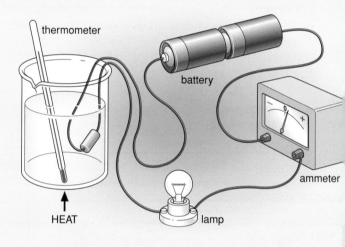

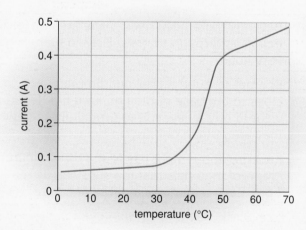

a Describe what the graph shows about how the resistance of the thermistor changes as it is heated.

b The lamp will light up if the current flowing through it is greater than 0.4 A. Describe how the brightness of the lamp will change as the water is heated, starting at 20 °C.

2 The diagram shows an experiment to investigate the factors which affect an induced voltage. The coil of wire is connected to a voltmeter. The magnet can be moved in and out of the coil.

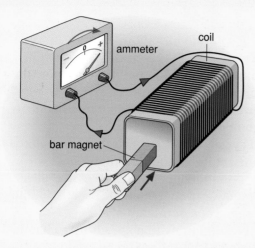

In the table below, the first column shows how the magnet can be moved in different ways. Copy the table and in the second column, write down how you would expect the reading on the voltmeter to change as a result. (The first row has been completed.)

Choose from:

Voltage increases

Voltage decreases

Voltage reverses

Voltage becomes zero

Movement of magnet	Reading on voltmeter
North pole moved in quickly	Large voltage
South pole moved in quickly	
North pole moved in slowly	
Magnet held still inside coil	

3 Alex was writing up her lab work at home. Unfortunately she had rushed her work in class and had forgotten to write down some important information about her results.

During the class she had tested a lamp and a diode. For each she measured the current flowing through the component and the voltage across it. She then reversed the connections to each component and tried again.

Here is Alex's results table:

Voltage (V)	Current in component A (amps)		Current in component B (amps)	
	Normal	Reversed	Normal	Reversed
0	0	0	0	0
2	0.4	−0.4	0.2	0
4	0.7	−0.7	0.4	0
6	0.87	−0.87	0.6	0
8	0.95	−0.95	0.8	0
10	1.0	−1.0	1.0	0

a Draw two sets of axes to show Alex's results. (You will need to put current on the y-axis and voltage on the x-axis).

b Plot the results for each component onto your axes.

c Is component A a lamp or a diode? Give reasons for your decision.

4 Ali measured the current through and the voltage across a resistor and recorded his results.

Voltage (V)	Current (A)
2.50	0.04
4.10	0.07
5.90	0.10
9.70	0.16
11.50	0.19

a Plot a graph of his results, with current on the x-axis.

b Draw a best fit straight line through his points.

c Comment on the accuracy of his readings.

d Use the graph to estimate the current at 8V.

e Extrapolate the graph to estimate the current at 15V.

5 In a simple electric motor, a coil spins in a magnetic field. What would happen to the spinning motor if each of the following changes was made:

a The current was increased.

b The current were reversed.

c The number of turns in the coil was reduced.

Glossary of terms

acceleration   The rate of change of velocity; acceleration = change of velocity/time taken.

activation energy   The energy needed to start a reaction: used to break bonds.

adapt   To become more suitable for.

adaptation/s   A feature or features that make a structure more suitable for its function.

air resistance   The drag force on an object moving through the air; a form of friction.

albino   Lack of a pigment in the skin, fur or feathers causing an animal become white.

alkali metal   A reactive metal, such as sodium from group 1 of the periodic table, that reacts with water to form an alkaline solution.

allele   Some genes have two different forms called alleles.

amplitude   The height of a wave; its maximum disturbance.

anaemia   A disorder affecting red blood cells. Because of this, blood cannot carry enough oxygen.

analogue   An analogue signal has a shape which corresponds to the shape of the signal being carried; the opposite of a digital signal.

anhydrous   Without water of crystallisation.

antibiotics   Chemicals used to destroy bacteria in the body.

asexual reproduction   Reproduction that does not involve the formation of gametes. New organisms formed by asexual reproduction are genetically identical to the parent organism.

atomic number   The number of protons in an atom; same as the proton number.

atoms   The smallest part of an element that still has the properties of that element.

background radiation   We are exposed to background radiation all the time, from radioactive substances around us, and from cosmic rays.

balanced equation   A way of describing a chemical reaction using formulae for reactants and products; the number of each type of atom must be the same on both sides of the equation.

batch process   A process such as fermentation where a fixed amount of reagents are reacted in discrete units.

biomass   The mass of living organisms in an area.

boiling point   The temperature at which all of a liquid turns to a gas.

braking distance   The distance travelled by a car while the brakes are applied.

brine   A solution of sodium chloride in water, such as sea water.

camouflage   A feature that makes it more difficult to spot an organism.

carbohydrase   An enzyme that breaks down carbohydrates.

carbon cycle   The flow of carbon compounds through plants, animals and decomposers.

carrier   An individual with a recessive allele that does not show as a characteristic because of the presence of a dominant allele.

catalyst   Something that speeds up a chemical reaction without itself being used up.

chemical formula   A description of a chemical compound using symbols and numbers to show how many of each type of atom is found in that compound.

chromosomes   Long threads containing many genes, found in the nucleus of a cell.

clone   Group of genetically identical organisms.

closed system   A reacting system is closed if none of the products can escape.

communications satellite   A spacecraft orbiting the Earth used to transmit telephone and TV signals.

compete   Try to gain an advantage over another organism.

competition   What happens when there are not enough resources for all the organisms in a habitat.

compost   Decaying remains of plants.

compounds   A new substance formed when atoms from two or more elements become chemically joined together.

concentration   The amount of a chemical in a fixed volume of solution.

condense   To turn from a gas to a liquid.

continuous process   A process such as oil refining where reagents are continually fed into the reacting vessel and the products continually removed.

contraceptive pill   A pill containing hormones that prevent an egg becoming fertilised.

count rate   The reading on a Geiger counter showing the rate at which radiation has been detected.

covalent bonds   Chemical bonds formed when non-metals share electrons; molecules have covalent bonds.

covalent compound   A compound formed when atoms from two or more elements are joined by covalent bonds.

critical angle If a light ray strikes an internal surface at a greater angle than this, it will be reflected; none is refracted.

cuttings Small pieces of plant stem, root or leaf that grow into new plants.

cycle A series of processes that always occur in the same order.

cystic fibrosis An inherited disorder affecting the breathing and digestive systems. It is caused by a faulty recessive allele.

daughter atom An atom produced when a radioactive atom, the parent atom, decays.

decay The breakdown of dead and waste material. When a radioactive atom decays, it emits radiation and becomes a different type of atom.

decomposers Organisms that break down waste material and dead material.

diffraction The spreading out of waves when they pass through a gap or around an obstacle.

digital A digital signal carries information in the form of a string of on and off pulses; the opposite of an analogue signal.

distance–time graph A graph showing how the distance travelled by an object depends on the time.

dominant An allele that produces a characteristic when it is present on only one of a pair of chromosomes.

egg cell The female sex cell (gamete).

elastic potential energy Energy stored by an elastic object when it is stretched or squashed.

electrolysis The tearing apart of a molten (or dissolved) ionic compound using electricity.

electromagnetic radiation Energy travelling in the form of waves.

electromagnetic spectrum All types of electromagnetic radiation, arranged in order according to their wavelengths and frequencies.

electron A small particle with tiny mass and a single negative charge.

electron shells The positions that electrons can occupy around an atom – same as energy levels.

electronic structure The way electrons are arranged around an atom.

element Something made of one type of atom only.

ellipse A squashed circle; objects orbiting under gravity have orbits shaped like ellipses.

empirical formula The formula found by experiment given in terms of the simplest ratio of the elements.

endothermic A reaction that takes in energy.

energy levels The positions that electrons can occupy around an atom – same as electron shells.

enzyme An organic catalyst.

equilibrium The balance point in a reversible reaction reached when the rates of the forward and back reactions are equal.

evaporation When a liquid turns to a gas below its boiling point.

evolution The process of gradual change taking place in organisms over many generations. Organisms become better adapted to their environment.

exothermic A reaction that gives out energy.

extinct Extinct species used to live on the Earth but no longer exist.

fermentation The conversion of sugar to ethanol and carbon dioxide.

fertilisation The fusion of egg and sperm cells to form the first cell of a new individual.

fertilisers Chemicals that are used to make plants grow better and to increase the yield of crops.

fertility drug A drug used to increase the chances of a woman becoming pregnant.

fluids Liquids and gases are fluids; they are substances that can flow.

food chain A series of organisms, each dependent on the previous one for food.

food web A series of interconnected food chains.

force A push or a pull; measured in newtons (N).

formula mass (M_r) The sum of the relative atomic masses of all the atoms in a compound (e.g. for water H_2O: $2 \times 1 + 16 = 18$).

fossils The 'remains' of plants and animals from many years ago, found in rocks.

freezing When a liquid cools and turns to a solid.

frequency The number of waves per second; measured in hertz (Hz).

fructose A sweet sugar found in fruit.

galaxy A cluster of billions of stars, held together by gravity.

galena Lead sulphide, the ore of lead (PbS).

gametes Specialised sex cells involved in sexual reproduction in plants and animals.

gas syringe A graduated syringe used to measure the volume of a gas.

gene Part of a chromosome, which controls an inherited characteristic.

genetic engineering Changing the genes of an organism. For example, genes from humans can be added to bacteria.

geostationary A satellite in a geostationary orbit takes 24 hours to complete one orbit.

giant ionic structure A giant structure formed from positive and negative ions and held together by strong electrostatic forces.

glucose The simple sugar produced by photosynthesis.

GM crops   Genetically modified crops. These are crop plants that have had new genes added from another species.

gravitational potential energy (GPE)   The energy stored by an object that has been raised up against the force of gravity.

group   Name given to the vertical columns of the periodic table; elements in the same group have similar properties.

Haber process   The industrial process used to make ammonia from nitrogen and hydrogen.

haematite   An oxide ore of iron (Fe_2O_3).

half-life   The average time taken for half the atoms in a sample of a radioactive substance to decay.

halide   An ionic compound of one of the halogens, such as chlorine.

halogens   A member of group 7 of the periodic table, such as chlorine.

heat   Energy moving from a hotter place to a colder place, because of the temperature difference.

herbicides   Chemicals used to kill weeds.

hormones   Chemicals that are transported around the body in the blood. These chemicals control body processes.

immobilised enzyme   An enzyme that has been fixed in some way for use in an industrial process.

inherited disorders   Disorders that are caused by dominant or recessive alleles, which are passed from parents to their children.

insulation   A way of reducing heat loss.

intercropping   Growing one type of crop in between another type of crop.

ion   A charged particle.

ionic bond   A bond formed by the electrostatic attraction between oppositely charged ions.

ionic compound   A compound formed by the electrostatic attraction between oppositely charged ions.

ionic lattice   A giant structure formed from positive and negative ions and held together by strong electrostatic forces.

ionised   An ionised atom or molecule is electrically charged because it has lost or gained electrons.

isomerase   An enzyme that converts glucose to fructose.

isotopes   Atoms of an element come in different forms, depending on the numbers of neutrons they have in their nuclei.

kinetic energy   The energy of a moving object.

lactic acid   The acid that makes milk turn sour.

lactose   The sugar in milk.

light wave   A form of electromagnetic radiation which we can see.

limewater   A solution of calcium hydroxide; used as the test for carbon dioxide.

lipase   An enzyme that breaks down fats and oils.

longitudinal wave   Any wave in which particles move back and forth, along the direction in which the wave is travelling.

melting point   The temperature at which a solid turns to a liquid.

microbe   Another word for a microorganism.

microorganism   An organism so small that it can only be seen through a microscope.

Milky Way   Our galaxy.

model   In science we use models to help us explain ideas.

mole   The amount of a substance containing 6.02×10^{23} particles (e.g. the relative atomic mass or formula mass in grams).

molecules   Particles made from atoms joined by covalent bonds.

monatomic gases   Gases that exists as single atoms, such as helium or the other noble gases.

mutation   Change in a gene that produces new forms of the gene.

natural selection   Factors such as predation and competition for food affect the survival of organisms. Because of these factors, the best adapted organisms are selected for survival.

negative ion   An atom or cluster of atoms with a net negative charge.

neutron   A sub-atomic particle with no electric charge and a relative mass of 1.

neutron star   One way in which a star may end its life, as a giant ball of neutrons.

newton   The unit of force; symbol N.

noble gas   A member of group 0 (or 8) of the periodic table, such as neon.

non-renewable   Once used it cannot be replaced.

nuclear model   The picture of an atom with a tiny nucleus at its centre, and electrons orbiting it.

nucleon number   The number of nucleons (protons and neutrons) in a nucleus.

nucleus   The central part of the atom containing the proton(s) and, for all except hydrogen, the neutrons; has most of the mass of the atom.

open system   A reacting system is open if some of the products can escape (or are removed).

optical fibre   A fine glass fibre; a ray of light bounces along inside the fibre by total internal reflection, following its curves.

organic farming   Farming without using pesticides or manufactured fertilisers.

ovary   Female sex organ where eggs are produced.

parent atom   A radioactive atom which decays to become a daughter atom.

period   Horizontal row of the periodic table.

periodic table   A way of arranging all the different elements in a table to link up those with similar properties.

pesticides   Chemicals that kill pests such as insects.

photosynthesis   A series of reactions in which plants use light energy to make food.

pituitary gland   A gland in the brain that produces hormones, including hormones that control reproduction.

plum pudding model   The picture of an atom as a sphere of positive charge with negatively-charged electrons embedded in it.

pollen grains   Grains containing male gametes produced by the male parts of flowers.

positive ion   An atom or cluster of atoms with a net positive charge.

precipitate   An insoluble solid that sometimes forms when two reacting solutions are mixed.

pressure   The force a gas exerts over unit area.

prey   Animals that are eaten by other animals.

producers   Green plants that use light energy to make food.

products   The chemicals that form as a result of a chemical reaction.

protease   An enzyme that breaks down proteins.

proton   A sub-atomic particle with a positive charge and a relative mass of 1.

proton number   The number of protons in an atom.

pyramid of biomass   A diagram that shows the mass of living organisms at each stage in a food chain.

pyramid of numbers   A diagram that shows the number of organisms at each stage in a food chain.

pyrite   Fool's gold – the sulphide ore of iron (FeS_2).

radioactive isotopes   Atoms of an element may come in several forms or isotopes; some are radioactive.

reactants   The chemicals that react together in a chemical reaction.

reaction rate   The rate at which products are formed (or reactants are lost) in a chemical reaction.

recessive allele   An allele that produces a characteristic only when the dominant allele is not present.

recycle   Convert back into a useful material.

red giant   A stage in the life of a star; it swells up and becomes dimmer.

reflection   When waves bounce off a surface.

refraction   When waves change direction because they move into a different material where their speed changes.

relative atomic mass (A_r)   The number of protons added to the number of neutrons in an atom.

renewable   Can be replaced after being used up.

resistant   Antibiotic-resistant bacteria are not destroyed by the action of antibiotics.

respiration   A series of reactions in which living organisms release energy from food.

reversible reaction   A reaction which can occur in either direction.

rock salt   The natural mineral form of sodium chloride.

satellite   A spacecraft or other object in orbit around (for example) the Earth.

seismic wave   A shock wave travelling through the Earth; usually set off by an earthquake.

seismograph   An instrument for detecting seismic waves.

selective breeding   Selection of plants and animals for breeding because they have useful and desired characteristics.

sex chromosomes   The chromosomes that control the sex of a person. In humans, XY is male and XX female.

sickle cell disease   An inherited disease affecting red blood cells. People with the disease suffer from severe anaemia.

skin cancer   Cancer of skin cells, which can be caused by over-exposure to sunlight.

spectrum   A series of waves, arranged in order according to their wavelengths and frequencies.

speed   How far an object travels in a given time; speed = distance travelled/time taken.

sperm   The male sex cell (gamete).

stabilised enzyme   An enzyme that has been treated so that it will last for a long time in an industrial process.

starch   A carbohydrate made from glucose molecules joined together.

stomata   Tiny holes on the surfaces of plant leaves, which are used for exchanging gases with the atmosphere (singular: stoma).

stopping distance   The distance travelled by a vehicle between the time when the driver notices the need to stop and when the vehicle stops.

sublimation   When a solid turns straight into a gas (or vice versa).

sucrose   The sweet sugar used at home.

supernova   When a star explodes towards the end of its life.

surface area   The area of surface available for a chemical reaction to take place.

sustainable development   Development that conserves natural resources.

terminal velocity   The top speed of an object falling through the air.

testis Male sex organ where sperm cells are produced (plural: testes).

thinking distance The distance travelled by a vehicle between the time when the driver notices the need to stop and when the brakes are applied.

tissue culture A cloning technique involving growing groups of cells into new plants.

total internal reflection (TIR) When a ray is entirely reflected within a transparent material because its angle of incidence is greater than the critical angle.

transverse wave A wave in which particles move from side to side, at right angles to the direction in which the wave is moving.

ultrasound Sound which is too high-pitched to hear; its frequency is above 20 kHz.

Universe All the matter and energy that exists.

vapour A gas formed by evaporation from a liquid.

velocity The speed of an object in a particular direction.

wavelength The length of a single wave, measured from one wave crest to the next.

weight The force on an object caused by the pull of the Earth's gravity.

white dwarf A stage in the life of a star when it is relatively small, dense and bright.

womb Part of the female reproductive system. The lining of the womb provides food and oxygen for a growing embryo.

word equation A way of describing a chemical reaction by naming the reactants and products.

work Energy transferred by a force. Work done = force × distance moved in the direction of the force.

yeast A single-celled organism that ferments sugar to alcohol and carbon dioxide.

yield The amount of product you get; often expressed as a percentage of what is theoretically possible.

Data sheets

Reactivity Series of Metals

Potassium   most reactive

Sodium

Calcium

Magnesium

Aluminium

Carbon

Zinc

Iron

Tin

Lead

Hydrogen

Copper

Silver

Gold

Platinum   least reactive

(elements in italics, though non-metals, have been included for comparison).

Formulae of Some Common Ions

Positive ions		Negative ions	
Name	Formula	Name	Formula
Hydrogen	H^+	Chloride	Cl^-
Sodium	Na^+	Bromide	Br^-
Silver	Ag^+	Fluoride	F^-
Potassium	K^+	Iodide	I^-
Lithium	Li^+	Hydoxide	OH^-
Ammonium	NH_4^+	Nitrate	NO_3^-
Barium	Ba^{2+}	Oxide	O^{2-}
Calcium	Ca^{2+}	Sulphide	S^{2-}
Copper(II)	Cu^{2+}	Sulphate	SO_4^{2-}
Magnesium	Mg^{2+}	Carbonate	CO_3^{2-}
Zinc	Zn^{2+}		
Lead	$Pb2^+$		
Iron(II)	Fe^{2+}		
Iron(III)	Fe^{3+}		
Aluminium	Al^{3+}		

The periodic table of elements

KEY

Mass number A	1
	H
	Hydrogen
Atomic number (Proton number) Z	1

1	2		3	4	5	6	7	0
								4 **He** Helium 2
7 **Li** Lithium 3	9 **Be** Beryllium 4		11 **B** Boron 5	12 **C** Carbon 6	14 **N** Nitrogen 7	16 **O** Oxygen 8	19 **F** Fluorine 9	20 **Ne** Neon 10
23 **Na** Sodium 11	24 **Mg** Magnesium 12		27 **Al** Aluminium 13	28 **Si** Silicon 14	31 **P** Phosphorous 15	32 **S** Sulphur 16	35 **Cl** Chlorine 17	40 **Ar** Argon 18
39 **K** Potassium 19	40 **Ca** Calcium 20	45 **Sc** Scandium 21 48 **Ti** Titanium 22 51 **V** Vanadium 23 52 **Cr** Chromium 24 55 **Mn** Manganese 25 56 **Fe** Iron 26 59 **Co** Cobalt 27 59 **Ni** Nickel 28 63 **Cu** Copper 29 64 **Zn** Zinc 30	70 **Ga** Gallium 31	73 **Ge** Germanium 32	75 **As** Arsenic 33	79 **Se** Selenium 34	80 **Br** Bromine 35	84 **Kr** Krypton 36
85 **Rb** Rubidium 37	88 **Sr** Strontium 38	89 **Y** Yttrium 39 91 **Zr** Zirconium 40 93 **Nb** Niobium 41 96 **Mo** Molybdenum 42 99 **Tc** Technetium 43 101 **Ru** Ruthenium 44 103 **Rh** Rhodium 45 106 **Pd** Palladium 46 108 **Ag** Silver 47 112 **Cd** Cadmium 48	115 **In** Indium 49	119 **Sn** Tin 50	122 **Sb** Antimony 51	128 **Te** Tellurium 52	127 **I** Iodine 53	131 **Xe** Xenon 54
133 **Cs** Caesium 55	137 **Ba** Barium 56	139 **La** Lanthanum 57 178 **Hf** Hafnium 72 181 **Ta** Tantalum 73 184 **W** Tungsten 74 186 **Re** Rhenium 75 190 **Os** Osmium 76 192 **Ir** Iridium 77 195 **Pt** Platinum 78 197 **Au** Gold 79 202 **Hg** Mercury 80	204 **Tl** Thallium 81	207 **Pb** Lead 82	209 **Bi** Bismuth 83	210 **Po** Polonium 84	210 **At** Astatine 85	222 **Rn** Radon 86
223 **Fr** Francium 87	226 **Ra** Radium 88	227 **Ac** Actinium 89						

Elements 58–71 and 90–103 have been omitted.

The value for mass number is normally that of the commonest isotope, e.g. ^{35}Cl not ^{37}Cl.

Bromine is approximately equal proportions of ^{79}Br and ^{81}Br.

Formulae List

This list shows the formulae for quantitative relationships in the Physical Processes section of the specification which candidates will be expected to recall (N.B. for convenience, formulae are also given here in symbolic form even though this form is not required by the specification).

$$\begin{array}{l} \text{potential difference} \\ \text{(volt, V)} \end{array} = \begin{array}{l} \text{current} \\ \text{(ampere, A)} \end{array} \times \begin{array}{l} \text{resistance} \\ \text{(ohm, } \Omega) \end{array} \qquad V = IR$$

$$\begin{array}{l} \text{power} \\ \text{(watt, W)} \end{array} = \begin{array}{l} \text{potential difference} \\ \text{(volt, V)} \end{array} \times \begin{array}{l} \text{current} \\ \text{(ampere, A)} \end{array} \qquad P = VI$$

$$\begin{array}{l} \text{energy transferred} \\ \text{(kilowatt hour, kWh)} \end{array} = \begin{array}{l} \text{power} \\ \text{(kilowatt, W)} \end{array} \times \begin{array}{l} \text{time} \\ \text{(hour, h)} \end{array} \qquad E = Pt$$

$$\text{total cost} = \text{number of Units} \times \text{cost per Unit}$$

$$\begin{array}{l} \text{energy transferred} \\ \text{(joule, J)} \end{array} = \begin{array}{l} \text{power} \\ \text{(watt, W)} \end{array} \times \begin{array}{l} \text{time} \\ \text{(second, s)} \end{array} \qquad E = Pt$$

$$\text{acceleration (metre/second squared, m/s}^2) = \frac{\text{change in velocity (metre/second m/s)}}{\text{time taken for change (second, s)}} \qquad a = \frac{v - u}{t}$$

$$\begin{array}{l} \text{wave speed} \\ \text{(metre/second, m/s)} \end{array} = \begin{array}{l} \text{frequency} \\ \text{(hertz, Hz)} \end{array} \times \begin{array}{l} \text{wavelength} \\ \text{(metre, m)} \end{array} \qquad v = f\lambda$$

$$\text{efficiency} = \frac{\text{useful energy transferred by device}}{\text{total energy supplied to device}}$$

$$\text{work done} = \text{energy transferred}$$

$$\begin{array}{l} \text{work done} \\ \text{(joule, J)} \end{array} = \begin{array}{l} \text{force applied} \\ \text{(newton, N)} \end{array} \times \begin{array}{l} \text{distance moved in direction of force} \\ \text{(metre, m)} \end{array} \qquad W = Fs$$

$$\text{power (watt, W)} = \frac{\text{work done (joule, J)}}{\text{time taken (second, s)}} \qquad p = \frac{W}{t}$$

$$\begin{array}{l} \text{weight} \\ \text{(newton, N)} \end{array} = \begin{array}{l} \text{mass} \\ \text{(kilogram, kg)} \end{array} \times \begin{array}{l} \text{gravitational field strength} \\ \text{(newton/kilogram, N/kg)} \end{array} \qquad w = mg$$

$$\begin{array}{l} \text{change in gravitational potential} \\ \textit{energy (joule, J)} \end{array} = \begin{array}{l} \text{weight} \\ \textit{(newton, N)} \end{array} \times \begin{array}{l} \text{change in vertical} \\ \textit{height (metre, m)} \end{array} \qquad gpe = mg\Delta h$$

$$\begin{array}{l} \text{kinetic energy} \\ \text{(joule, J)} \end{array} = \frac{1}{2} \times \begin{array}{l} \text{mass} \\ \text{(kilogram, kg)} \end{array} \times \begin{array}{l} \text{speed}^2 \\ \text{[(metre/second)}^2, \text{(m/s)}^2\text{]} \end{array} \qquad ke = \frac{1}{2} mv^2$$

Hazard symbols
You will need to be able to recognise, and explain the significance of, the following hazard symbols.

Oxidising
These substances provide oxygen which allows other materials to burn more fiercely.

Harmful
These substances are similar to toxic substances but less dangerous.

Highly flammable
These substances easily catch fire.

Corrosive
These substances attack and destroy living tissues, including eyes and skin.

Toxic
These substances can cause death. They may have their effects when swallowed or breathed in or absorbed through the skin.

Irritant
These substances are not corrosive but can cause reddening or blistering of the skin.

Index